Scott Foresman - Addison Wesley

MATH

Extend Your Thinking

Enrichment Masters

Grade 4

Scott Foresman - Addison Wesley

Editorial Offices: Menlo Park, California • Glenview, Illinois
Sales Offices: Reading, Massachusetts • Atlanta, Georgia • Glenview, Illinois
Carrollton, Texas • Menlo Park, California

http://www.sf.aw.com

ISBN 0-201-31263-8

Printed in the United States of America

4 5 6 7 8 9 10 – BW – 01 00 99

Contents

Overview

Extend Your Thinking (Enrichment Masters) enhance student learning by actively involving students in different areas of mathematical reasoning. Activities often involve students in real-world situations, some of which may have more than one right answer. Thus, the masters motivate students to find alternate solutions to a given problem.

How to use

The *Extend Your Thinking* masters are designed so that the teacher can use them in many different ways.

- **a.** As a teaching tool to guide students in exploring a specific type of thinking skill. Making a transparency of the worksheet provides an excellent way to expedite this process as students work at their desks along with the teacher.
- **b.** As an enrichment worksheet that challenges and motivates students to hone their thinking skills.
- **c.** As independent or group work.
- **d.** As a homework assignment that encourages students to involve their parents in the educational process.

Description of the masters

The *Extend Your Thinking* masters consist of four types of motivating and challenging activities that focus on these four categories of higher-order thinking skills:

Patterns activities encourage students to develop skills in recognizing patterns that exist and are used in all facets of mathematics. Students are challenged to describe, extend, analyze, and generalize patterns. The study of patterns allows students to gain an appreciation for the inter-relatedness and beauty in the structure of mathematics.

These activities provide students with consistent exposure to *Patterns in Data, Patterns in Numbers, Patterns in Algebra,* and *Patterns in Geometry.*

Critical Thinking activities challenge students to examine and evaluate their own thinking about math. The problems and situations involve higher-order thinking skills such as analysis, synthesis, and evaluation. As students become more aware and more critical of their thinking, they learn to evaluate their own reasoning as they become better problem solvers.

The critical-thinking strategies students use include the following: *Classifying and Sorting, Ordering and Sequencing, Using Logic, Drawing Conclusions, Using Number Sense, Finding/Extending/Using Patterns, Making Generalizations, Reasoning with Graphs and Charts, Explaining Reasoning/Justifying Answers, Developing Alternatives, Evaluating Evidence and Conclusions, and Making and Testing Predictions.*

Visual Thinking activities focus on students' ability to perceive and mentally manipulate visual images. These types of activities are extremely important because visualization can often help develop students' critical thinking and problem solving skills.

Students are provided an opportunity to explore spatial perception as well as visual patterns using both two- and three-dimensional figures. Visual analogies provide practice in exploring logical reasoning. Many visual thinking pages integrate patterns and emphasize the integration of the mathematics strands.

Decision Making activities present enriching real-world situations that require students to make a decision. There are often no clearly right or clearly wrong answers. This gives the students the opportunity to make choices and consider alternatives.

You may wish to encourage students to use these steps as they make and evaluate their decisions.

Understand Encourage students to define the problem. They need to consider why a decision is needed, what goal they wish to meet, and what tools and techniques they can use to reach their decision.

Plan and Solve At this stage, students need to identify the options by isolating information that is relevant to the decision-making process. As they consider the advantages and disadvantages of each option, they are using skills that enable them to make an informed decision.

Make a Decision After students evaluate the data and consider both the positive and negative consequences of each possible decision, they decide which choice is best.

Present the Decision Students are often asked to explain why they feel a certain choice is more advantageous. Because different students may weigh each advantage and disadvantage differently, this concluding step can often lead to a useful, worthwhile class discussion.

Name ______________________

Decision Making

Ms. McCarthy owns a small grocery store. She needs to hire extra help for the cold weather. Normally, Ms. McCarthy earns about $16,000 per month. The bar graph shows how much Ms. McCarthy earns during these months.

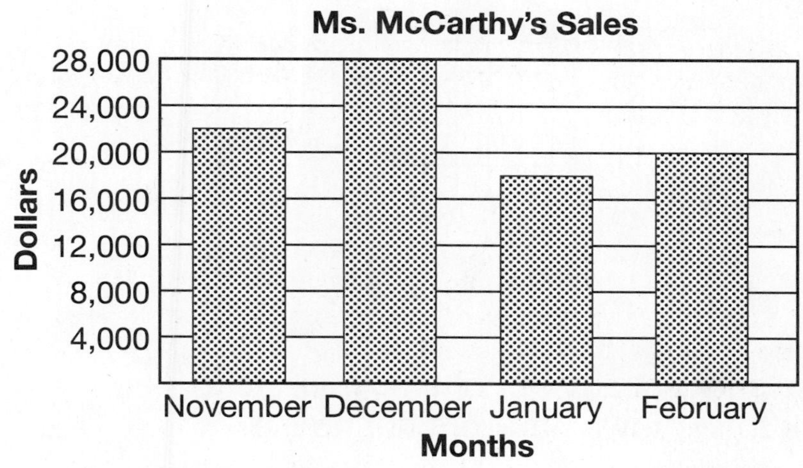

Ms. McCarthy needs to hire 1 worker for every extra $2,000 she earns in a month. How many extra workers does she need:

1. in November? ______________
2. in December? ______________
3. in January? ______________
4. in February? ______________
5. Draw a pictograph for Ms. McCarthy's data. Let one symbol show each extra worker that must be hired.

Number of Extra Workers to be Hired

November	
December	
January	
February	

(symbol) = 1 extra worker

6. Ms. McCarthy doesn't want to hire new workers every month. She decides to hire some in November and more in December. How many workers should Ms. McCarthy hire each time? Explain your reasoning.

____

____

Name ______________________

Critical Thinking

The grid below represents the town near Ms. Klein's house. Use the grid to help you answer the questions.

It takes Ms. Klein 5 minutes to walk a block.

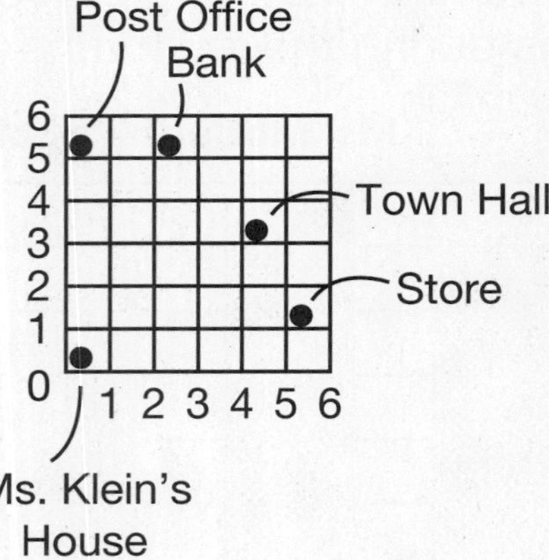

1. What is the shortest amount of time it will take her to walk to the town hall from her house? ______

2. Ms. Klein leaves the town hall at 10:00 A.M. and then goes to the bank. At what time will she get there if she takes the shortest route? ______

3. She spends 10 minutes at the bank. Then she goes to the post office. At what time will she arrive at the post office? ______

4. Next, Ms. Klein goes to the store. How long will it take her to get there if she takes the shortest route? ______

5. Ms. Klein goes home when she is finished shopping at the store. How long will it take her to walk home by the shortest route? ______

6. a. Ms. Klein has gone to the town hall, the bank, the post office, the store, and home. What order could Ms. Klein have walked in order to save time?

   ____

   b. How much walking time would this trip take? ______

   c. How much time could she have saved if she used this suggestion? ______

Name ______________________________

Critical Thinking

Rainbow's Ice Cream Parlor displayed these graphs to show that they are much more popular than Sunny's Ice Cream Parlor.

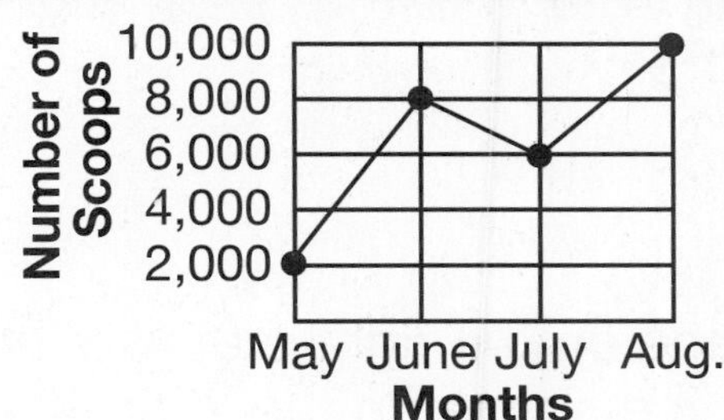

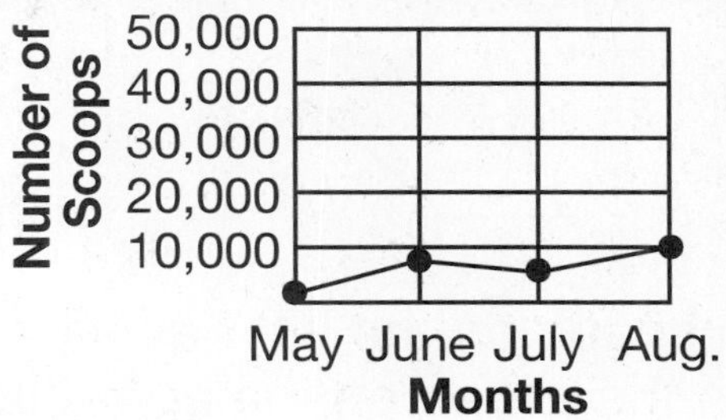

Use the graph to answer **1–3.**

1. a. About how many scoops were sold in June at Rainbow's Ice Cream Parlor? ____________

b. About how many were sold in June at Sunny's? ____________

2. a. About how many scoops total did Rainbow's sell that summer? ____________

b. About how many scoops were sold at Sunny's? ____________

3. Do these graphs show that one ice cream parlor sold more than the other? Explain.

____

____

The following year, Sunny's Ice Cream Parlor displayed these graphs to show that they were more popular than Rainbow's Ice Cream Parlor.

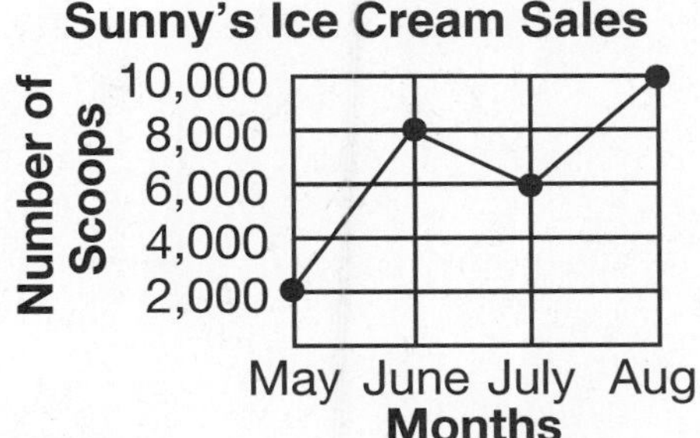

4. Can you tell from these two graphs, which ice cream parlor is more popular? Explain.

____

Name ______________________________________

Visual Thinking

These two shapes are the same. One is just turned.

Each shape on the left has a matching shape on the right that was turned. Circle the shape on the right that matches the shape on the left.

1. 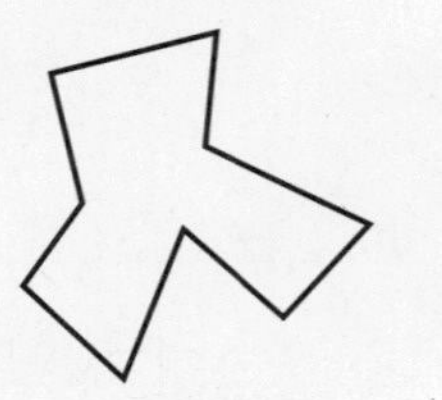 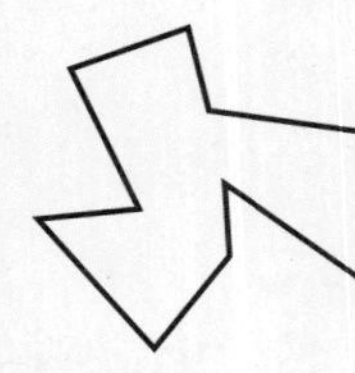   

2.  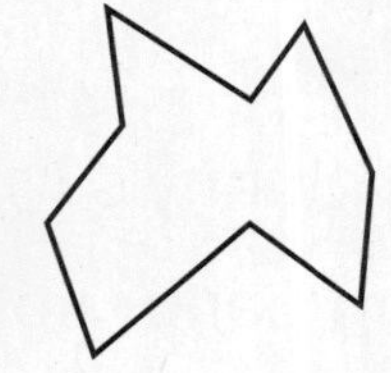 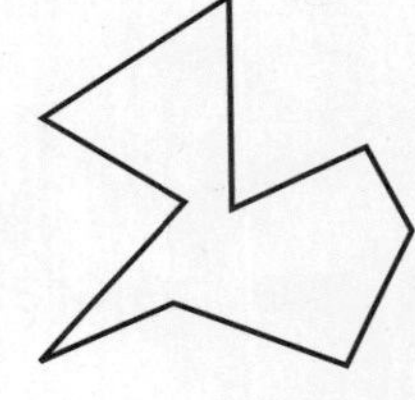  

3.     

4. 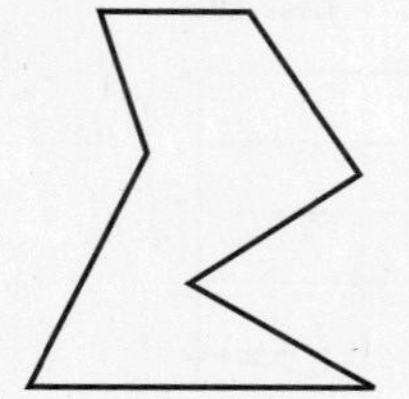 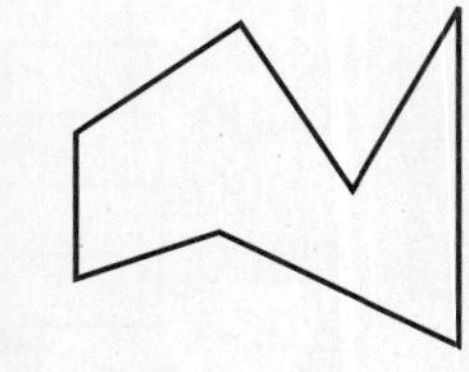  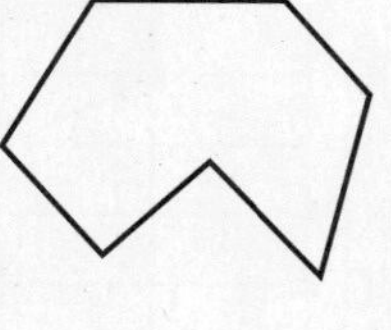 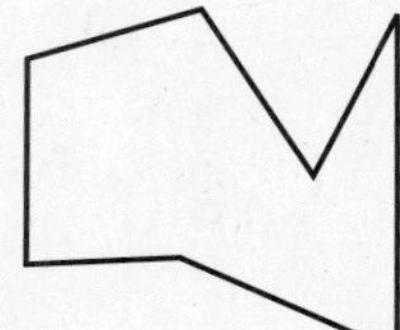

5.    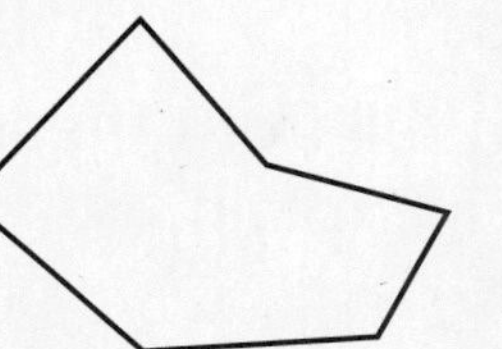 

Name ______________________________

Visual Thinking

Draw the missing figure.

Example

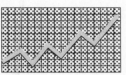

1. 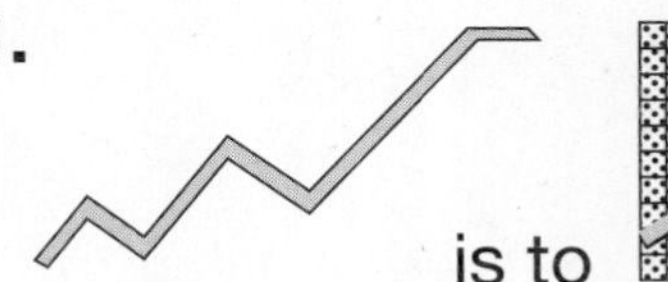 is to 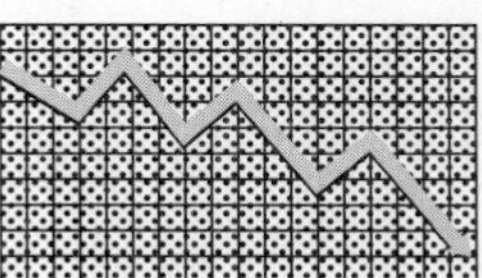 as __________ is to

2. 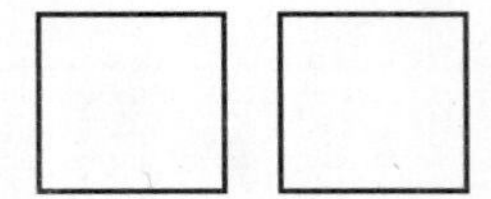 is to 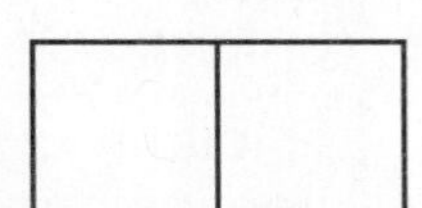 as __________ is to 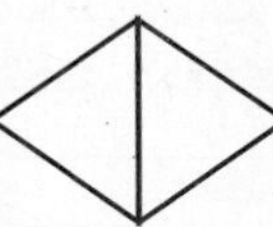

3. 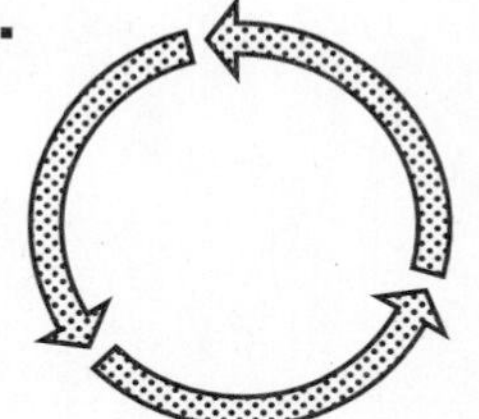 is to  as __________ is to 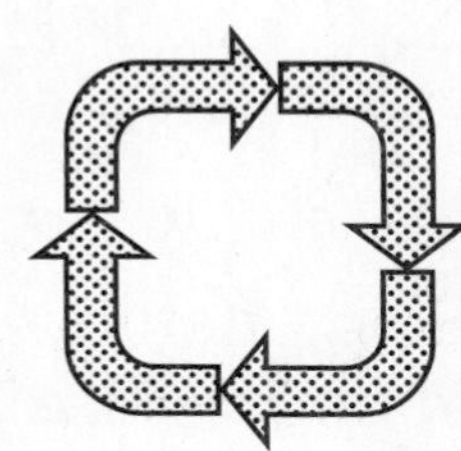

4.  is to 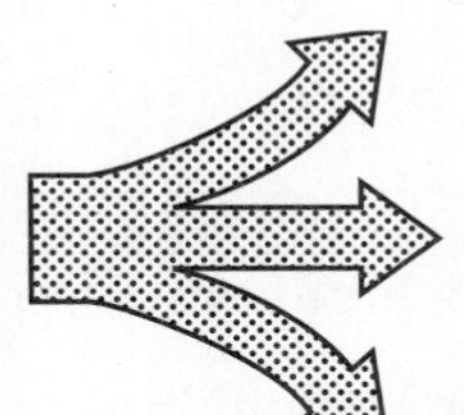 as 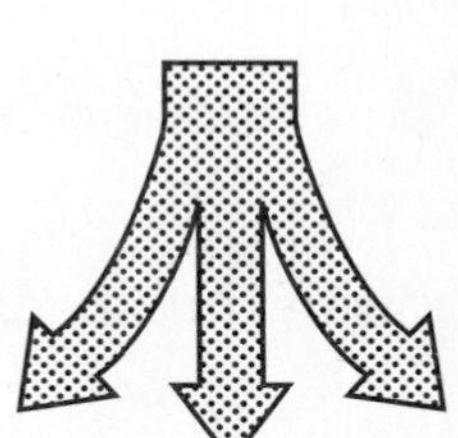 is to __________

5. 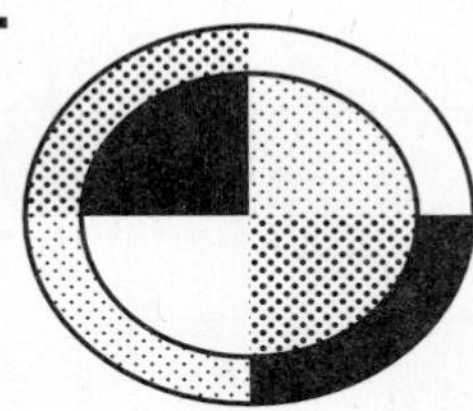 is to 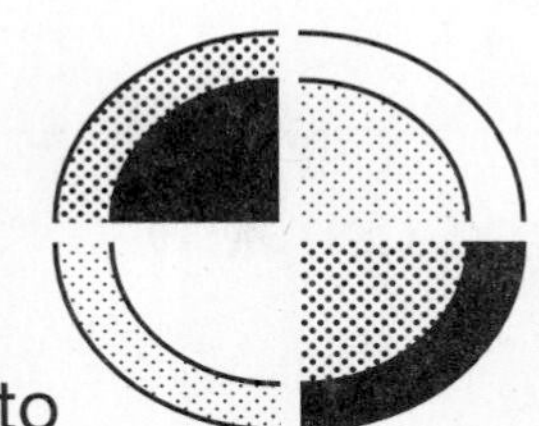 as 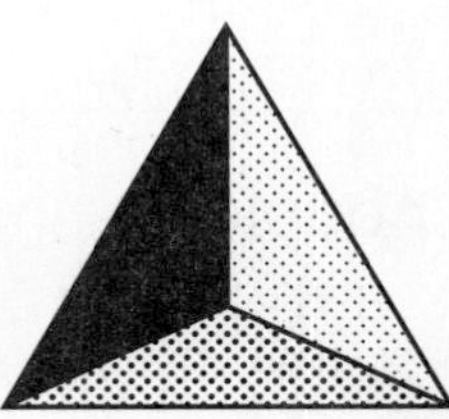 is to __________

Name ______________________________

Extend Your Thinking
1-6

Patterns in Data

Automatic Teller Machines (ATMs) are like banks. People can use them to withdraw or deposit money into their accounts. The two graphs below show different information about ATMs and how people use them. Use the graphs to answer the questions.

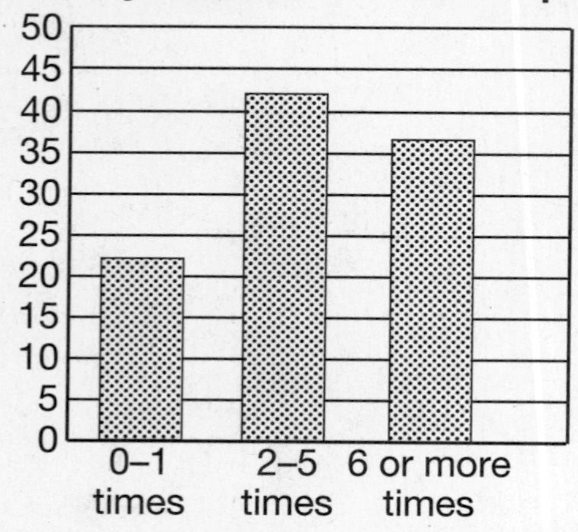

How ATMs Are Used on Vacation

Planned	ATM ATM ATM ATM ATM ATM
Unplanned emergency	ATM ATM
Unplanned convenience	ATM ATM ATM ATM ATM ATM ATM ATM ATM ATM ATM ATM

ATM = 5 people

1. How often do the greatest number of people use ATMs? ______________

2. Why does the largest group of people use ATMs while they are on vacation? ______________

3. a. Which sentences describe the average ATM user? ______

> I. "I use ATMs about once a month. On vacation I only use them for emergencies."
>
> II. "I use ATMs 4 times a month. On vacation I use them for convenience."

b. Explain your reasoning.

____

4. About how many people per hundred use ATMs more than 6 times a month? ______________

5. How does the second largest group of people use ATMs while on vacation? ______________

Name ______________________________

Decision Making

Janice has 6 dogs to feed. Each dog eats 2 pounds of food a week. Which food should she buy?

Dog's Delicacy	Dog Delight	Nature's Best
$4 for 3 pounds	$3 for 2 pounds	$5 for 4 pounds
We add important vitamins your dog needs!	All natural! Your dog will live years longer.	Dogs love our tasty food!!

1. What is the total amount of food the dogs eat per week?

____

2. Compare costs.

a. weekly supply of Dog's Delicacy costs ________.

b. weekly supply of Dog Delight costs ________.

c. weekly supply of Nature's Best costs ________.

3. Why might Janice buy Dog's Delicacy?

____

4. Why might Janice buy Dog Delight?

____

5. Why might Janice buy Nature's Best?

____

6. Which dog food should she buy? Explain.

____

____

7. Which part or parts of each ad is probably opinion?

____

____

____

Name ______________________________ **Extend Your Thinking 1-8**

Critical Thinking

1. Fill in the number of times each letter appears in these directions. Then use the data to make a bar graph below.

Letter	Number of Times	Letter	Number of Times
f		e	
i		u	
l		a	
n		c	
t		p	

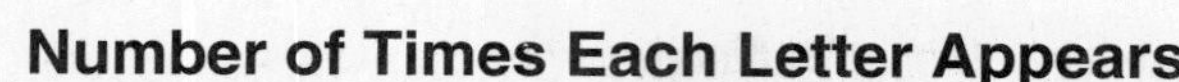

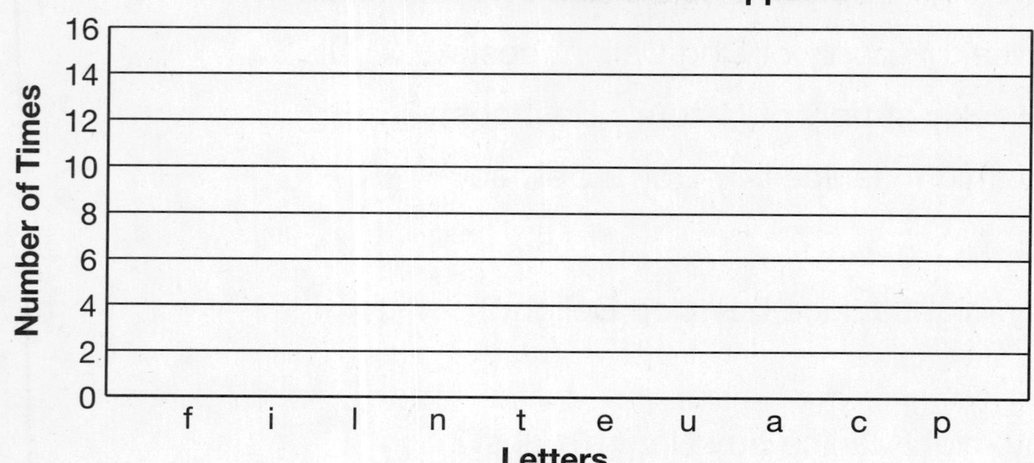

2. Which letters appeared the same number of times?

____

3. Based on the data here, which two letters would you predict are most common in written English? Explain your reasoning.

____

____

____

Name ______________________________

Visual Thinking

Circle the hole that the shape will fit in exactly.

1. 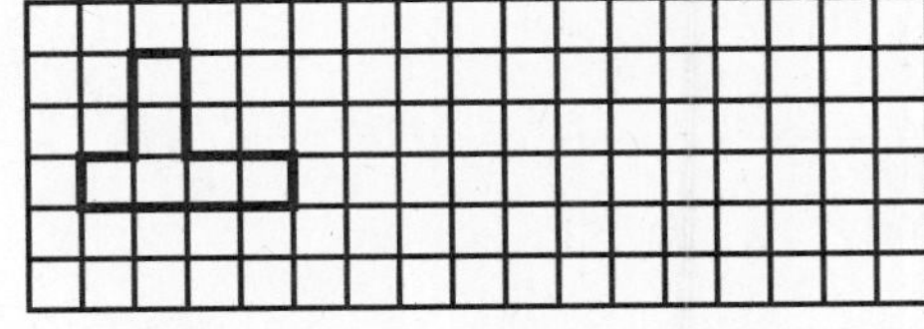

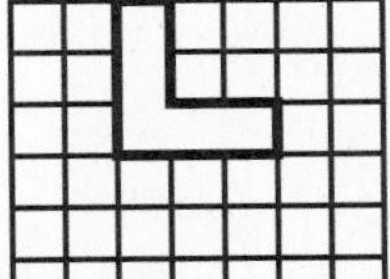 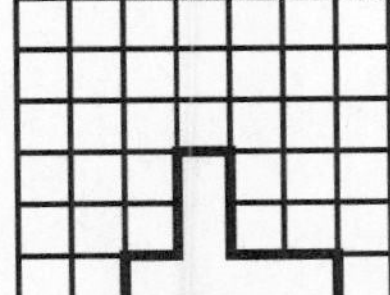 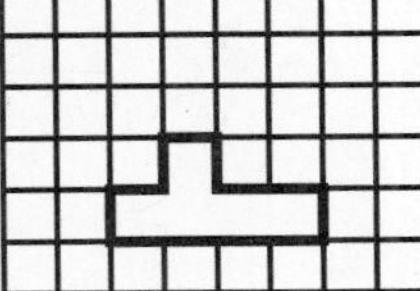

2. 

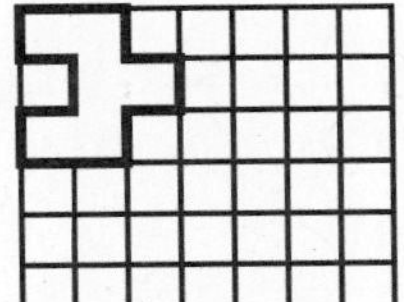 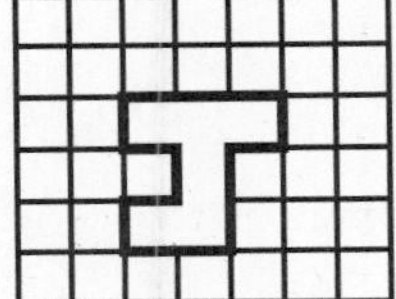 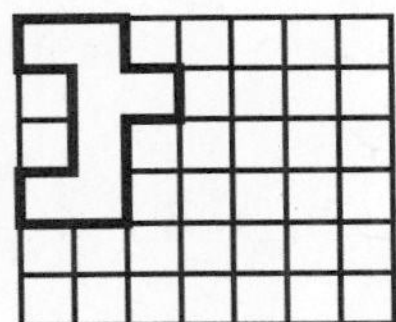

3. 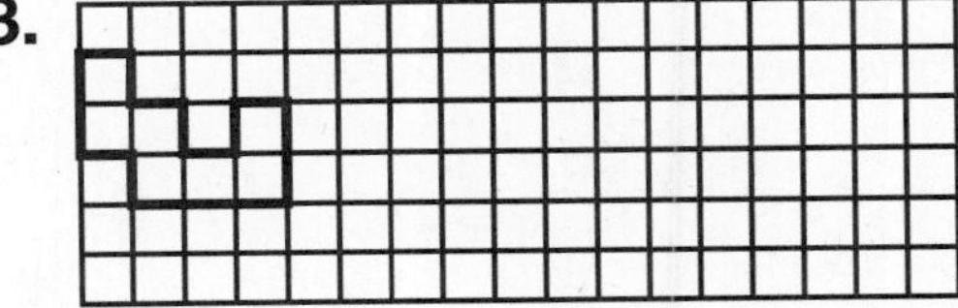

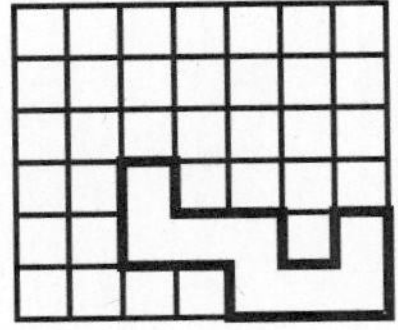 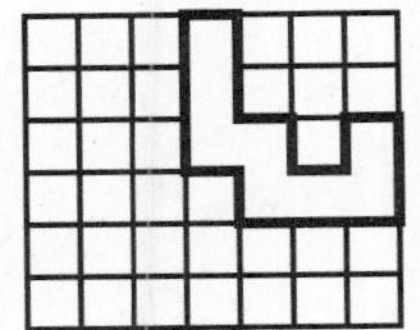 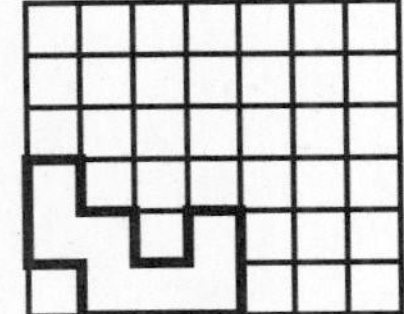

4. 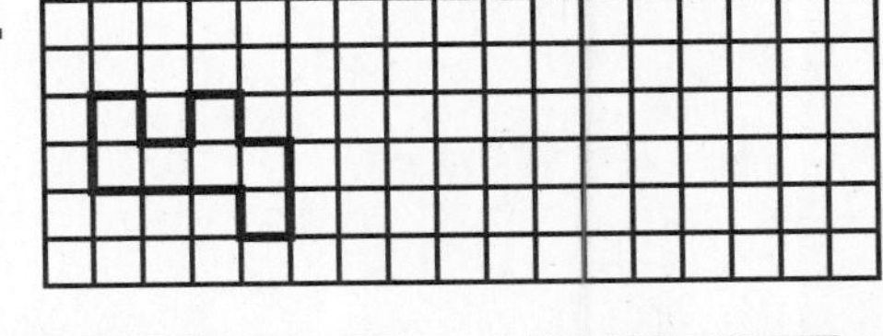

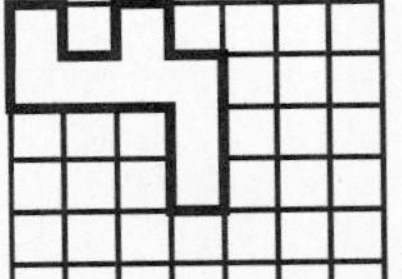 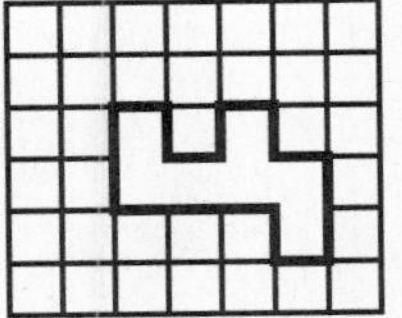 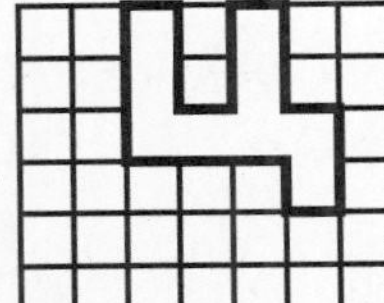

Name ______________________________

Critical Thinking

Choose a number from the box to make each sentence true. Write the number on the line. Use each number exactly once.

5	7	28	17	6	55	8	22	14	4

1. The mode is 7. 3, 4, 5, 6, 7, ________
2. The range is 7. 1, 3, 4, 7, ________
3. The mode is 22. 3, 4, 8, 8, 18, 22, 24, 22, ________
4. The median is 17. 5, 10, 20, 18, ________
5. The range is 12. 2, 4, 6, 8, 10, 12, ________
6. The mode is 6. 5, 6, 6, 18, 3, 2, 2, ________
7. The range is 50. 5, 15, 10, 8, 30, ________
8. There is no mode. 5, 7, 17, 6, 4, ________
9. The median is 4. 2, 3, 4, 5, ________
10. The median is 10. 10, 2, 12, 15, ________

Name ________________________________

Patterns in Numbers

Tell what rule was used to make the pattern. What are the next three numbers?

1. 5; 50; 500; ________; ________; ________

Rule: ________________________________

2. 12, 24, 36, ________, ________, ________

Rule: ________________________________

3. 120, 240, 360, 480, ________, ________, ________

Rule: ________________________________

4. 401; 801; 1,201; ________; ________; ________

Rule: ________________________________

5. 1,100; 950; 800; ________; ________; ________

Rule: ________________________________

6. 45, 90, 135, ________, ________, ________

Rule: ________________________________

7. 100,000; 10,000; 1,000; ________; ________; ________

Rule: ________________________________

Write three addition or subtraction patterns of your own. Give your rule.

8. ________________________________

Rule: ________________________________

9. ________________________________

Rule: ________________________________

10. ________________________________

Rule: ________________________________

Name ______________________________________ Extend Your Thinking 1-12

Patterns in Geometry

Continue the pattern. Draw the next two beads.

1. 

2. 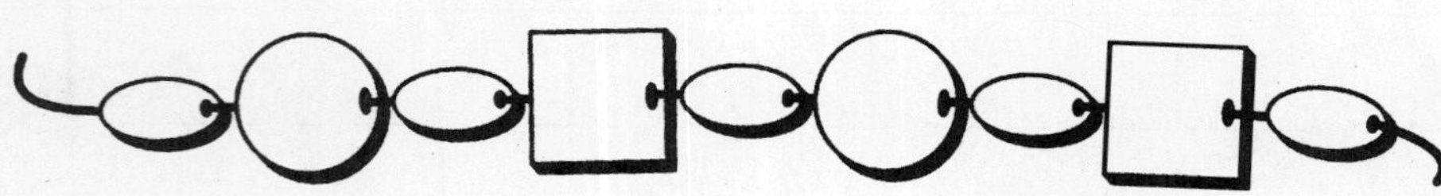

3. 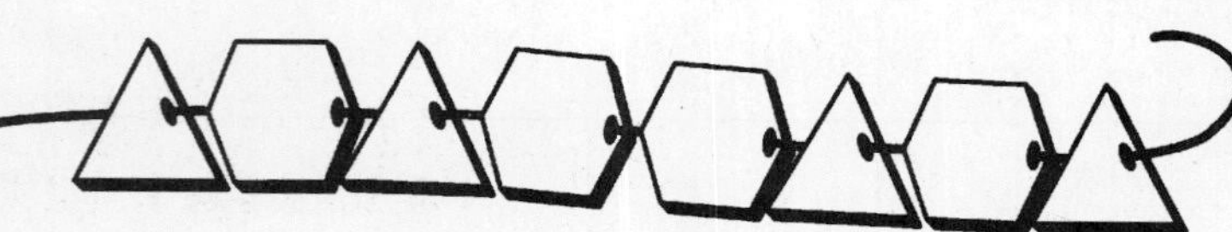

4. 

5. 

6. 

7.

Name ______________________________

Visual Thinking

Estimation About how many shapes are in each drawing?

1. ______________

2. ______________

3. ______________

4. ______________

5. ______________

6. ______________

Name ______________________

Extend Your Thinking
2-2

Critical Thinking

Hundreds

S H O E L A C E S

1 2 3 4 5 6 7 8 9

Tens

P O R C U P I N E

1 2 3 4 5 6 7 8 9

Ones

C O N D U C T O R

1 2 3 4 5 6 7 8 9

Each letter in the words above has been assigned a digit. "Shoelaces" represents the hundreds digits, "porcupine" represents the tens digits, and "conductor" represents the ones digits.

Use the code to write the word for each number.

Example

1 7 7

S I T

1. 5 2 7 ________

2. 2 5 7 ________

3. 9 7 9 ________

4. 7 2 4 ________

5. 1 5 3 ________

6. 7 2 7 ________

7. 5 7 4 ________

8. 2 2 7 ________

9. 7 5 7 ________

Name ______________________

Critical Thinking

Estimation How much is a million? Read each situation. Circle your best guess. Explain what you could do to check your estimate.

1. If one million kids climbed onto each other's shoulders they would be:

a. as tall as a 110-story building

b. farther up than airplanes can fly

c. past the moon

____

____

2. If you wanted to count from one to one million, it would take you about:

a. 12 days

b. 2 years

c. 95 years

____

____

3. The world's largest peanut measured 4 in. How far would a million similar peanuts stretch if they were laid end to end?

a. 1 mile

b. 63 miles

c. 40 feet

____

____

Name ______________________________ Extend Your Thinking **2-4**

Patterns in Numbers

Tell what rule was used to make the pattern. What are the next two numbers?

1. 30, 40, 50, 60, ____________, ____________

Rule: ______________________________

2. 1; 10; 100; 1,000; ____________; ____________

Rule: ______________________________

3. 2, 4, 8, 16, ____________, ____________

Rule: ______________________________

4. 26; 260; 2,600; 26,000; ____________; ____________

Rule: ______________________________

5. 22,195; 22,190; 22,185; 22,180; ____________; ____________

Rule: ______________________________

6. 3; 30; 300; 3,000; ____________; ____________

Rule: ______________________________

7. 360,000; 36,000; 3,600; ____________; ____________

Rule: ______________________________

8. 520,000; 52,000; 5,200; ____________; ____________

Rule: ______________________________

Make up your own number patterns. Leave some blank spaces. Give them to a classmate to solve.

9. ________, ________, ________, ________, ________

10. ________, ________, ________, ________, ________

Name ______________________________ **Extend Your Thinking 2-5**

Decision Making

Have you ever needed to decide which of two choices is a better deal for you? At the Amazing Amusement Park you can buy rides and food in two different ways.

	Ticket A	Ticket B
Rides	Unlimited rides $10/hour (first hour) Unlimited rides $5/hour (after the first hour) Must buy and use tickets in pairs	Each ride $1 apiece No requirements
Food	Free juice and hot dog	Juice costs $0.75. Hot dogs cost $1.50.
Extras	Free camera rental	Camera rental $5 a day

You are going with a friend and plan on staying for 3 hours. You figure you can ride on 8 rides per hour. You have your own camera.

1. Which ticket will cost less for you and your friend?

____

____

2. If you only go on 6 rides an hour which ticket will be the better deal?

____

____

3. What if another friend joins you? Which tickets will you buy?

____

____

4. Why might you choose Ticket A?

____

____

Name ______________________________

Critical Thinking

Find your way through the mazes following the rule above each.

Striped

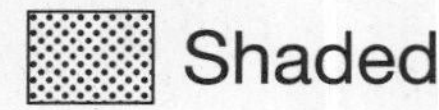

Rule: If you are on a shaded square, you cannot enter a white square.

1.

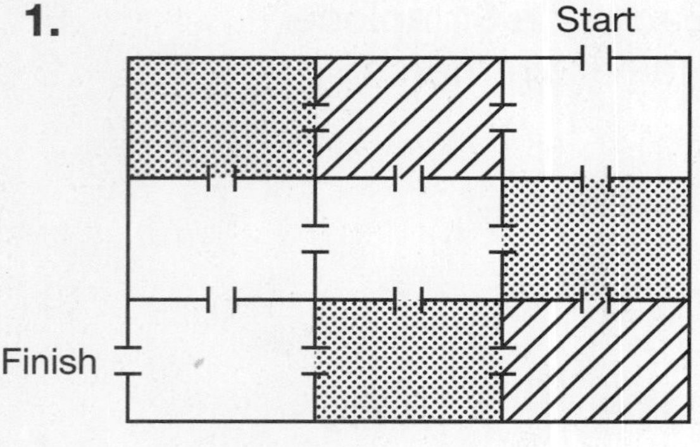

2.

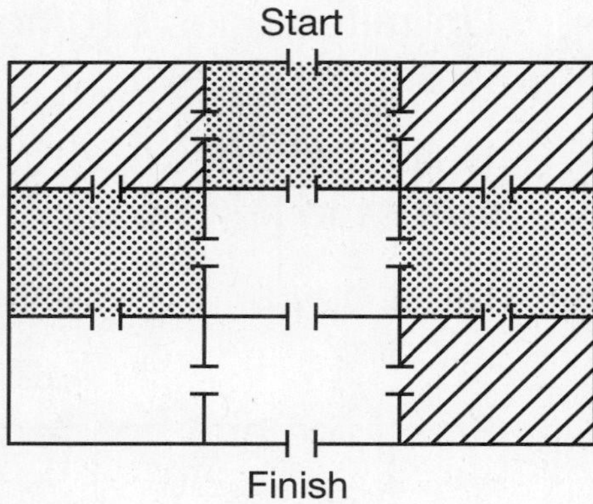

Rule: You can only enter a striped square from a white square.

3.

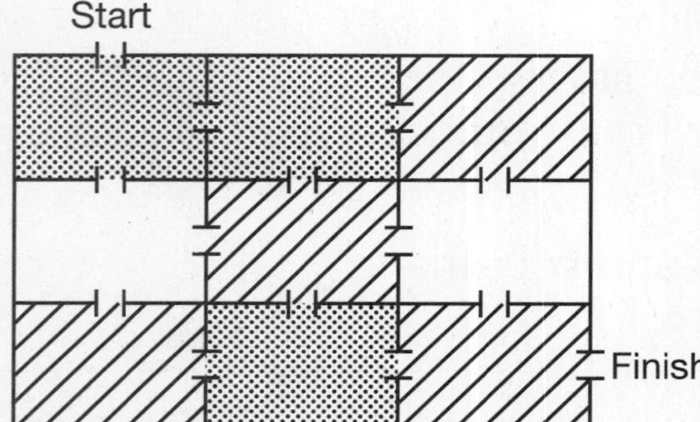

4.

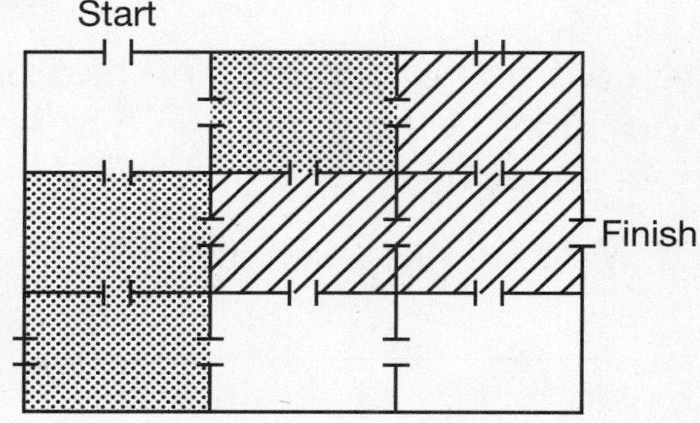

5. If start and finish were reversed, would the path through each maze stay the same for each exercise? Explain.

____

____

____

6. Draw your own maze and write a rule for it. Give it to a classmate to solve.

Name ______________________________ **Extend Your Thinking 2-7**

Critical Thinking

Solve the riddles by using the clues given.

1. I am a 3-digit number.

My ones digit is a 7.

I am 570 when rounded to the nearest ten.

I am __________.

2. I am a 2-digit number.

My ones digit is a 6.

I am 90 when rounded to the nearest ten.

I am __________.

3. I am a 4-digit number.

I am greater than 7,500.

My ones digit is a 4.

I am 7,600 when rounded to the nearest hundred.

I am 7,550 when rounded to the nearest ten.

I am __________.

4. I am a 3-digit number.

My ones digit is a 2.

I am 1,000 when rounded to the nearest hundred.

I am less than 960.

I am __________.

5. I am a 3-digit number.

My ones digit is a 6.

I am 560 when rounded to the nearest ten.

I am __________.

Name ______________________________

Extend Your Thinking
2-8

Decision Making

Suppose your class is going on a camping trip. You are assigning the chores for the trip. Each of you has to take 1 of the chores listed. Use the information below to help you decide who should do each chore.

Marilyn "I am good at tending fires, but I can also set up the tents."

Fred "I'll do anything except clean the grounds."

Martha "I don't want to cook or do the dishes."

José "I don't mind doing the dishes, but I don't want to set up the tents."

Write the name of the person who will do each chore. Remember to include yourself. Explain why you assigned the chores as you did.

1. Set up tents.

____

2. Cook.

____

3. Clean the grounds.

____

4. Do the dishes.

____

5. Tend the fire.

____

Name ______________________________

Decision Making

Look at each period of time and choose an activity you think would take that amount of time.

1. less than 1 second ______________________________

2. between 1 second and 1 minute ______________________________

3. between 1 minute and 1 hour ______________________________

4. between 1 hour and 1 day ______________________________

5. between 1 day and 1 week ______________________________

6. between 1 week and 1 month ______________________________

7. between 1 month and 1 year ______________________________

8. between 1 year and 1 decade ______________________________

9. between 1 decade and 1 century ______________________________

Name ______________________ **Extend Your Thinking 2-10**

Patterns in Data

Find a pattern to answer each question. Then write the rule.

1. Eric takes his medicine at 8:15 A.M., 11:15 A.M., and 2:15 P.M. When will he take his medicine next? __________

   Rule: ______________________

2. WRKO plays Carla's favorite song at 10:05 A.M., 10:35 A.M. and 11:05 A.M. When will they probably play it next? __________

   Rule: ______________________

3. A news program is on the radio at noon, 6:00 P.M., and midnight. When will the news be on again? __________

   Rule: ______________________

4. Anita's grandmother drinks a glass of water at 8:30 A.M., 10:30 A.M., and 12:30 P.M. When will she have another? __________

   Rule: ______________________

5. Mayflies hatch in the stream at 5:12 A.M., 5:18 A.M., 5:30 A.M., and 5:54 A.M. When will mayflies hatch again? __________

   Rule: ______________________

   ____

6. Mr. Kim, the baker, takes bread out of the oven at 4:30 A.M., 5:30 A.M., 7:00 A.M., 8:00 A.M., and 9:30 A.M. When will he take bread out of the oven again? __________

   Rule: ______________________

Name ____________________

Critical Thinking

A Chinese one-year calendar has 12 months. It is based on cycles of the moon. It is similar to the calendar you use every day, but only has 29 or 30 days in each month.

Each year is named after one of 12 animals.

Rooster	Dog	Pig	Rat	Ox	Tiger
1981	1982	1983	1984	1985	1986
1993	1994	1995	1996	1997	1998

Rabbit	Dragon	Snake	Horse	Sheep	Monkey
1987	1988	1989	1990	1991	1992
1999	2000	2001	2002	2003	2004

1. Look at the years in the calendar. Find a pattern. Then fill in the next year for each animal.
2. Describe the pattern you found.

   ____

3. What animal is this year named after? ____________________
4. Name the animal for which the year you were born is named. ____________________
5. What animal will 2018 be named for? Explain how you found your answer. ____________________

   ____

6. What animal was 1978 named for? ____________________

   ____

   ____

Name ______________________________

Extend Your Thinking
2-12

Critical Thinking

Here's a pictograph of a videotape schedule.

Video: Downtown School of Kempo Karate		
Opening:	(music and scenes)	½ clock
Part I:	Welcome to the Downtown School	2 clocks
Part II:	What is Kempo Karate?	5 clocks
Part III:	The Sensei	3 clocks
Part IV:	Let's Visit some Classes	7 clocks
Part V:	How to Enroll	3 clocks
Closing:	(music and titles)	1 clock

(clock) = 1 minute

1. Which part of the videotape do you think will have the most information? Why?

____

2. How long will it take to explain Kempo Karate? How do you know?

____

3. How long will the whole videotape last? ______________

4. Francine is videotaping Parts I and IV. She has 20 minutes of tape. Can she use all of it? Explain.

____

5. a. If you started to watch this tape at 3:00 P.M., when would the part about The Sensei start? ______________

   b. When would you finish watching the tape? ______________

6. Frank started viewing the tape at 10:45. Will he be able to watch the entire tape before 11:00? Explain.

____

Name ______________________________

Decision Making

Georgia makes beaded bracelets. She needs to make 10 bracelets like the one shown below.

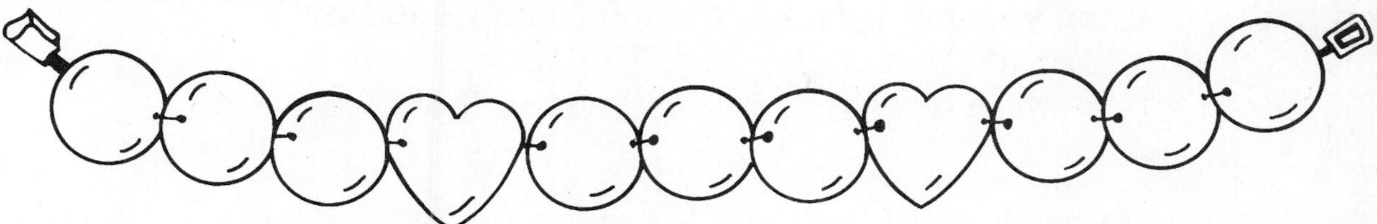

Georgia has the following choices when she buys beads.

1. How many round beads will Georgia need to make 10 bracelets? ______
2. How many heart-shaped beads will Georgia need to make 10 bracelets? ______
3. How much will it cost Georgia to buy all the round beads she needs if she only buys the 25-bead packets? ______
4. How much will it cost Georgia to buy all the round beads she needs if she only buys the 10-bead packets? ______
5. Describe 1 combination of large and small packets of round beads Georgia could buy.

____

____

6. Describe the combination of large and small packets of round and heart-shaped beads you would buy to make the 10 bracelets. Explain your decision.

____

____

Name ______________________________

Critical Thinking

Mel's Music World had a sale for five days. On day 1, the store sold 200 of its supply of tapes. On day 2, half of the remaining amount was sold. The same thing happened on days 3, 4 and 5. At the end of the sale, Mel counted the number of tapes left in the store. He discovered there were only 50 tapes left.

1. Mel wanted a record of the sale. He made a chart for the five days of the sale. But, he was so busy waiting on customers that he forgot to fill in the chart! He only recorded the number of tapes left at the end of day 5. How can Mel figure out the number of tapes left at the end of each of the other days?

____

____

2. Use the plan you described above to complete the chart.

Day	Total Number of Tapes Left
1	
2	
3	
4	
5	50

3. Suppose Mel decided to hold the sale for one additional day. If the same pattern of sales continues, how many tapes will be left in the store at the end of day 6? ________

4. Mel also had a sale on CDs. He sold 120 the first day, twice that number on the second day and twice as many on the third day as on the second. How many CDs did he sell on the third day? ________

 Use with pages 96–97.

Name ____________________

Visual Thinking

A flip moves a figure to create a mirror image with the same size and shape.

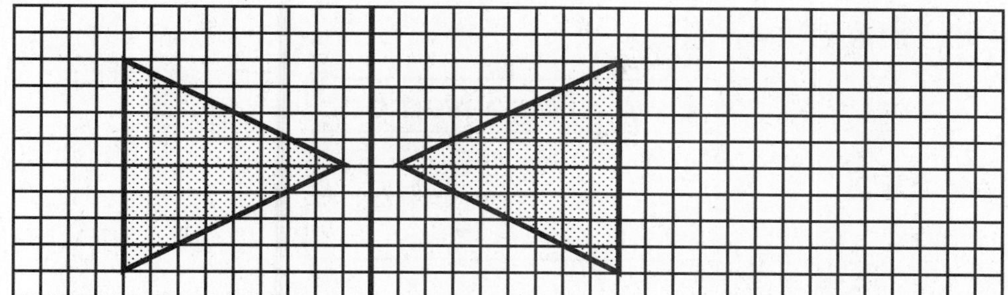

In each row, the figure on the left has been flipped over the line at its right. Circle the figure on the right that shows the position of the first figure after it has been flipped.

1. 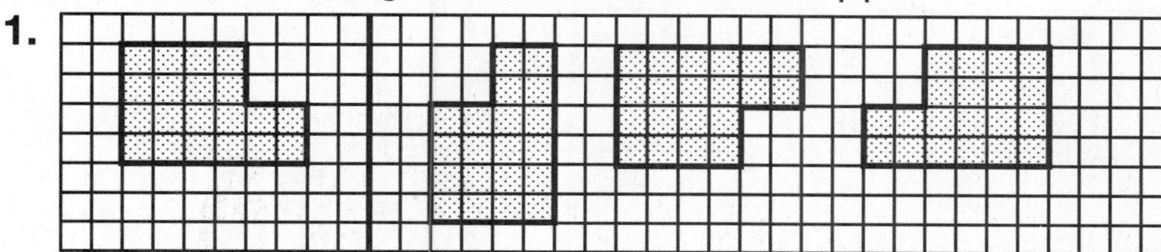

2. 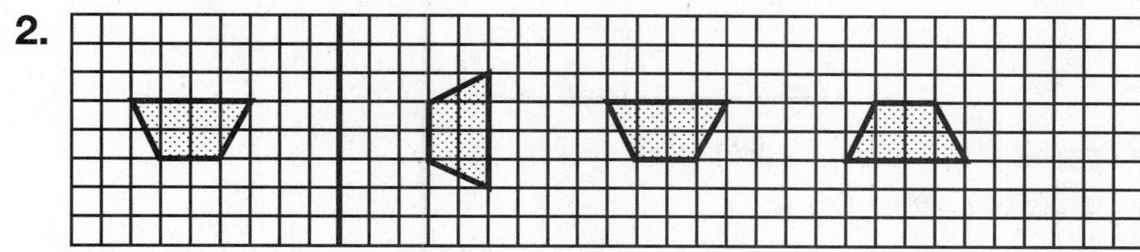

3. 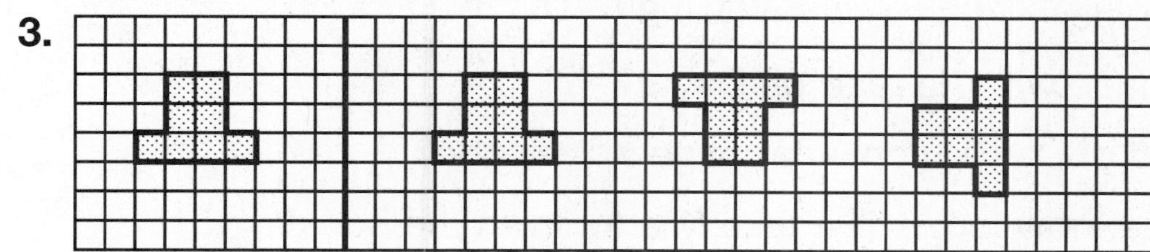

4. 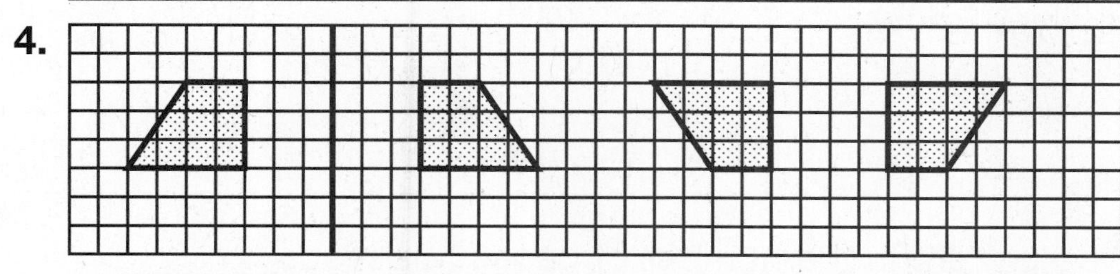

5. 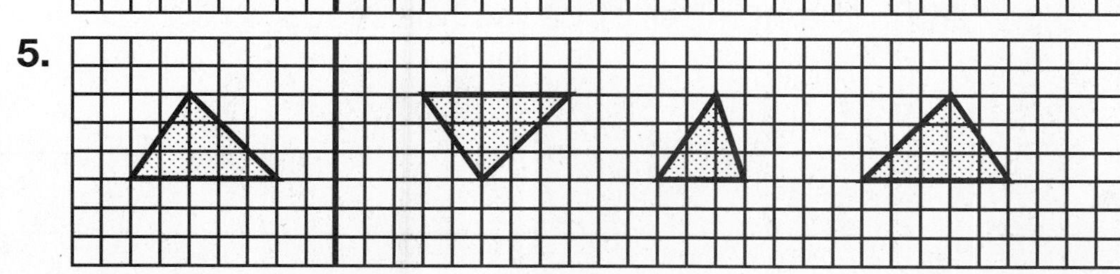

Name ______________________ **Extend Your Thinking 3-4**

Patterns in Data

Mia is reading a 128 page book. She is keeping a record of how many pages she reads each day.

Complete the chart.

Day	Page Number
1	6
2	14
3	24
4	30
5	38
6	48
7	
8	
9	
10	78

1. If Mia continues the same reading pattern, to what page will she read on Day 7? ________
2. To what page will Mia read on Day 8? ________
3. To what page will Mia read on Day 9? ________
4. At the end of Day 13, on what page will Mia be? ________
5. At this rate, how long will it take Mia to finish the book? Explain how you know.

____

____

6. Describe the pattern in the number of pages Mia reads each day.

____

____

Name ______________________

Patterns in Geometry

Draw the next three figures in each pattern. Use words to describe each pattern.

1.

Pattern: ______________________

2.

Pattern: ______________________

3.

Pattern: ______________________

4.

Pattern: ______________________

5.

Pattern: ______________________

Name ______________________________

Patterns in Numbers

Fill in the blanks to complete the pattern. Tell what rule was used to make the pattern.

1. 23, 56, 89, ________, ________, ________

Rule: ______________________________

2. 123, 199, 275, ________, ________, ________

Rule: ______________________________

3. 154, 376, 598, ________, ________, ________

Rule: ______________________________

4. 12, 24, 48, 96, ________, ________, ________

Rule: ______________________________

5. 12, 23, 34, 45, ________, ________, ________

Rule: ______________________________

6. 1, 2, 4, 7, ________, ________, ________

Rule: ______________________________

7. 25, 22, 32, 29, 39, ________, ________, ________

Rule: ______________________________

8. 10, ________, ________, 49, 62, 75, ________

Rule: ______________________________

Name ______________________________

Critical Thinking

Think about each person's conclusion. Do you think the conclusion is right or wrong? Explain.

1. Barbara counted the chairs in the auditorium. There were 484. Then she counted the programs that were available. There were 225. She concluded that the theater would need 259 more programs.

____

____

2. Stan inherited 212 books from his grandfather. He has a special bookcase for them. He has put 124 on the shelves already. He concludes that he still has to find room for 88 books.

____

3. The last pair of shoes Kim bought cost $29.99. Kim has $24.86. She concludes that she needs $5.13 before she can get another pair of shoes.

____

____

4. The goal of the library fund drive was $5,000. So far, $3,489 had been donated. Sean concluded that the library fund exceeded their goal by $1,511.

____

____

5. At the school fair, the bake stand sold 296 English muffins. They made 384 and conclude that if they sell another 88 muffins, they will be sold out.

____

Name ______________________________

Extend Your Thinking
3-8

Patterns in Numbers

In each of the tables below, the number in the second column is subtracted from the number in the first column and the result is in the third column.

Fill in the tables. Describe the patterns you found in each.

1,001	123	
2,002		1,879
	123	2,880
4,004		3,881
	123	
6,006		5,883

Pattern: ______________________________

	1,111	7,941
9,052	2,222	
9,052		5,719
	4,444	
9,052		
		2,386

Pattern: ______________________________

6,284		1,234
	5,050	2,345
8,506	5,050	
9,617		4,567
		5,678
11,839	5,050	

Pattern: ______________________________

Name ______________________________ **Extend Your Thinking 3-9**

Decision Making

You and your brother have $25 to spend on a birthday gift for your mom. You have a choice of three gifts.

Gift A: a pair of earrings for $14.99 and a box of candy for $8.95

Gift B: a bird feeder for $18.95 and some birdseed for $4.50

Gift C: a potted plant for $11.99, a vase for $8.50, and cut flowers for $4.50

Extra information: You will make your own card and wrapping paper. Sales tax is included.

1. List the gifts from most expensive to least expensive. Include the total cost of each.

____

2. How much money would you have left over if you bought

a. Gift A? __________

b. Gift B? __________

c. Gift C? __________

3. How much would Gift C cost if you didn't buy the vase? __________

4. Describe the strong and weak points of each gift choice.

Gift A: ______________________________

Gift B: ______________________________

Gift C: ______________________________

5. Which gift would you choose? Explain your reasoning.

____

____

6. If you had enough money for two gift choices, which two would you choose? Why?

____

Name ________________________________

Critical Thinking

Some of the tallest dams in the United States were built during the 1900s.

Dam	State	Height	Year Completed
Oroville	California	754 ft	1968
Hoover	Nevada	725 ft	1936
Glen Canyon	Arizona	708 ft	1966
Hungry Horse	Montana	564 ft	1953
Ross	Washington	541 ft	1949

1. What is the difference between the height of the tallest dam on the list and the shortest dam on the list?

____

2. How could you use mental math to find the difference in height between the Glen Canyon dam and the Hungry Horse dam? Explain.

____

3. How many years passed between the building of the oldest dam on the list and newest dam on the list?

____

4. Suppose the state of Arizona decided to build a dam which is 1,001 feet tall.

   a. How much taller would the new dam be than the Glen Canyon dam?

   ____

   b. If the new dam was completed this year, how many years would have passed from the completion of the Glen Canyon dam to the completion of the new dam?

   ____

Name ________________________________

Critical Thinking

An Idaho farmer is getting ready to plant his spring crop of corn, barley, and oats. He has to decide how much of each grain he will plant. The table shows the number of seeds that he needs for each crop and how much he must spend for each.

Crops	Number of Seeds	Cost
Corn	25,000	$1200
Barley	12,500	$1350
Oats	7200	$ 890

1. In order to make a profit, the farmer must make more money from the sale of his crops than he has spent for seeds. In order to make any profit at all, how much money would the farmer have to make on the sale of the crops? Explain.

____

____

2. Describe how you can use mental math to determine how many more corn seeds the farmer plans to buy than barley seeds.

____

____

3. Which seeds cost more per seed, corn or barley? Explain.

____

____

____

____

Name ______________________________

Extend Your Thinking
3-12

Critical Thinking

The units of currency known as dollars and cents are used in other countries besides the United States, such as Australia and Canada, for example. But many countries have different currencies. Use the information given to answer each question.

1. In Germany, there are 100 pfennigs to the mark. If you had 2 marks and 70 pfennigs, and someone gave you 3 10-pfennig coins, how much money would you have?

   ____

2. In France, there are 100 centimes to the franc. If you had 8 francs and 45 centimes, and someone gave you a 5-franc coin and a 20-centime coin, how much money would you have?

   ____

3. In Japan, the currency is called yen. If you had 490 yen and someone gave you two 500-yen coins and a 10-yen coin, how much money would you have?

   ____

4. In Greece, the currency is called drachma. If you had 1,000 drachma and someone gave you one 50-drachma bill, two 20-drachma coins and three 5-drachma coins, how much money would you have?

   ____

5. In Saudi Arabia, there are 100 halalahs to the riyal. If you had 6 riyals and 34 halalahs and someone gave you a 5-riyal bill, a 50-halalah coin and three 10-halalah coins, how much money would you have?

   ____

6. In Zambia, there are 100 ngwee to the kwacha. If you had 54 ngwee and someone gave you one 20-ngwee coin, six 10-ngwee coins, three 2-ngwee coins and one 1-ngwee coin, how much money would you have?

   ____

7. In the United Kingdom, there are 100 pence to the pound. If you had 5 pounds and someone gave you two 1-pound coins, one 20-pence coin, two 5-pence coins, six 2-pence coins and four 1-pence coins, how much money would you have?

   ____

Name ________________________________

Decision Making

Winchester High School is putting on a school play. The expenses of the show have to be covered by ticket sales. You are in charge of the budget.

Salary for director	$ 500
Salary for conductor	$ 300
Lumber	$ 120
Nails	$ 16
Paint	$ 29
Costumes:	
Fabric	$ 112
Thread, buttons, trim	$ 13
1 new stage light	$ 226
Makeup for actors	$ 57

1. What are the total expenses for the play? ________

2. Last year, Winchester's school play made $1000 in profit. If they still have that money to spend this year, what is the extra amount that must be made in order to meet the total expenses? ________

3. The costume maker was able to buy fabric and trim on sale for $75. By how much did this lower the budget? ________

4. What are some options you have in making sure expenses are covered? List three ways you could make sure all expenses are covered.

____

____

5. Which way listed in question **4** would you choose to make sure all expenses were paid for?

____

Name ______________________________

Critical Thinking

The United Kingdom uses a system of money that is very much like ours. Instead of the dollar bill, the British use a coin called the pound. Their bills are called notes and the symbol they use for a pound looks like this: £. They also have 5-pound, 10-pound, 20-pound and 50-pound notes. A pound is worth about $1.70 in American money.

1. About how much in American money would the British 5-pound note be worth? ____________
2. Below is a picture of some British money. How many pounds are shown here? ____________
3. About how much is this worth in American money? ____________

4. Imagine that you work in a store that accepts British money, but gives change in American money! A British tourist makes a purchase of $7.60. She hands you £10.

   a. Will this be enough money to pay for her purchase? Explain.

   ____

   b. How much change will you give her in American money?

   ____

Name ______________________________

Visual Thinking

Use the pictures to help you determine the value of *n*. Draw a picture to represent *n* in each box. Write the value of *n*.

1. 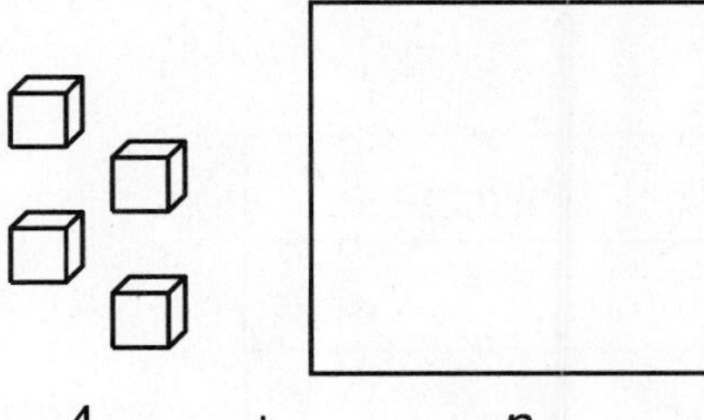 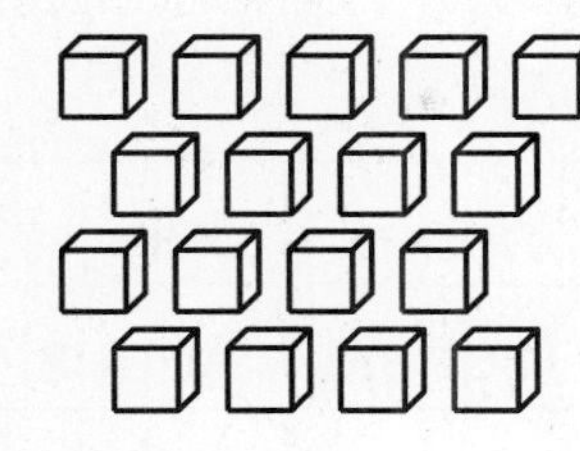

4 + *n* = 17 *n* = ________

2.  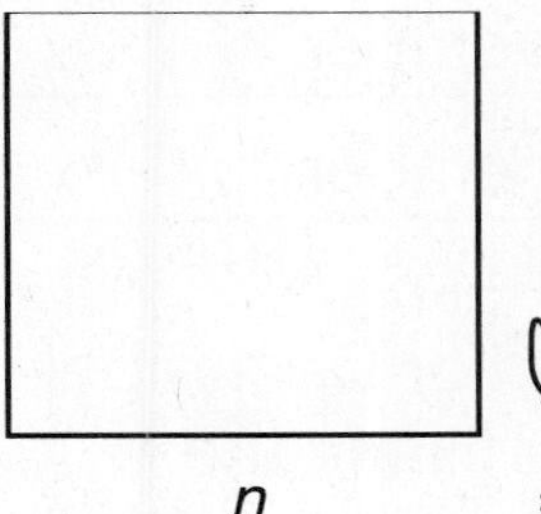 

8 + *n* = 9 *n* = ________

3. 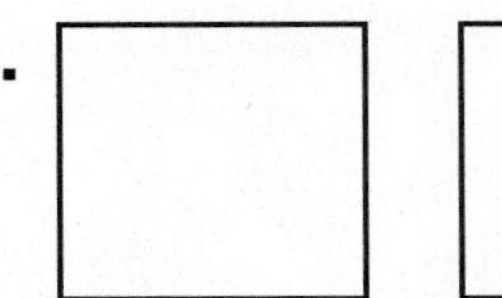 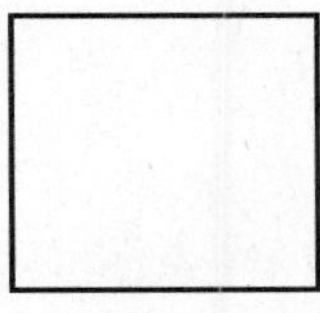  

n + *n* + 3 = 13 *n* = ________

4. 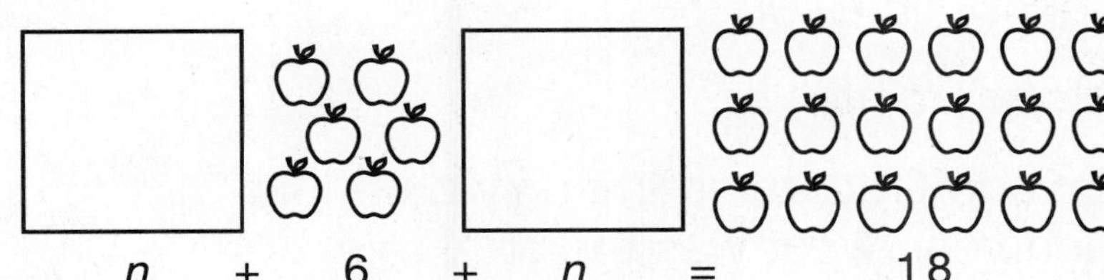

n + 6 + *n* = 18 *n* = ________

5. 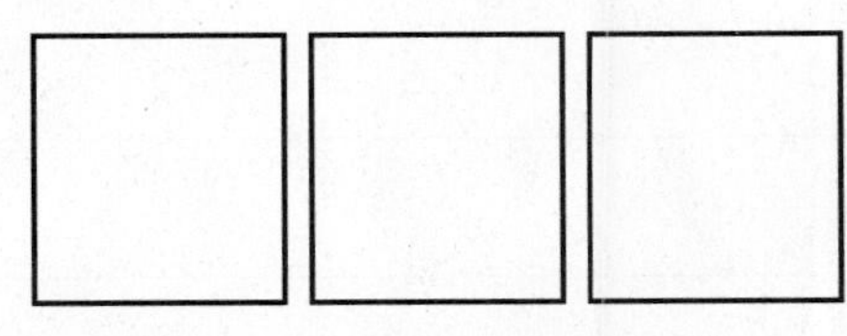 

n + *n* + *n* = 9 *n* = ________

Name ________________________________

Patterns in Data

Henderson Lake in British Columbia, Canada is a very wet place. During one year, rain and snowfall measured 262 inches! Here are rain and snowfall measurements for the first 7 months of that year.

January	22 inches	July	2 inches
February	25 inches	August	
March	32 inches	September	
April	40 inches	October	
May	10 inches	November	
June	2 inches	December	

1. The rain and snowfall measurements for December are the same as those of January. Similarly the measurements for November are the same as those of February. Use the pattern to complete the table.

2. What is the total rain and snowfall for the year shown in the table? ____________

3. Suppose that in the following year, the rainfall in August is twice that of May, while the rainfall in October is half that of March.

   a. What would the August rainfall be? ____________

   b. What would the October rainfall be? ____________

4. If the rainfall for August and October is the only data that changed in the following year, what was the total rain and snowfall for the year? Explain how you found your answer.

____

____

Name ____

Visual Thinking

Circle the figure with the same pattern as the figure on the left.

1.  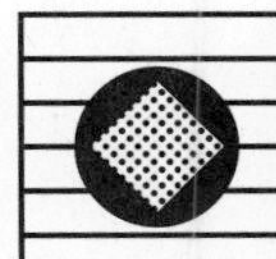  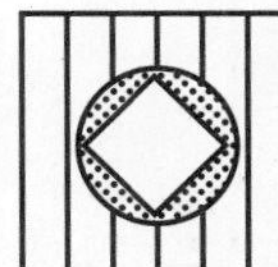 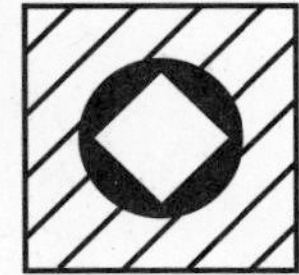

2.  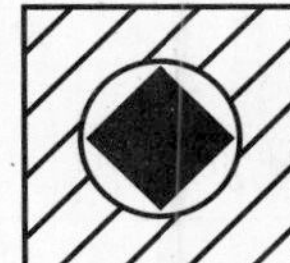   

3. 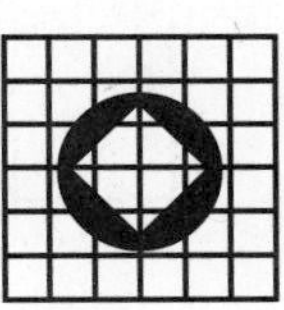 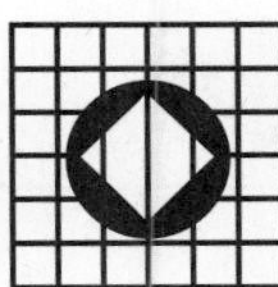 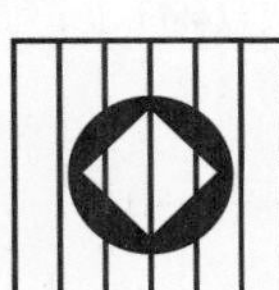 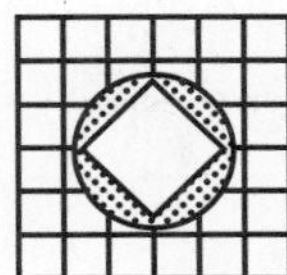 

4. 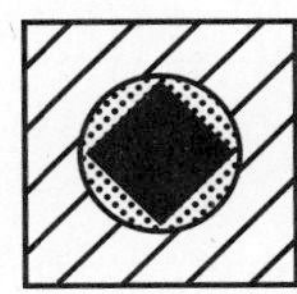 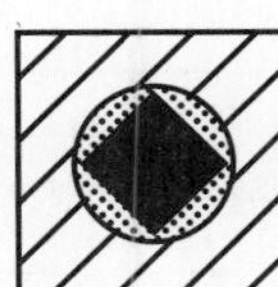  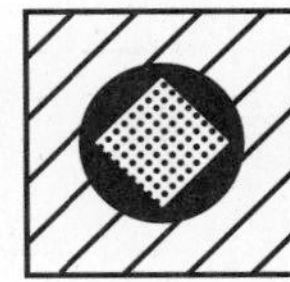 

5. 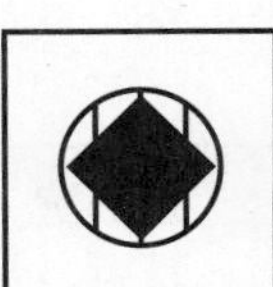 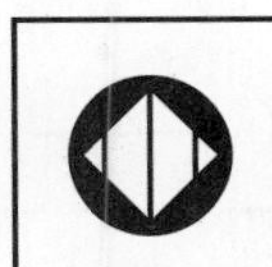 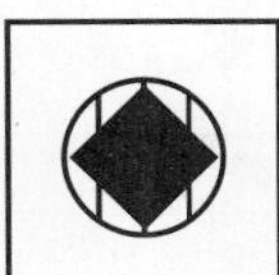 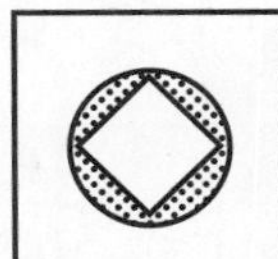 

Name ______________________________

Visual Thinking

These figures are mirror images of each other because their positions are reversed.

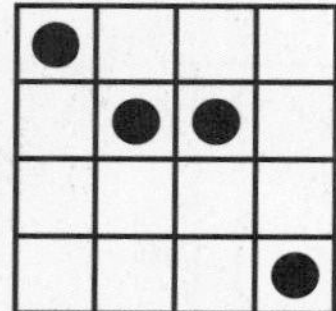
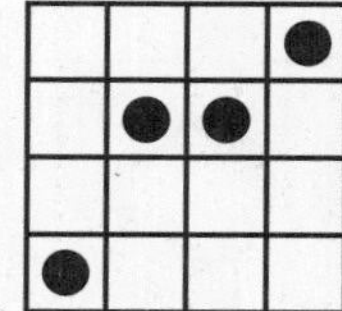

Circle the figure on the right that is the mirror image of the figure on the left.

1. 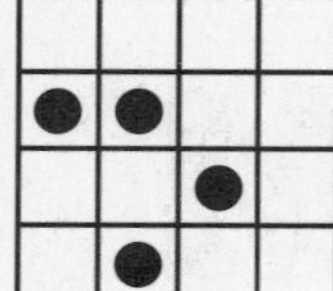 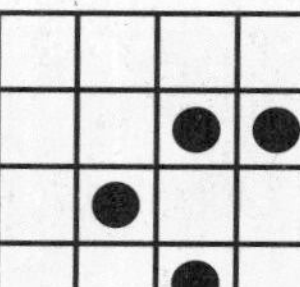 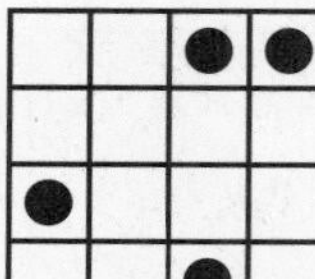 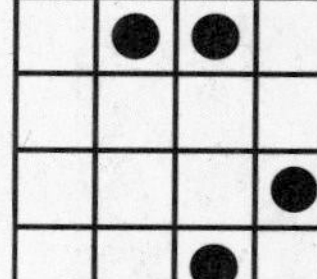

2. 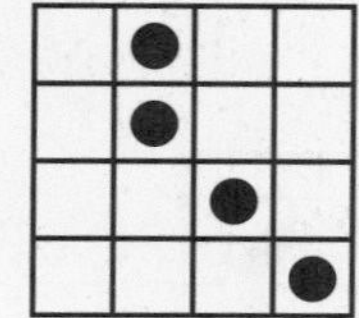 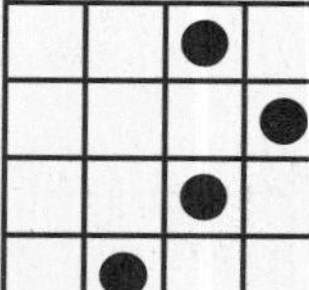 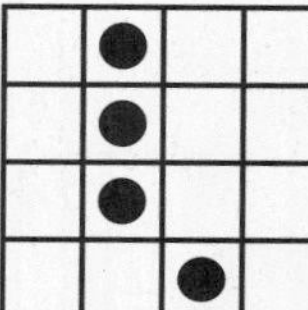 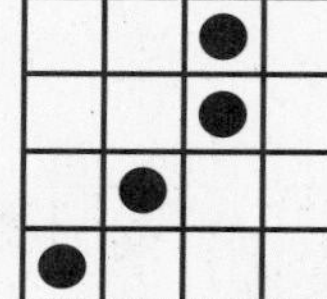 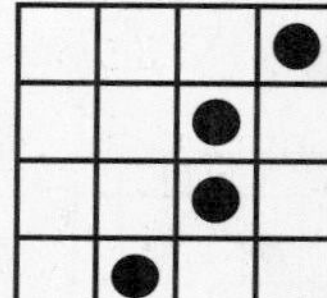

3. 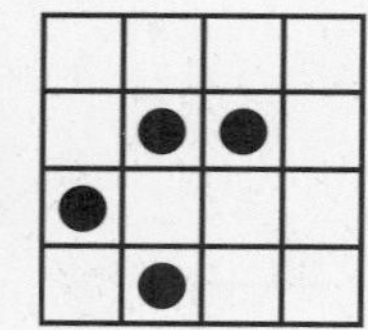 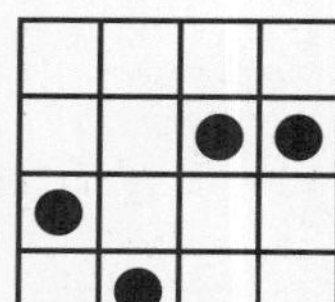 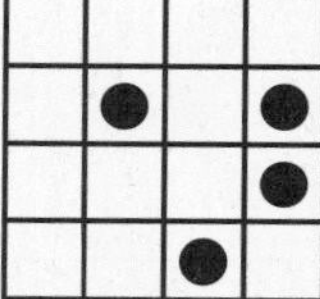 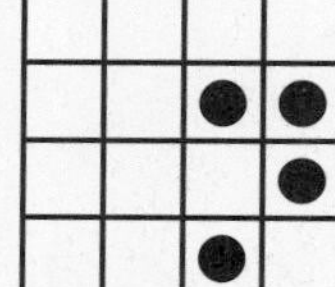 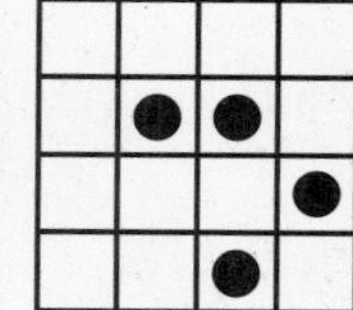

4. 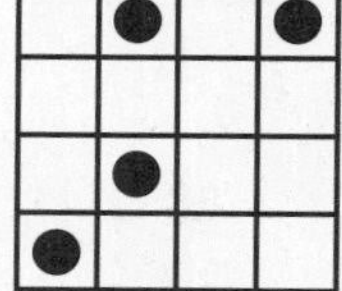 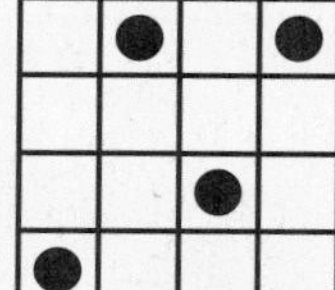 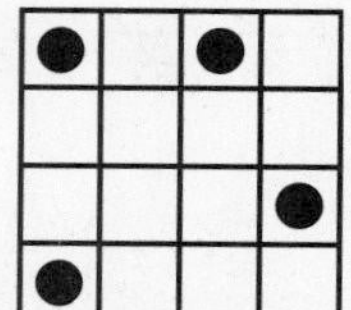

5. 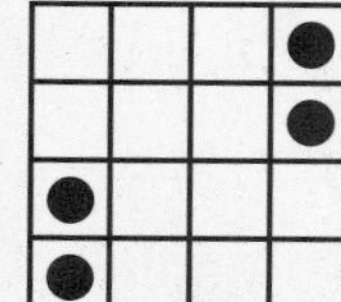 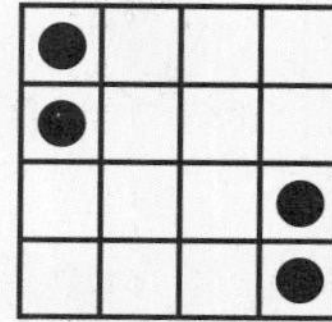 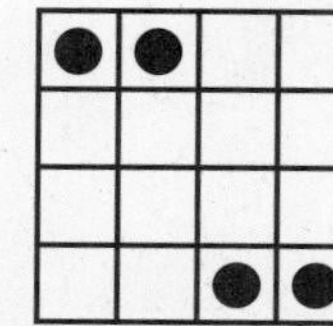

Name ______________________

Decision Making

You are having a party for 24 people. You have $60 to spend on supplies. You can choose between two stores for supplies.

Store A is 3 miles away
- Forks: set of 4 for $1.00
- Plates: set of 6 for $3.00
- Cups: set of 3 for $2.00

Store B is 2 miles away
- Forks: set of 6 for $3.00
- Plates: set of 8 for $5.00
- Cups: set of 6 for $3.00

1. Suppose you buy all your supplies at Store A.

a. How many sets of each item would you have to buy?

forks __________ plates __________ cups __________

b. How much would each item cost?

forks __________ plates __________ cups __________

c. How much would you pay all together? __________

2. Suppose you buy all your supplies at Store B.

a. How many sets of each item would you have to buy?

forks __________ plates __________ cups __________

b. How much would each item cost?

forks __________ plates __________ cups __________

c. How much would you pay all together? __________

3. Suppose you buy the least expensive items from Store A and Store B.

a. How much money would each item cost?

forks __________ plates __________ cups __________

b. How much money would you pay all together? __________

4. Would you choose to buy all your supplies at one store, or go to both stores to get the least expensive supplies? Explain.

____

____

Name ______________________________ **Extend Your Thinking 4-4**

Critical Thinking

You can add products to find other products.

1. Draw an array of 5×9. Shade the array to show that $(3 \times 9) + (2 \times 9) = 5 \times 9$.

2. How could you use the product of 9×7 and the product of 8×7 to find the product of 17×7?

____

3. Find 12×17 by adding two products.

   a. $12 \times 17 = (12 \times$ ________$) + (12 \times$ ________$)$

   b. $12 \times 17 =$ ________ $+$ ________

   c. $12 \times 17 =$ ________

   d. What other numbers have a sum of 17? ________

4. Find what number multiplied by 9 equals 135.

   a. $9 \times$ ________ $= 81$

   b. $9 \times$ ________ $= 54$

   c. $81 + 54 =$ ________

   d. $9 \times$ ________ $= 135$

5. $7 \times 11 = 77$ and $25 \times 7 = 175$. Explain how you could use these products to find 7×14. Then find 7×14.

____

6. Find 24×4 by adding 3 products.

   a. $24 \times 4 = ($________ $+$ ________ $+$ ________$) \times 4$

   b. $24 \times 4 = ($________ $\times 4) + ($________ $\times 4) + ($________ $\times 4)$

   c. $24 \times 4 =$ ________ $+$ ________ $+$ ________

   d. $24 \times 4 =$ ________

Name ______________________

Patterns in Numbers

Complete each pattern. Then write the rule used for each pattern.

1. 8, 16, 24, ______, ______, ______

Rule: ______________________

2. 4, 8, 12, ______, ______, ______

Rule: ______________________

3. 5, 10, 15, ______, ______, ______

Rule: ______________________

4. 0, 24, 48, 72, ______, ______, ______

Rule: ______________________

Look at **1–4** again. Describe each pattern in terms of multiples.

5. **1** shows multiples of ______

6. **2** shows multiples of ______

7. **3** shows multiples of ______

8. **4** shows multiples of ______

9. Write your own patterns of multiples. Describe each pattern using multiples and then by an addition rule.

Pattern: ______________________

Multiples of: ______________________

Rule: ______________________

Pattern: ______________________

Multiples of: ______________________

Rule: ______________________

Name ______________________________ **Extend Your Thinking 4-6**

Visual Thinking

Draw the next figure in each row to continue the pattern.

1. 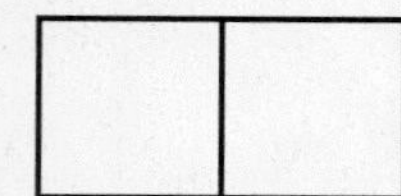 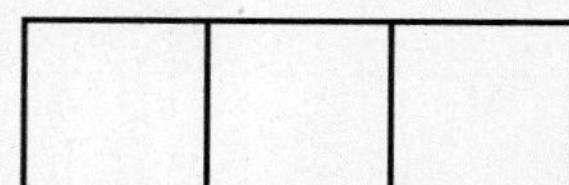

2. 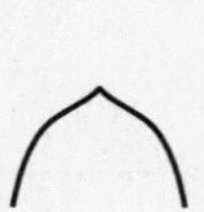 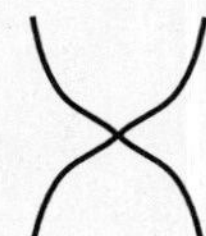 

3.   

4. 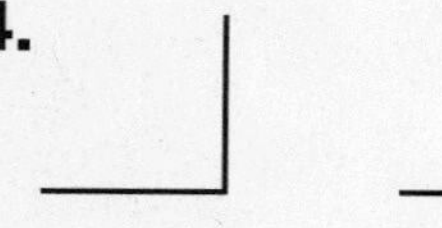  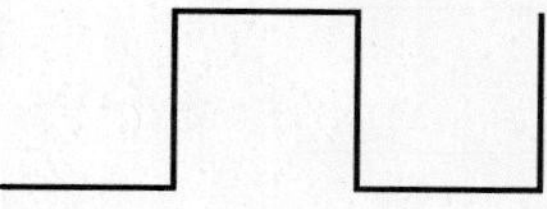

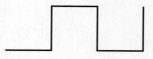

5.  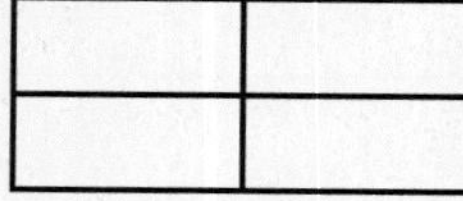 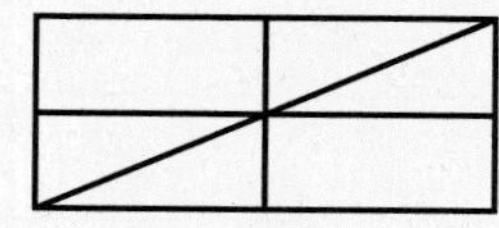

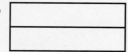

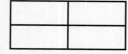

6. 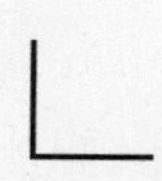  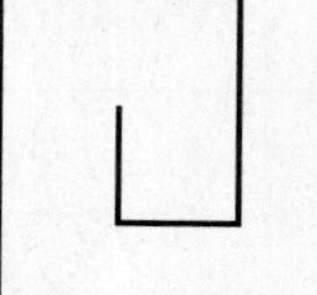

Name ____________________

Critical Thinking

Answer the riddles using the numbers below.

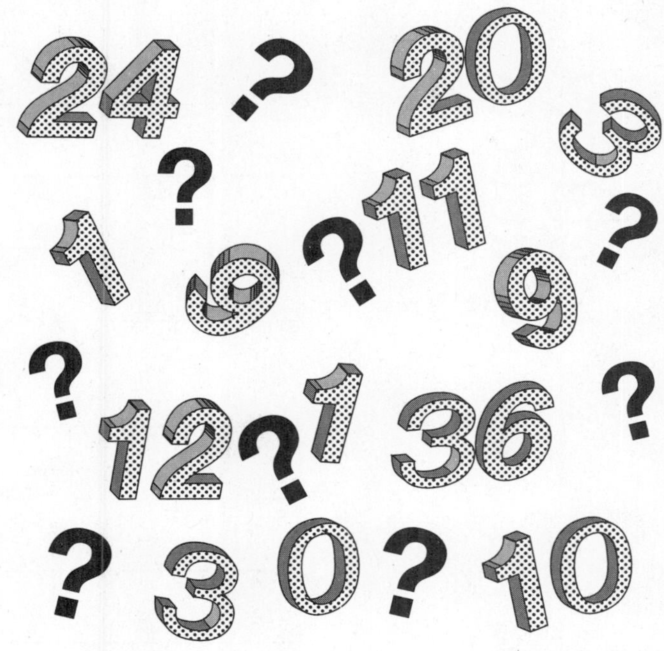

1. I am a 2-digit number. I am divisible by 5 and 2. I am less than 20. What number am I? ________
2. I am a 1-digit number. I am only divisible by myself. If you multiply a number by me, you get that number. What number am I? ________
3. I am a 2-digit number. I am divisible by 1, 2, 3, 4, 6, 9, 12, 18, and 36. I am less than 50. What number am I? ________
4. I am a 1-digit number. I am a factor of 18, 27, 36, and 45. I am not 1. I am less than 5. What number am I? ________
5. I am a 2-digit number. I am divisible by 6 different numbers that include 3, 4, and 6. I am a factor of 12, 24, 36, and 48. What number am I? ________
6. I am a 2-digit number. I am a factor of 80, 60, 40, and 20. I am divisible by 6 different numbers that include 4, 5, and 10. What number am I? ________
7. I am a 1-digit number. I only have 2 factors. I am a factor of 6, 9, and 12. What number am I? ________
8. I am a 1-digit number. If you multiply any number by me, you always get the same product. What number am I? ________

Name ______________________________ Extend Your Thinking 4-8

Visual Thinking

Write the multiplication and division fact families for the following pictures.

1. ⬭⬭⬭⬭⬭⬭⬭ (6 rows of 7)

____

____

____

____

2. ⬭⬭⬭⬭

____

____

____

____

Write fact families for each set of numbers.

3. 21, 3, 7 ______________________________

4. 36, 6, 6 ______________________________

5. 56, 7, 8 ______________________________

6. Choose one of the fact families from **3–5** and draw a picture for it.

7. Write a story using your own fact family and picture.

____

____

____

____

____

Name ______________________________

Patterns in Numbers

Write the next three numbers in each pattern below. Write the rule used for each pattern. Then write what the numbers in the pattern have in common.

1. 2, 4, 6, 8, ________, ________, ________

   Rule: ______________________________

   What do they have in common? ______________________________

2. 45, 40, 35, 30, ________, ________, ________

   Rule: ______________________________

   What do they have in common? ______________________________

3. 12, 15, 18, 21, ________, ________, ________

   Rule: ______________________________

   What do they have in common? ______________________________

4. 72, 63, 54, 45, ________, ________, ________

   Rule: ______________________________

   What do they have in common? ______________________________

5. 42, 36, 30, 24, ________, ________, ________

   Rule: ______________________________

   What do they have in common? ______________________________

6. 21, 28, 35, 42, ________, ________, ________

   Rule: ______________________________

   What do they have in common? ______________________________

7. 64, 56, 48, 40, ________, ________, ________

   Rule: ______________________________

   What do they have in common? ______________________________

Name ______________________________ **Extend Your Thinking 4-10**

Patterns in Numbers

Write the rule. Then find the next number to continue the pattern.

1. 3, 6, 9, 12, 15, ________

Rule: ______________________________

2. 16, 8, 4, 2, ________

Rule: ______________________________

3. 14, 17, 20, 23, 26, 29, 32, ________

Rule: ______________________________

4. 14, 24, 34, 44, 54, 64, ________

Rule: ______________________________

5. 114, 116, 119, 121, 124, 126, ________

Rule: ______________________________

6. 59,049; 6,561; 729; 81; ________

Rule: ______________________________

7. 81, 83, 86, 90, ________

Rule: ______________________________

8. 65; 130; 260; 520; ________

Rule: ______________________________

9. 1, 1, 2, 3, 5, 8, ________

Rule: ______________________________

10. 779, 776, 773, 770, ________

Rule: ______________________________

11. 1, 1, 2, 6, 6, 12, 36, ________

Rule: ______________________________

Name ________________________________

Decision Making

Andrew, Belinda, and Carl went to a fruit stand. They each had the following amounts of money.

Andrew: 30¢
Belinda: 20¢
Carl: 40¢

Price List	
Apples	5¢ each, bags of 6 for 15¢
Oranges	10¢ each, bags of 6 for 30¢
Bananas	2¢ each, bags of 6 for 5¢

1. If they each only buy one type of fruit, how many individual pieces (not in bags) of fruit can each person buy with the money they have?

Andrew: Apples ________ Oranges ________ Bananas ________

Belinda: Apples ________ Oranges ________ Bananas ________

Carl: Apples ________ Oranges ________ Bananas ________

2. If they each only buy one type of fruit, how many bags of six can each person buy with the money they have?

Andrew: Apples ________ Oranges ________ Bananas ________

Belinda: Apples ________ Oranges ________ Bananas ________

Carl: Apples ________ Oranges ________ Bananas ________

3. If they put their money together, can they buy more fruit? Explain your answer.

____

____

____

4. How do you think Andrew, Belinda, and Carl should spend their money for fruit? Explain your reasoning.

____

____

____

Name ______________________________

Critical Thinking

Your teacher has given you this challenge.

"Here are 150 squares of paper. Create 3 pyramid shapes on the bulletin board. Each pyramid must be one row higher than the last. The top row of every pyramid will be one block long and every row must be two squares longer than the row above it. The team that uses the most squares wins."

Your team won! You used 149 squares to make 3 pyramids on the board.

1. **a.** How many rows did your first pyramid have? _____

   b. How many total blocks? _____

2. **a.** How many rows did your second pyramid have? _____

   b. How many total blocks? _____

3. **a.** How many rows did your third pyramid have? _____

   b. How many total blocks? _____

4. Describe patterns you see in the number of blocks for each pyramid.

   ____

   ____

5. Draw a pyramid with 25 blocks using the pattern above.

Pyramid Challenge

Name ______________________________ Extend Your Thinking 4-13

Patterns in Numbers

Write what comes next in each pattern. Then write the rule used for each pattern.

1. 11, 13, 15, 17, ________, ________, ________

Rule: ______________________________

2. 48, 41, 34, 27, ________, ________, ________

Rule: ______________________________

3. 3, 7, 12, 18, ________, ________, ________

Rule: ______________________________

4. 3, 9, 27, ________, ________, ________

Rule: ______________________________

5. 12, 13, 15, 16, 17, 19, 20, ________, ________, ________

Rule: ______________________________

6. 1, 2, 6, 24, ________, ________, ________

Rule: ______________________________

7. 1; 10; 101; 1,010; ________; ________; ________

Rule: ______________________________

____

8. Write your own number pattern. Write its rule.

Pattern: ______________________________

Rule: ______________________________

Name ______________________________

Extend Your Thinking
4-14

Critical Thinking

Suppose you are an ancient Egyptian stone worker. The Queen has hired you to make a pyramid sculpture for her garden.

"I will give you 140 blocks of stone," she said. "Do not waste them."

The Queen showed you a model using 14 blocks. The model is 3 blocks high. The top layer has 1 block, the 2nd layer has 4 blocks, and the 3rd layer has 9 blocks.

A mathematician whispered to you, "You will be able to use all the blocks if you follow the Queen's model. Just look for the pattern."

After a while, the pattern becomes clear. You build the pyramid, using all the blocks, and are richly rewarded by the Queen.

1. How many layers did your finished pyramid have? __________

2. How many blocks did you use for each layer?

   ____

3. Describe the pattern the mathematician was talking about.

   ____

   ____

   ____

4. Could you make another pyramid with 200 blocks following the same pattern? Explain.

   ____

   ____

5. How many blocks of stone would you need to follow the same pattern and make a pyramid:

   a. 8 blocks high? __________

   b. 9 blocks high? __________

   c. 10 blocks high? __________

Name ______________________________

Extend Your Thinking
4-15

Decision Making

The Math Club has raised $450 for this year's trip. They've decided to go to New York City. Today, all 8 members will vote on what to do when they get there. They must choose from among the following choices:

A. Go to a Broadway play.
- Each matinee ticket costs $28.
- A play lasts for 2 or 3 hours.
- There is 1 matinee a day, usually at 2:00 P.M.

B. See a show at Radio City Music Hall.
- Each ticket costs $12.
- A show lasts about 90 minutes.
- There are 5 shows a day, starting at 9:00 A.M.

C. Go to the Museum of Natural History.
- Each ticket costs $5.
- The museum is free to the public on Wednesdays.
- The museum is across the street from Central Park.

D. Go to the Statue of Liberty.
- Each ticket costs $11.
- The statue is in New York Harbor.
- The ferry ride to the statue takes about 20 minutes.

The train ride to New York takes 1 hour and costs $12 each way. Lunch costs about $10 per person, unless you bring your own.

If you were in the Math Club, how would you vote to spend the day? Explain.

____

____

____

____

____

____

____

____

____

Name ______________________________ **Extend Your Thinking 4-16**

Decision Making

The astronomy club is putting on a school dance to raise money for a field trip. They surveyed 50 students and found out that 25 read the school bulletin board, 29 read the newspaper, and 41 listen to announcements.

1. Make a bar graph in the space below to show the data above.

2. The astronomy club wants to advertise their dance to get as many students to attend as possible. How should they do this?

____

____

____

3. Suppose there are the following limits:

- The dance can only be talked about on the announcements one time during a week.
- A poster advertising the dance can only be posted on the school bulletin board for one week.
- An advertisement in the newspaper costs $10 for each day that it runs.

How would these limits affect your answers to **2**? Explain.

____

____

____

____

____

Name ___________________________

Critical Thinking

Mr. Jones had 10 chickens on his farm. Each chicken lays an average of 1 egg a day.

1. Finish the table recording the number of eggs laid in a week on Mr. Jones' farm.

Days	1	2	3	4	5	6	7
Eggs							

Answer the questions using your data.

2. How many eggs did Mr. Jones collect after 4 days? ___________

3. Estimate the number of eggs Mr. Jones will collect in two weeks. Explain your reasoning.

____

4. If he sells half the eggs each day, how many eggs would he have left on the third day? Explain.

____

5. Suppose Mr. Jones adds 10 more chickens to his flock.

a. How many eggs will he collect in a week? Explain.

____

b. Why is the number of eggs collected in one week the same as the answer to **3**?

____

____

____

Name ______________________________

Extend Your Thinking
5-2

Visual Thinking

In each row, circle the figure on the right that will complete the analogy.

1. is to as is to

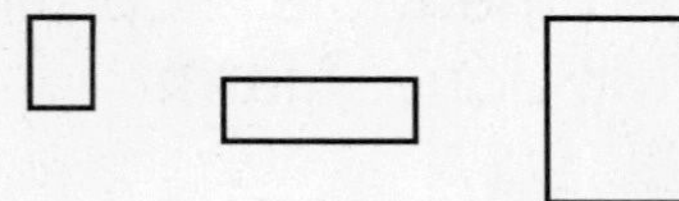

2. is to as is to

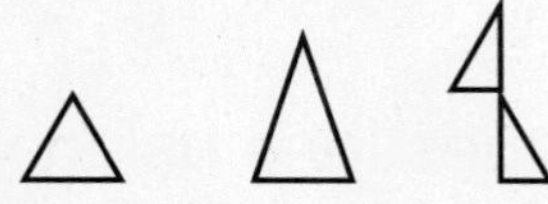

3. is to as is to

4. is to as is to

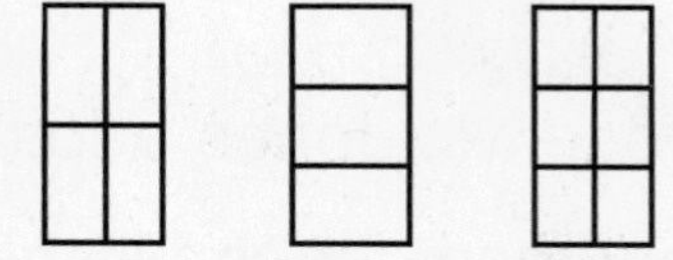

5. is to as is to

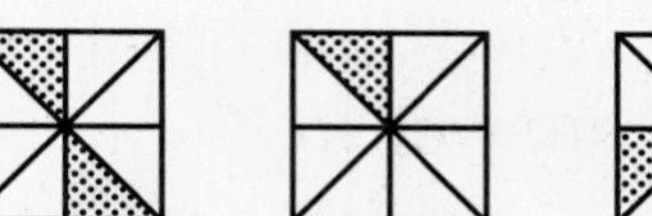

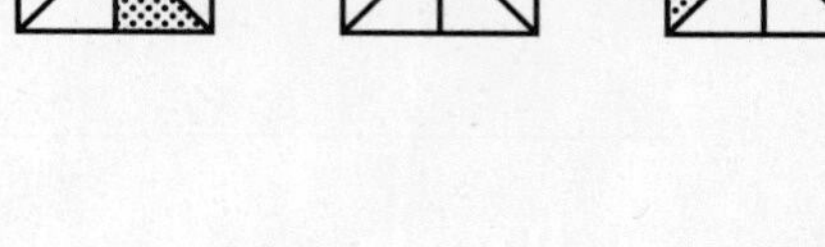

6. is to as is to

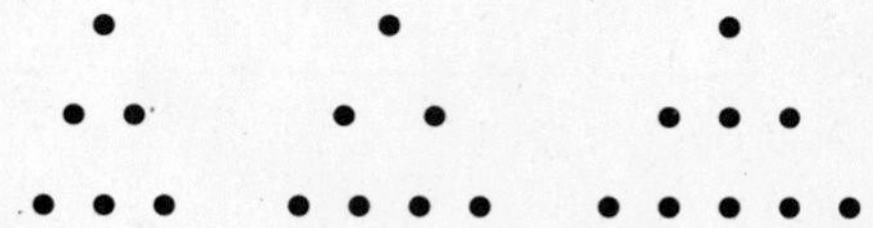

Name ______________________________

Decision Making

The student council at Greenway Elementary needs to choose an event to raise money for their school. Here are three possible choices:

A. Rent-a-Student. Costs involved in the Rent-a-Student program total $100. The Council estimates that 27 students are available for 8 hours each. The cost to rent a student is $1 an hour.

B. Ticket Raffle. The students raffle two tickets to a professional basketball game. Each ticket to the game costs $74. Each raffle ticket will sell for $2. The students should be able to sell 378 tickets in a week.

C. Juice Sale. The students sell juice at the school carnival. They think they can sell 6 cases of juice at $18 a case. The booth is open for 6 hours. The juice costs $12 for 1 case.

1. Estimate the cost of each choice.

Choice A __________ Choice B __________ Choice C __________

2. About how much money will each choice earn?

Choice A __________ Choice B __________ Choice C __________

3. About how much profit does the school earn from each choice?

Choice A __________ Choice B __________ Choice C __________

4. Besides profit, what other factors should the student council consider before making their decision?

____

____

____

5. Which event would be the best choice? Explain.

____

____

Name ___________________________ **Extend Your Thinking 5-4**

Visual Thinking

Which musical instruments match the ones on the left?
Write the correct answer on the blank.

1. ________

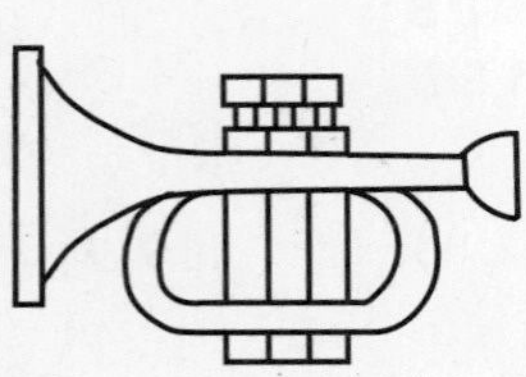

a.

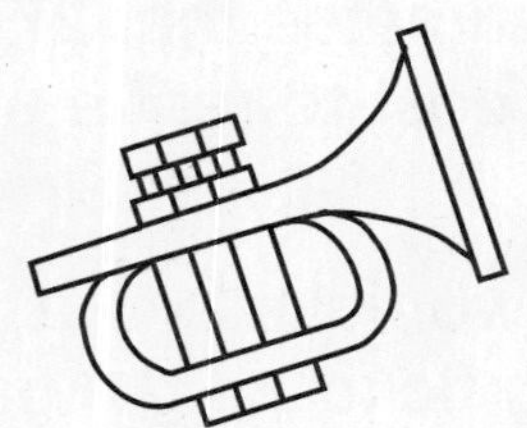

b.

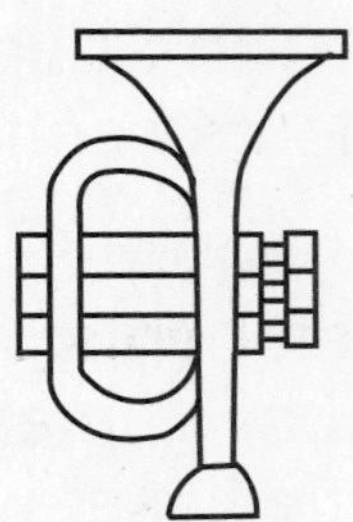

c.

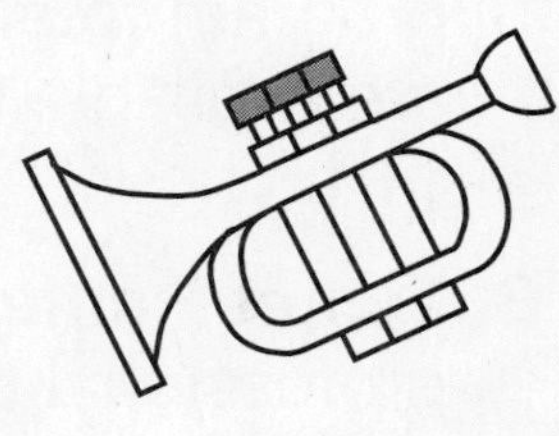

2. ________

a.

b.

c.

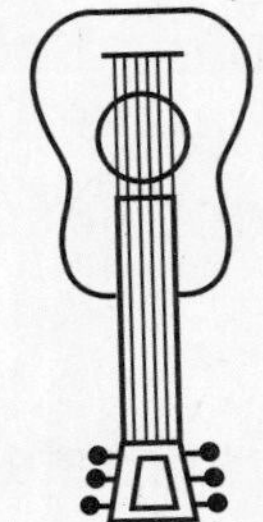

3. ________

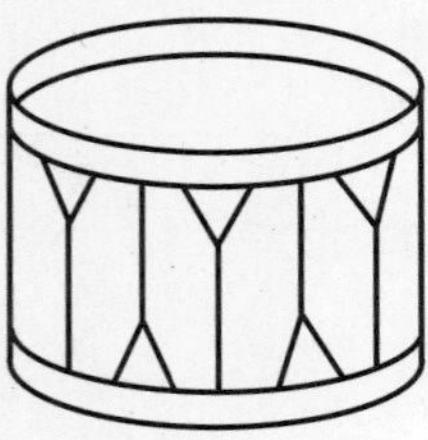

a.

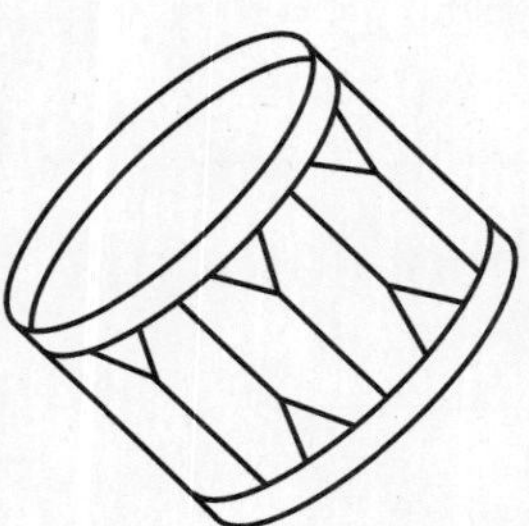

b.

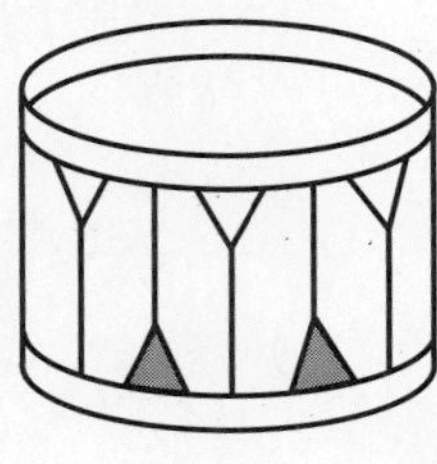

c.

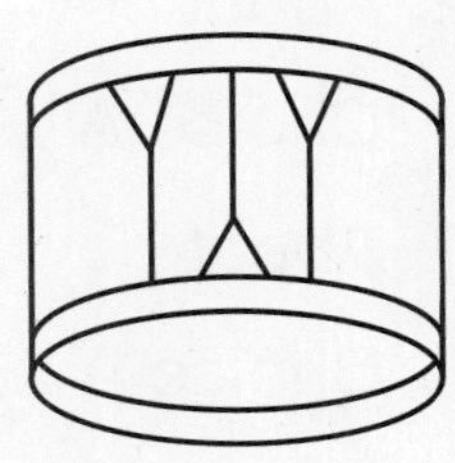

4. ________

a.

b.

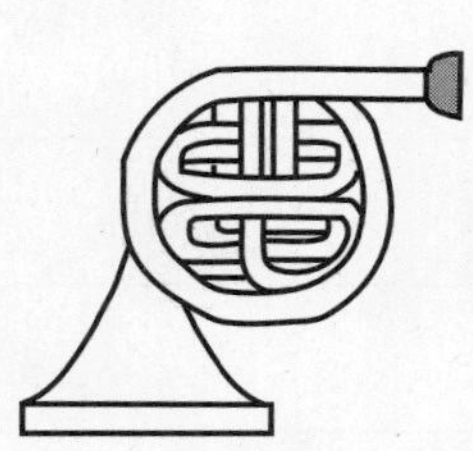

c.

Name ______________________________

Critical Thinking

Complete each multiplication exercise.

1. 16 × 7 = 11_

2. 3_ × 4 = 124

3. 48 × 5 = 24_

4. 56 × 4 = 2_4

5. _6 × 5 = 180

6. 41 × _ = 164

7. 6_ × 2 = 122

8. 77 × 8 = 6_6

9. 62 × 7 = _34

10. 1_ × 6 = 108

11. 62 × 2 = 1_4

12. _8 × 7 = 266

13. 62 × 6 = _2

14. _4 × 5 = 170

15. 4_ × 6 = 264

16. 75 × 9 = 6_5

17. Describe how you found a missing digit in the product.

____

____

18. Describe how you found a missing digit in one of the factors.

____

____

Name ______________________________

Critical Thinking

Use a calculator to find the missing numbers.

1. $\begin{array}{r} \$143 \\ \times \quad \_ \\ \hline \$1,001 \end{array}$

2. $\begin{array}{r} \_\_\_ \\ \times \quad 8 \\ \hline \$1,648 \end{array}$

3. $\begin{array}{r} \_\_\_ \\ \times \quad 4 \\ \hline \$1,332 \end{array}$

4. $\begin{array}{r} \$807 \\ \times \quad \_ \\ \hline \$7,263 \end{array}$

5. $\begin{array}{r} \_\_\_ \\ \times \quad 3 \\ \hline \$2,961 \end{array}$

6. $\begin{array}{r} \$456 \\ \times \quad \_ \\ \hline \$3,648 \end{array}$

7. $\begin{array}{r} \_\_\_ \\ \times \quad 5 \\ \hline \$4,615 \end{array}$

8. $\begin{array}{r} \$499 \\ \times \quad \_ \\ \hline \$2,994 \end{array}$

9. $\begin{array}{r} \$586 \\ \times \quad \_ \\ \hline \$4,102 \end{array}$

10. $\begin{array}{r} \_\_\_ \\ \times \quad 6 \\ \hline \$1,152 \end{array}$

11. $\begin{array}{r} \_\_\_ \\ \times \quad 3 \\ \hline \$1,395 \end{array}$

12. $\begin{array}{r} \$787 \\ \times \quad \_ \\ \hline \$5,509 \end{array}$

 Use with pages 214–215.

Name ______________________________

Decision Making

Approximately 220 dinosaur egg sites have been found around the world in Asia, North America, Europe, South America, and Africa.

Professor Jenkins and her assistant are planning a scientific research trip to visit a dinosaur egg site. These 3 trips are available. Which destination should they choose?

Destination	Number of Days	Cost per Person	Other Information
Asia	8	$1,750	Asia has the greatest number of dinosaur egg sites.
North America	10	$979	There is only one dinosaur egg site in North America.
Europe	7	$ 1,549 (meals not included)	Europe has two dinosaur egg sites.

1. Which trip could Professor Jenkins and her assistant take for less than $3,000? Explain.

____

2. If meals in Europe cost an additional $175 per person, how much would a trip to Europe for 2 cost? __________

3. On which trip(s) will Professor Jenkins and her assistant be able to see at least 2 dinosaur egg sites?

____

4. What additional information could you use to help Professor Jenkins and her assistant make their decision?

____

____

____

5. Which trip should they choose? Explain how you made your decision.

____

Name ______________________

Critical Thinking

Joe Smith is an all-star running back for his football team. This card shows his record for five years.

Year	Total Yards	Touchdowns	Carries
1990	1,220	9	210
1991	1,340	7	264
1992	1,220	6	190
1993	1,640	9	283
1994	1,084	8	186

1. a. Estimate the total number of yards Joe ran from 1990 to 1994. Should you use a calculator? Explain.

____

____

b. Explain how you used multiplication to estimate the total number of yards.

____

____

____

2. Estimate the total number of carries Joe made. Can you use multiplication? Explain.

____

____

3. Would you estimate to find the total number of touchdowns Joe made? How many did he make?

____

Name ______________________________

Visual Thinking

Analogies are often use to show the relationship between pairs of items.

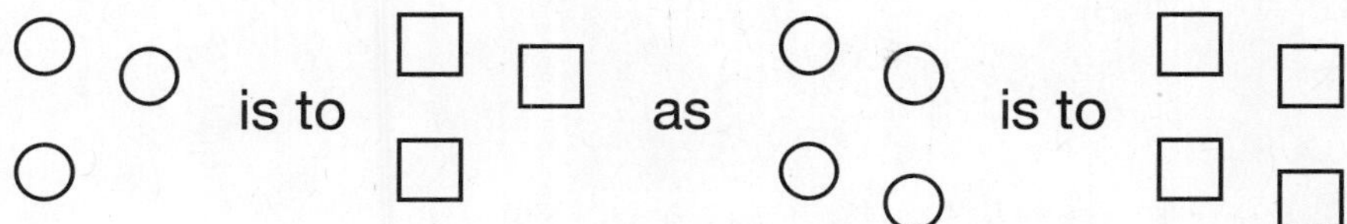

1. How are the first two drawings related?

____

____

2. Describe how the second pair of drawings are related in the same way.

____

____

Draw the fourth item for each analogy.

3. 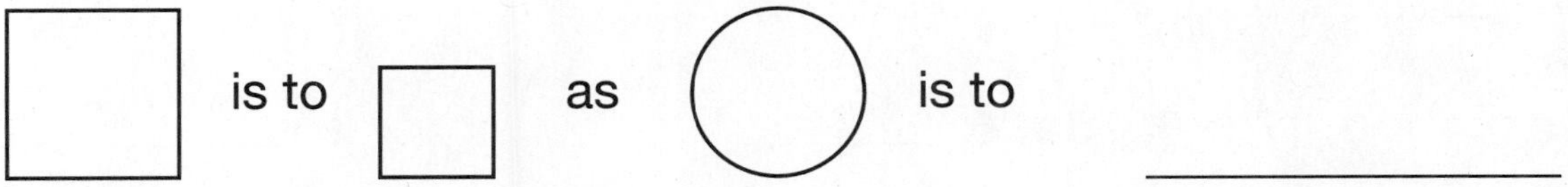 is to as is to ______________

4. 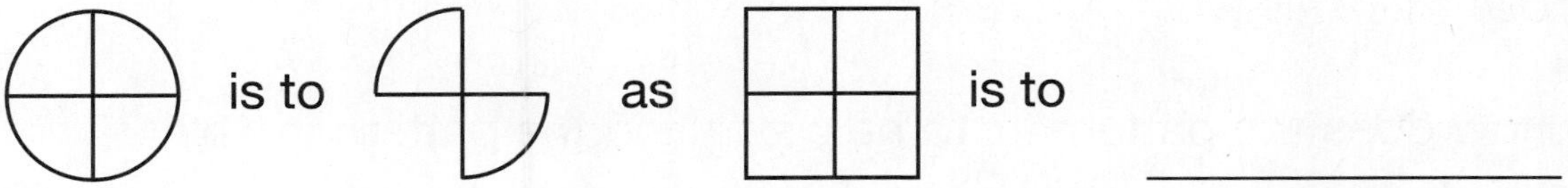 is to as is to ______________

5. 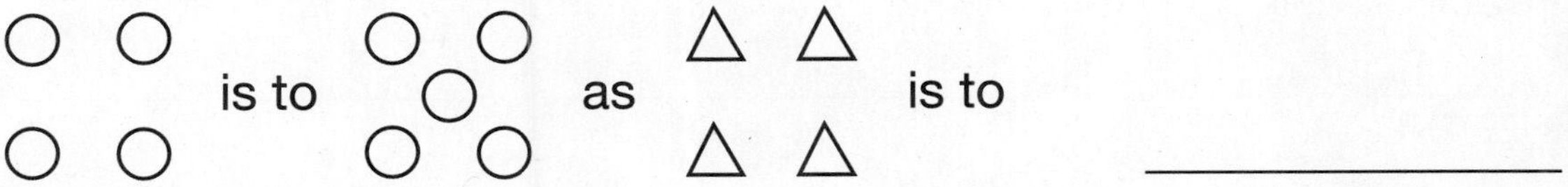 is to as is to ______________

Name ______________________________ Extend Your Thinking 5-10

Patterns in Numbers

What are the next three numbers in each **a.** pattern?
Use mental math to find the missing factors.
Then find the next numbers in each **b.** pattern of products.

1. a. 12 × 4, 18 × 4, 24 × 4, ________ × 4, ________ × 4, ________ × 4

b. 48, 72, 96, 120, ________, ________, ________, 216, ________

2. a. 60 × 3, 52 × 3, 44 × 3, ________ × 3, ________ × 3, ________ × 3

b. 180, ________, ________, 108, ________, ________, ________, 12

3. a. 20 × 7, 34 × 7, 48 × 7, ________ × 7, ________ × 7, ________ × 7

b. 140, ________, 336, ________, ________, ________, 728, ________

4. a. 84 × 6, 77 × 6, 70 × 6, ________ × 6, ________ × 6, ________ × 6

b. ________, ________, ________, 378, ________, ________, 252, ________

5. How does the pattern in **1a** help you find the pattern in **1b**?

____

____

____

Name ____________________

Critical Thinking

An architect is building a skyscraper. The building will have 42 floors. The plans include 27 offices on each of the bottom 2 floors, 22 offices on each of the middle 7 floors, and 9 offices on each of the 33 top floors. There will be 4 people working in each office on the bottom 2 floors, 3 people working in each office on the middle 7 floors, and 2 people working in each office on the top 33 floors.

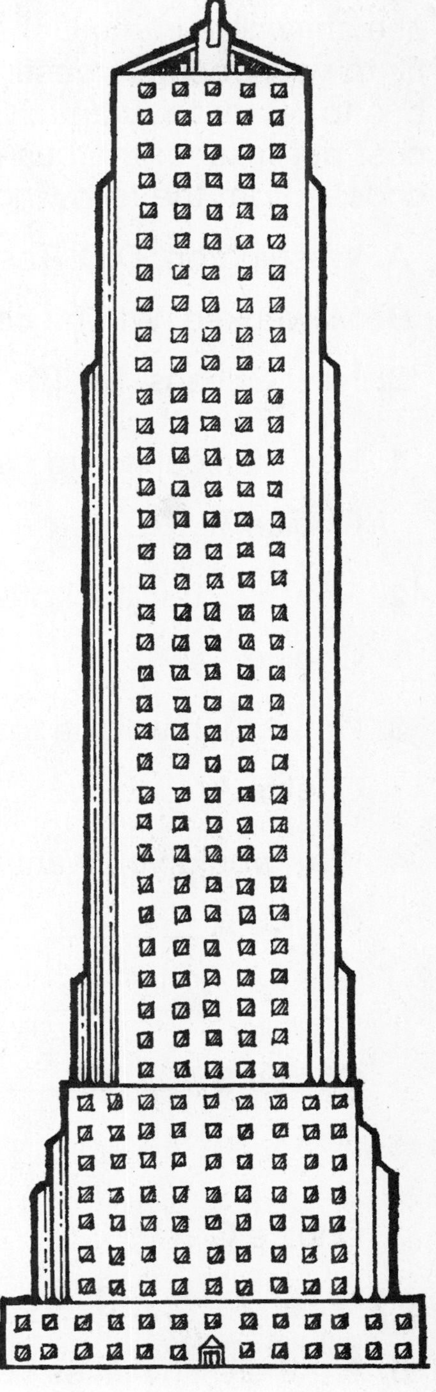

1. How many people can work on the 1st floor? ________

2. How many people can work on the 39th floor? ________

3. How many people can work on the 8th floor? ________

4. How many people in all can work on the middle 7 floors?

____

5. How many people in all can work on floors 22, 23, and 24?

____

6. How many people in all can work on floor 2 and floor 3?

____

7. How many people can work in the entire building?

____

____

Name ______________________

Extend Your Thinking
5-12

Decision Making

Your family won one-way plane tickets to use anywhere in the United States. You will fly to your vacation destination and take a bus to return to Atlanta, GA. The average cost per mile for the bus is $0.14. You must choose from the following locations:

	Atlanta
Washington, D.C.	608 mi.
Milwaukee, WI	761 mi.
New Orleans, LA	479 mi.

A. Washington, D.C. The cost for a hotel room is $65.45 per night.

B. Milwaukee, WI The cost for a hotel room is $30.99 per night.

C. New Orleans, LA The cost for a hotel room is $44.50 per night.

1. Use a calculator to determine the cost to return home from each city.

Choice A ________ Choice B ________ Choice C ________

2. How much will 2 hotel rooms cost in each city for 7 nights?

Choice A ________ Choice B ________ Choice C ________

3. How much will the total cost be for each city?

Choice A ________ Choice B ________ Choice C ________

4. Why would you want to visit each city?

Choice A ______________________

____

Choice B ______________________

____

Choice C ______________________

____

5. Are there any cities you would not want to visit? Why not?

____

6. To which city would you choose to travel? Why?

____

Name ______________________________

Visual Thinking

Complete the patterns in the problems below. Circle the letter for the shape that comes next in the pattern. Follow the sample below.

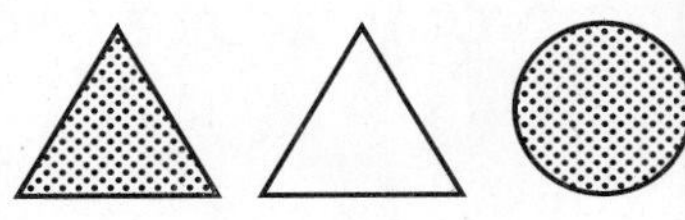

1. 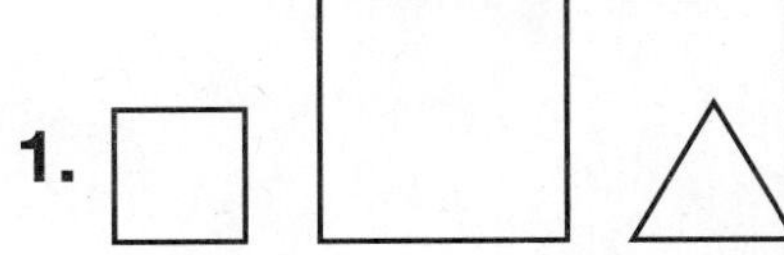

2. 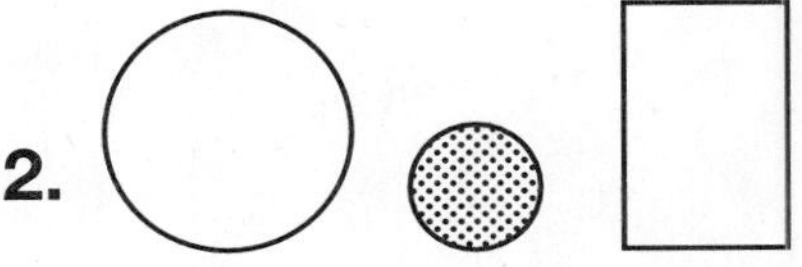

3. 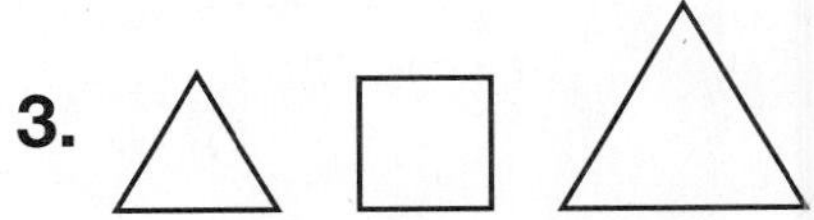

4. 

5. 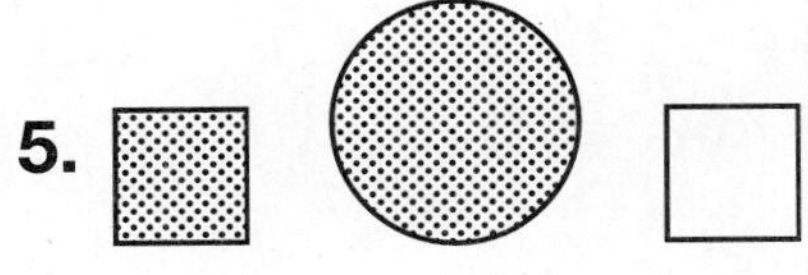

6.

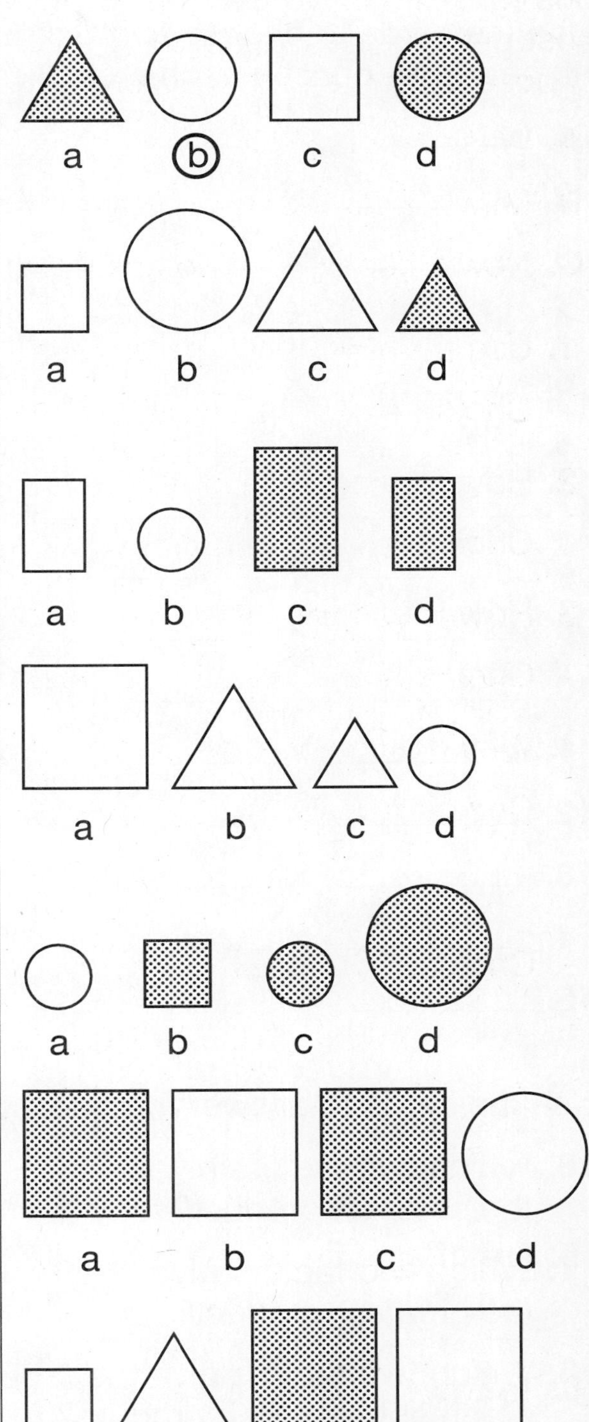

Name ______________________ Extend Your Thinking 6-1

Critical Thinking

600	40	2,000	30	80	5	70	9

Use the cards to choose two factors that will give the product. Use each number only once in each multiplication sentence.

1. ________ × ________ = 1,200

2. ________ × ________ = 42,000

3. ________ × ________ = 18,000

4. ________ × ________ = 2,400

5. ________ × ________ = 80,000

6. ________ × ________ = 360

7. ________ × ________ = 2,100

8. ________ × ________ = 48,000

9. ________ × ________ = 5,600

10. ________ × ________ = 60,000

11. ________ × ________ = 2,800

12. ________ × ________ = 5,400

13. ________ × ________ = 140,000

14. ________ × ________ = 3,000

15. ________ × ________ = 160,000

Use the cards to answer the questions.

16. Which two factors give the smallest product? ________

17. Which two factors give the greatest product? ________

18. Which two factors give the greatest three-digit product? ________

 Use with pages 250–251.

Name ______________________________

Visual Thinking

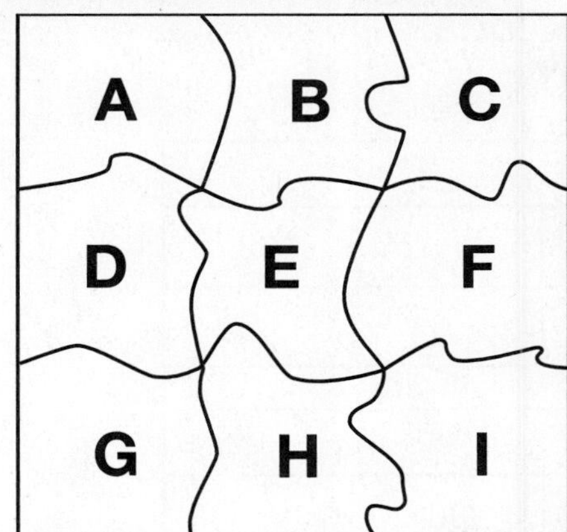

Match each puzzle piece below to the letter in the completed puzzle above.

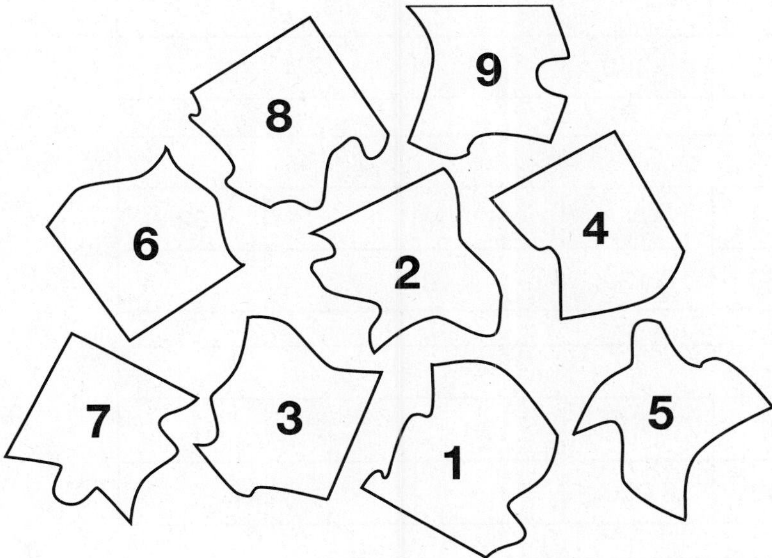

1. ________ 2. ________ 3. ________
4. ________ 5. ________ 6. ________
7. ________ 8. ________ 9. ________

Name ________________________________ **Extend Your Thinking 6-3**

Patterns in Numbers

Each factor is multiplied by a multiple of 10. Look for a pattern to find the multiple. Complete the table.

1.

Rule: Multiply by ____.						
Factor	12	22		42		62
Product	240	440	640			

2.

Rule: Multiply by ____.						
Factor	10	15		25	30	
Product	500	750	1,000			

3.

Rule: Multiply by ____.						
Factor	23	33			63	73
Product	1,840	2,640	3,440			

4.

Rule: Multiply by ____.						
Factor	32	42		62		82
Product	1,920	2,520	3,120			

5.

Rule: Multiply by ____.						
Factor	25	50		100	125	
Product	1,000	2,000	3,000			

6.

Rule: Multiply by ____.						
Factor	27	37			67	77
Product	2,430	3,330	4,230			

7. Make up a table of your own. Give it to a friend to solve.

Rule: Multiply by						
Factor						
Product						

Name ______________________________

Visual Thinking

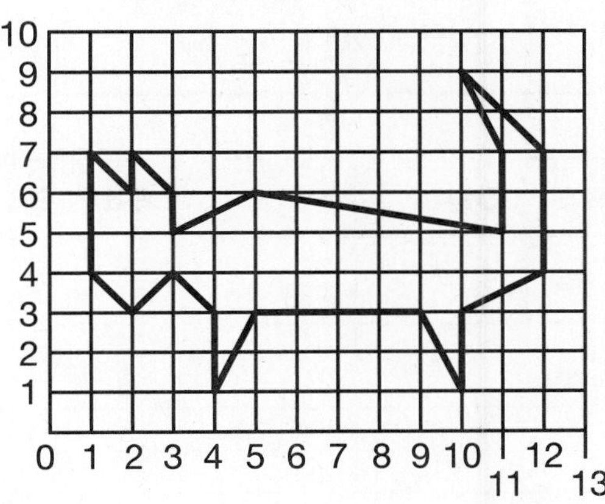

Shapes, the cat, has grown. Make a picture on the large grid to see just how big he has become. Find each point on Shapes' kitten picture. Then find the equivalent point on the larger grid. Use a ruler to join the points to show a picture of Shapes as an adult cat.

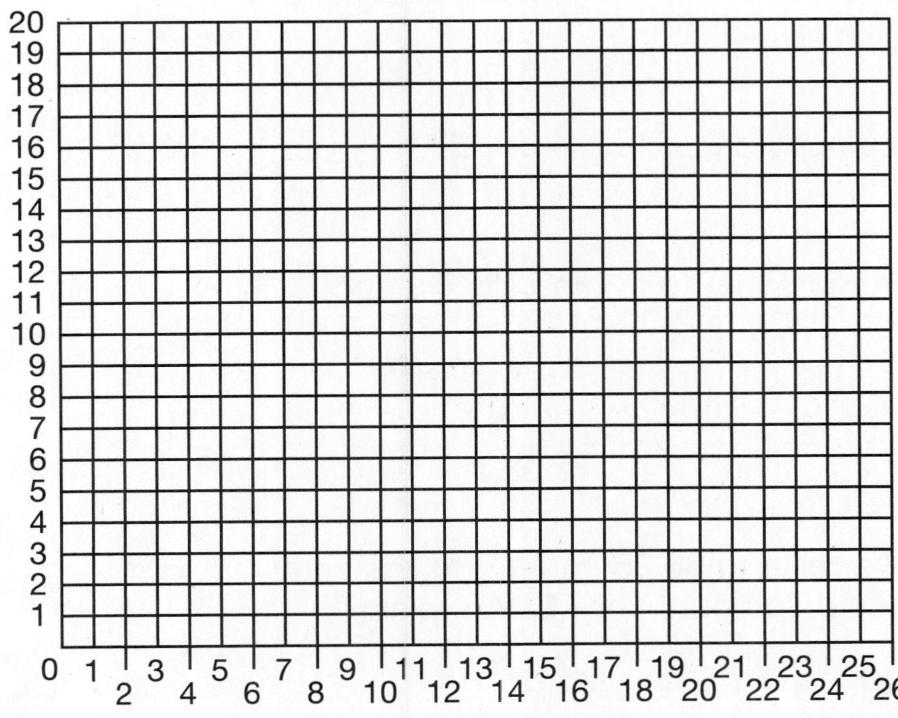

Name ________________________________

Critical Thinking

Mel has a part-time job at a sandwich shop. He earns $6 per hour. He made a spreadsheet so he could keep track of his earnings. Refer to the spreadsheet to answer the questions.

	A	B	C	D	E
1	**Day**	**Time in**	**Time out**	**Hours worked**	**Amount earned**
2	**Monday**	3:15 P.M.	5:30 P.M.		
3	**Tuesday**	3:30 P.M.	6:30 P.M.		
4	**Wednesday**	3:00 P.M.	6:15 P.M.		
5	**Thursday**	4:00 P.M.	6:45 P.M.		
6	**Friday**	3:45 P.M.	5:00 P.M.		
7	**Saturday**	10:00 A.M.	2:00 A.M.		
8			**Total:**		

1. How can you figure out what to put in cell **D4**?

____

____

2. How can you figure out what to put in cell **E7**?

____

3. How can you figure out what to put in cells **D8** and **E8**?

____

____

4. Complete the spreadsheet.

5. Suppose Mel gets a raise to $6.25 and keeps the same schedule. What would you put in cell **E8**? Explain.

____

 Use with pages 260–263.

Name ______________________

Decision Making

Rodney and his family visit a car factory in Detroit, Michigan.

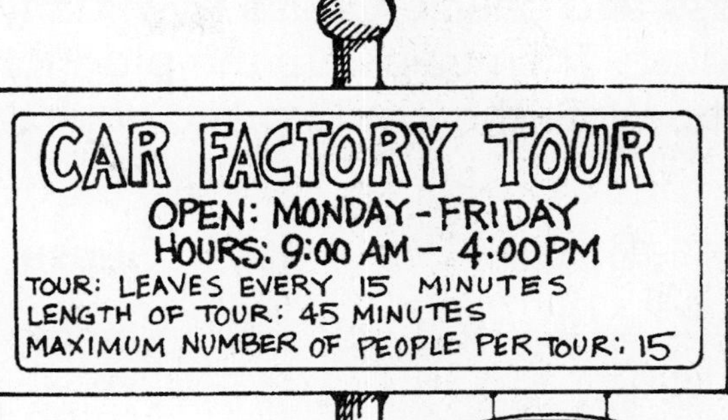

1. How many hours a day is the tour offered? ____________

2. What is the maximum number of tours each hour? ____________

3. If the tours must be completed by 4:00 P.M., what is the maximum number of tours that can be scheduled from 3:00 P.M. to 4:00 P.M.? ____________

4. What is the maximum number of tours that can be offered in one day? ____________

5. What is the maximum number of people that can tour the factory each day? ____________

6. How much will Rodney's family of 4 spend to take the tour? ____________

7. Plan a schedule for a trip to the car factory for you and your family. Assume the travel distance to the factory is one hour.

   a. List some things you will have to consider when making your schedule.

   ____

   ____

   b. Write your schedule with 15-minute intervals.

   ____________ ____________

   ____________ ____________

   ____________ ____________

   ____________ ____________

Name ______________________________

Extend Your Thinking
6-7

Critical Thinking

Guess and check. Guess how many digits are in each product. Then calculate the product to check the number of digits. Write the product and your calculation method.

1. $1{,}110 \times 14$

Guess __________ digits

Check __________ digits

Method ______________________

2. 322×23

Guess __________ digits

Check __________ digits

Method ______________________

3. $6{,}430 \times 25$

Guess __________ digits

Check __________ digits

Method ______________________

4. 750×33

Guess __________ digits

Check __________ digits

Method ______________________

5. 421×21

Guess __________ digits

Check __________ digits

Method ______________________

Name ______________________

Patterns in Data

The table below gives information about 2 rides at the fair. Read the information. Figure out the cost per minute for each ride. Then answer the questions.

	Giant Ferris Wheel $3.00 for 15 minutes		Flying Falcon $4.50 for 15 minutes	
	Minutes	**Cost**	**Minutes**	**Cost**
1.	1		1	
2.	2		2	
3.	3		3	
4.	4		4	
5.	5		5	
6.	6		6	

7. Which ride is the best buy per minute?

____

8. How many minutes would you get on the Giant Ferris Wheel for the cost of 4 minutes on the Flying Falcon? ________

9. How many minutes would you get on the Flying Falcon for the cost of 3 minutes on the Giant Ferris Wheel? ________

10. The Wind Tunnel costs $5.00 for 20 minutes. Is this better value per minute than the Giant Ferris Wheel? the Flying Falcon? Explain.

____

____

Decision Making

The table below shows how consumers rated each of 5 brands of mouthwash. Read over the table to decide which is the best buy.

= excellent   = good   = fair   = poor

Brand	Cost	Taste	Freshness	Time it Lasted	Overall
Bright Smile	$2.75	fair	fair	poor	fair
Shine	$3.25	good	good	excellent	excellent
Fresh Breath	$2.00	excellent	good	good	good
Winter Mint	$3.30	good	excellent	good	good
Mint Wave	$2.10	fair	poor	poor	poor

1. Which mouthwash costs the least? ____________

How much less is

a. Fresh Breath than Bright Smile? ____________

b. Fresh Breath than Shine? ____________

c. Mint Wave than Winter Mint? ____________

d. Mint Wave than Shine? ____________

2. Which mouthwash received the highest score for

a. taste? ____________

b. freshness? ____________

c. time it lasted? ____________

3. Which mouthwash has a combination of low cost and high ratings? ____________

4. Which mouthwash would you choose? Why?

____

____

 Use with pages 274–275.

Name ______________________

Decision Making

Dana and Austin are having a car wash to raise money for the local museum. They each made a sign. Which one should they use?

Sign 1	Sign 2
Support the Winston Museum Car Wash $2.50	**Support the Winston Museum Car Wash $3.50**

1. Dana estimates that they can wash 3 cars per hour. They expect to work for 7 hours. Should they overestimate or underestimate the number of cars they can wash? Explain.

____

____

2. How might they adjust the numbers to estimate many cars they could wash in one day?

____

____

3. Estimate the number of cars they can wash in a day. ____________

4. Based on your estimate, how much could they earn in one day with Sign 1? With Sign 2?

____

5. Which sign might bring in more cars? Explain.

____

6. Which sign would you use? Explain your reasoning.

____

____

Name ______________________________

Visual Thinking

Write a word problem to go with each picture. Give it to a friend to solve.

1. 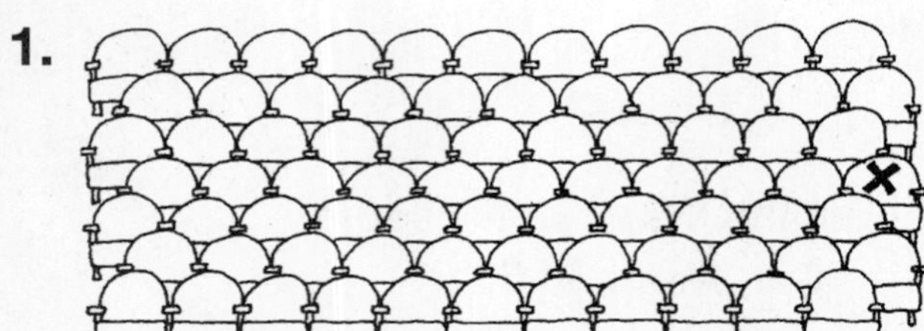

____

____

____

2. 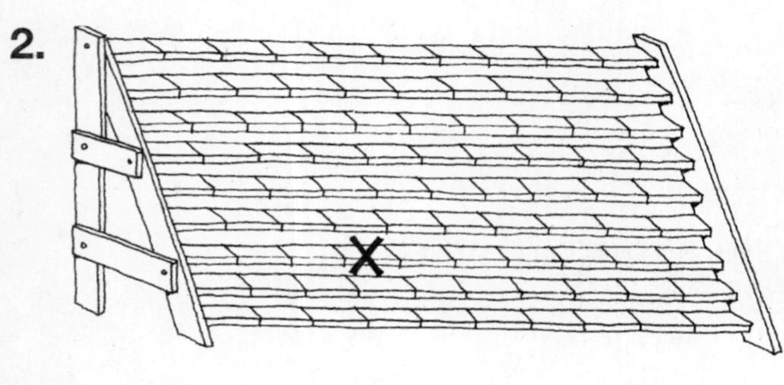

____

____

____

3. 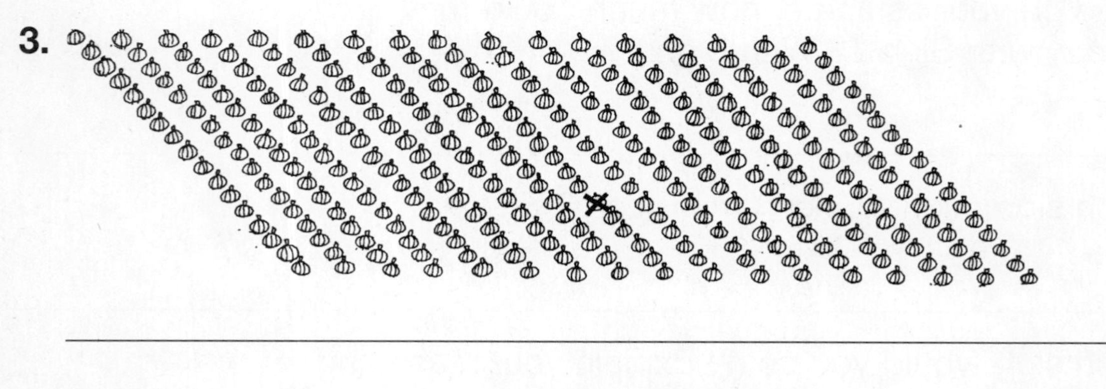

____

____

____

____

 Use with pages 280–281.

Name ________________________________

Visual Thinking

Circle the figure on the right that matches the figure on the left. The figures may be flipped or turned.

1.      

2.      

3. 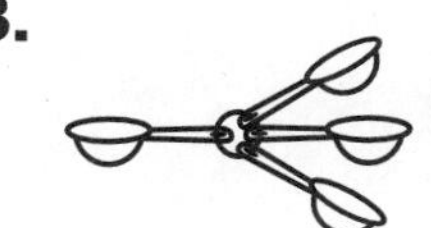  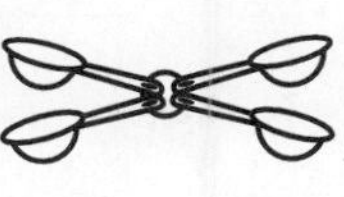  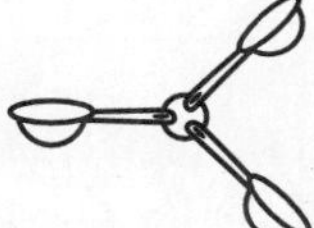 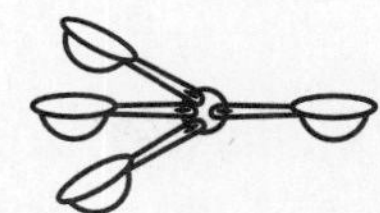

4.      

5.    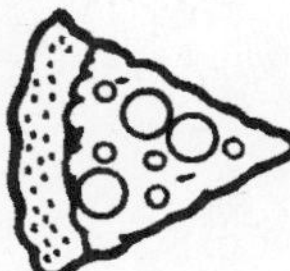  

Name ______________________________ **Extend Your Thinking 7-2**

Decision Making

Cheryl wants to bake a low-calorie cake for her father.

She looked in her cookbook and found three recipes for low-calorie cakes.

ChocoHeaven Cake	258 total calories	makes 8 servings
Perfect Banana Cake	210 total calories	makes 4 servings
Oatmeal Raisin Cake	331 total calories	makes 4 servings

1. Estimate the number of calories per serving of the ChocoHeaven Cake.

____

2. Estimate the number of calories per serving of the Perfect Banana Cake.

____

3. Estimate the number of calories per serving of the Oatmeal Raisin Cake.

____

4. Which cake has the most calories per serving?

____

5. Which cake should Cheryl make for her father's birthday? Why?

____

6. If the ingredients for ChocoHeaven Cake cost $15.27 and the ingredients for Perfect Banana Cake cost $5.33, which costs less per serving? Estimate to answer.

____

____

Name ______________________________

Patterns in Numbers

Find each quotient. Look for a pattern.

1. $3\overline{)6}$ _____ R _____
2. $3\overline{)7}$ _____ R _____
3. $3\overline{)8}$ _____ R _____
4. $3\overline{)9}$ _____ R _____
5. $3\overline{)10}$ _____ R _____
6. $3\overline{)11}$ _____ R _____
7. $3\overline{)12}$ _____ R _____
8. $3\overline{)13}$ _____ R _____
9. $3\overline{)14}$ _____ R _____
10. $3\overline{)15}$ _____ R _____
11. $5\overline{)16}$ _____ R _____
12. $5\overline{)17}$ _____ R _____
13. $5\overline{)18}$ _____ R _____
14. $5\overline{)19}$ _____ R _____
15. $5\overline{)20}$ _____ R _____
16. $5\overline{)21}$ _____ R _____
17. $5\overline{)22}$ _____ R _____
18. $5\overline{)23}$ _____ R _____
19. $5\overline{)24}$ _____ R _____
20. $5\overline{)25}$ _____ R _____

21. Describe the patterns that you see.

____

____

22. Why are there no remainders of 3 in **1-10**?

____

____

____

23. How would the patterns change if the divisor in each problem were 4?

____

____

24. If $79 \div 6 = 13$ R1, use the pattern to find $80 \div 6$. __________

Name ______________________________

Visual Thinking

An analogy pairs items that are related in the same way.
Circle the drawing that completes each analogy.

Example:

1.  is to  as 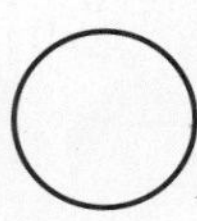 is to  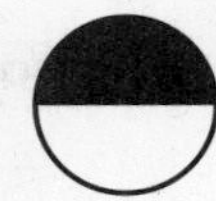

2. 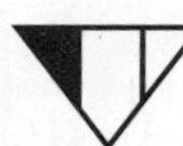 is to  as  is to   

3.  is to  as  is to  

4. 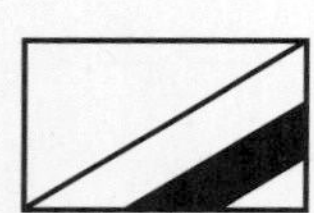 is to  as  is to 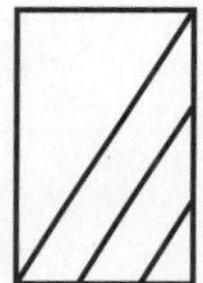 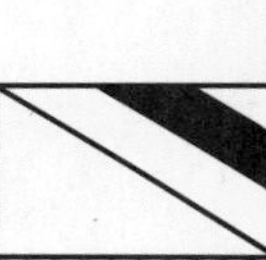  

5.  is to  as  is to    

Name ____________________

Extend Your Thinking
7-5

Patterns in Numbers

What happens when you divide the same 2-digit number by divisors that keep increasing by 1? Is there a pattern?

Solve the following problems to find out.

1. $2\overline{)67}$ __________

2. $3\overline{)67}$ __________

3. $4\overline{)67}$ __________

4. $5\overline{)67}$ __________

5. $6\overline{)67}$ __________

6. $2\overline{)83}$ __________

7. $3\overline{)83}$ __________

8. $4\overline{)83}$ __________

9. $5\overline{)83}$ __________

10. $6\overline{)83}$ __________

11. $7\overline{)83}$ __________

12. Describe the patterns you see.

____

____

____

13. If you divide 83 by 8, do you think the quotient would be greater or less than 11? Use **11** above to explain.

____

14. How can you use the fact that 91 ÷ 6 = 15 R1 and 91 ÷ 9 = 10 R1 to estimate the quotient of 91 ÷ 8?

____

Name ______________________

Decision Making

Harleyville Soccer League is planning its annual Awards Banquet. A total of 400 people will attend the banquet. You have been asked to help decide how many tables should be set up for the evening. This is the information you have been given:

a. Three rectangular head tables will be set up. Sixteen league officials will sit at the main head table.

b. Twelve coaches will sit at a second head table.

c. The third head table will be for the assistant coaches. Twelve people will be at this table.

All other people at the banquet will sit at round tables. The round tables come in 2 sizes that seat 8 or 12 people. There is room for 35 to 45 round tables.

1. What is the total number of people who will sit at the three head tables? ________

2. How many people will sit at the round tables? ________

3. Suppose you wanted to use the fewest number of tables possible. How many of each type would you use?

____

4. Suppose you wanted to use the greatest number of tables possible. How many of each type would you use?

____

5. What is another way you could set up the tables?

____

6. How would you set up the room? Explain.

____

____

____

Name ____

Visual Thinking

A figure has line symmetry if it can be folded along a line so that both sides match. Look at the figures in each row. Circle the figure that has line symmetry.

1.
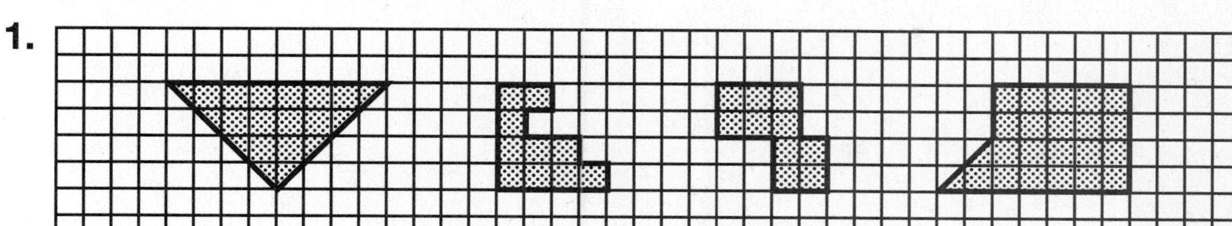

2.
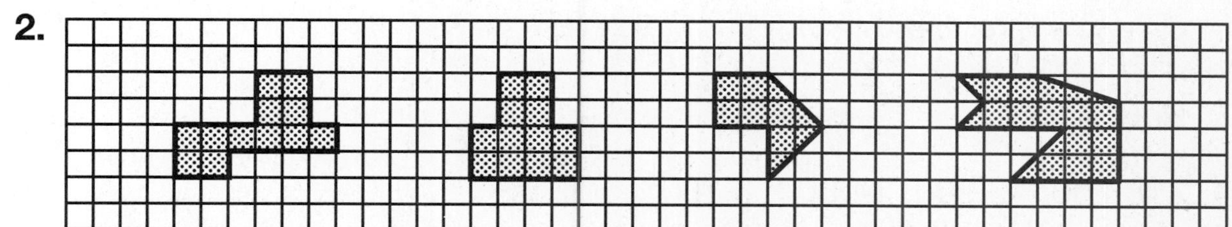

3.
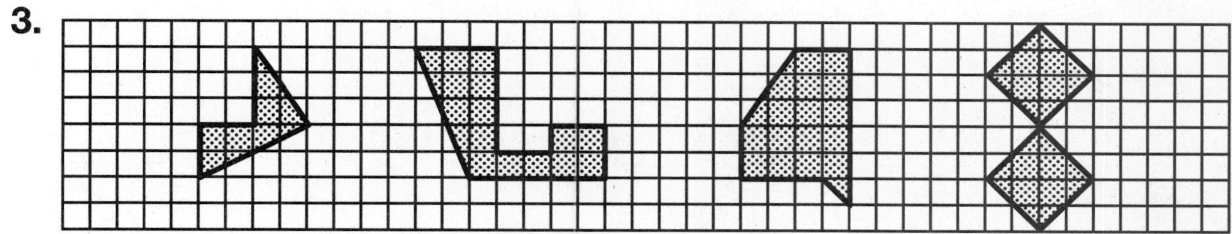

4.
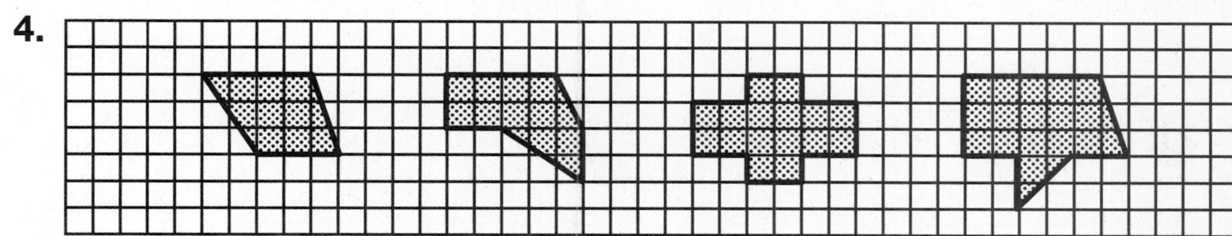

5.
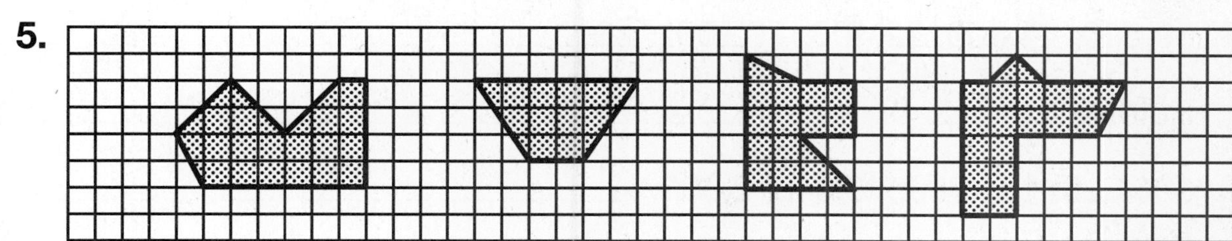

6.
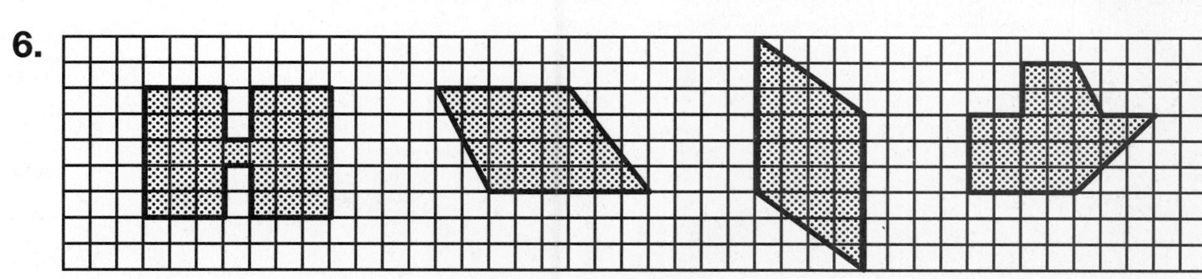

Name ______________________

Extend Your Thinking
7-8

Number Patterns

What are the next three numbers in each pattern? Tell what rule was used to make the pattern.

1. 26; 52; 104; 208; ________, ________, ________

Rule: ______________________

2. 46,875; 9,375; 1,875; 375; ________, ________, ________

Rule: ______________________

3. 8,192; 2,048; 512; 128; ________, ________, ________

Rule: ______________________

4. 218,700; 72,900; 24,300; 8,100; ________; ________; ________

Rule: ______________________

5. 34; 68; 136; 272; ________; ________; ________

Rule: ______________________

6. 11; 22; 66; 264; ________; ________; ________

Rule: ______________________

7. 21; 84; 336; 1,344; ________; ________; ________

Rule: ______________________

8. 89,600; 44,800; 22,400; 11,200; ________; ________; ________

Rule: ______________________

9. 606,528; 101,088; 16,848; 2,808; ________, ________, ________

Rule: ______________________

Name ______________________________

Critical Thinking

Who do you think is the greatest baseball hitter of all time? Many people would mention one of these five players. They were some of the best home run hitters of all time!

Player	Home Runs	At Bats
Hank Aaron	755	12,364
Harmon Killebrew	573	8,147
Willie Mays	660	10,881
Frank Robinson	586	10,006
Babe Ruth	714	8,399

1. Which hitter had the greatest number of home runs?

   ____

2. What does the number of times each player came to bat tell you about the players?

   ____

   ____

3. Which player had the greatest number of at bats? ______________

4. On the left side of the table, rank the players from the player who hit the greatest number of home runs to the player who hit the least. On the right side of the table, rank the players from the one who had the greatest number of at bats to the player who had the least.

5. Analyze your table. Who do you think was the best hitter? Explain.

   ____

   ____

   ____

   ____

Name ______________________________

Extend Your Thinking
7-10

Visual Thinking

Some shapes can be used to make a larger pattern of the same shape. For example, you can draw 3 more squares of the same size to make a larger square.

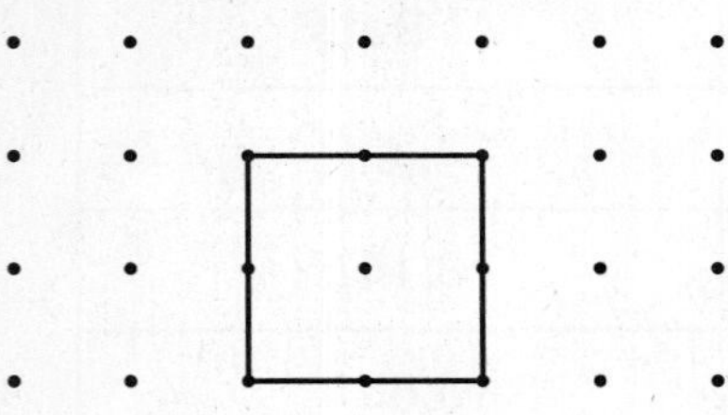

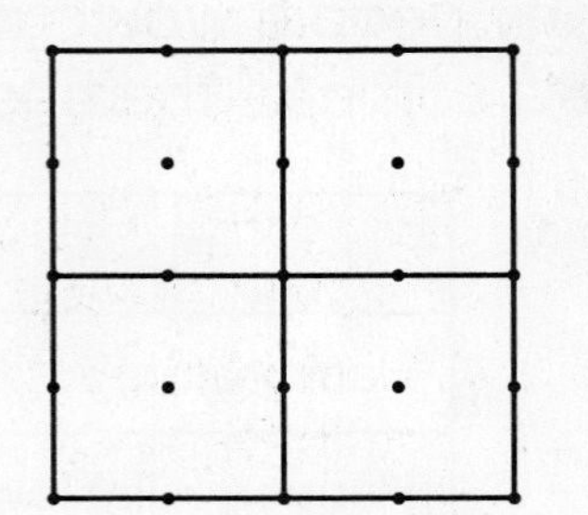

Make a large pattern of each shape using 4 of the smaller shapes.

1.

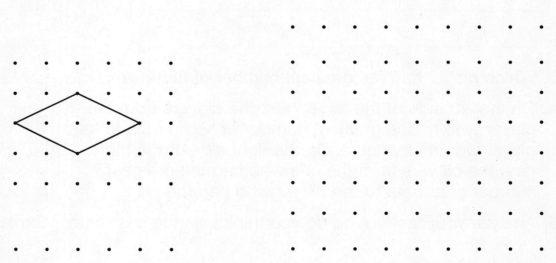

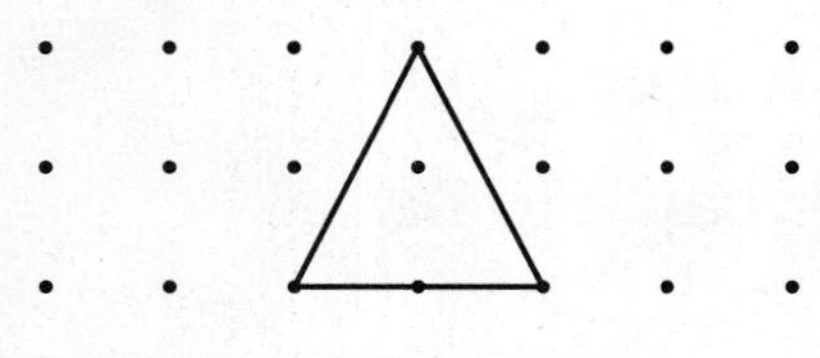

2.

3.

 Use with pages 320–321.

Name ______________________________

Decision Making

A group of students from your class is taking a field trip to a museum. There are 3 restaurants in the area of the museum where your class can eat lunch. Each restaurant offers a different price for group lunches. There are 12 students going on the field trip.

A. Darlene's Diner. Each student will be served a turkey sandwich, pretzels, and juice. The cost of lunch for 4 students is $9.88.

B. Rich's Restaurant. Each student will be served a tuna salad sandwich, soup, and juice. The cost of lunch for 3 students is $6.12.

C. Pat's Pit-Stop. Each student will be served a peanut butter and jelly sandwich, salad, and milk. The cost of lunch for 2 students is $4.52.

1. How much will lunch cost for each student at each restaurant? Write the number sentence and find the amount for each restaurant.

Restaurant A: ______________________________

Restaurant B: ______________________________

Restaurant C: ______________________________

2. a. If all of the students on the field trip eat lunch, what will the total cost be for the class to eat at each of the restaurants?

A: __________ B: __________ C: __________

b. How did you find the total cost for each restaurant?

____

____

3. Which restaurant would you choose for the class to go for lunch? Why?

____

____

____

Name ______________________________

Critical Thinking

A group of fourth- and fifth-grade classes took the same test. Here are the average scores for each class.

Fourth Grade Classes	Average Scores	Fifth Grade Classes	Average Scores
Mr. Andrew	82	Ms. Brown	88
Ms. Lim	85	Mr. Shapiro	85
Ms. Somers	86	Ms. King	81
Ms. Bouvet	79	Mr. Cohn	86

1. Find the overall average score for the fourth grade. ________

2. Find the overall average score for the fifth grade. ________

3. Which grade has the higher mean test score, fourth grade or fifth grade? Explain.

   ____

4. What is the mean score for fourth and fifth grade combined? ________

5. There are only 8 students in Mr. Andrew's class. The average score for his class is 82. Seven of his student's got the following scores: 81, 82, 89, 91, 72, 73, and 77. Find the eighth student's score. ________

6. A group of 4 sixth-grade classes took the test. If the mean score for the sixth grade is 90, what is the average score for fourth, fifth, and sixth grade combined? ________

7. Find the overall average for the top 2 average scores in fourth grade and the top 2 average scores in fifth grade.

   ____

Name ______________________

Patterns in Division

Write the factor or factors from 2 to 10 that each set of numbers has in common. Circle the largest factor. What rule can you use to figure out if a number is divisible by the largest factor?

1. 10, 15, 45, 60, 115

Common factors: ____________

Rule: ______________________

____

2. 12, 15, 105, 54, 24

Common factors: ____________

Rule: ______________________

____

3. 40, 70, 20, 130, 90

Common factors: ____________

Rule: ______________________

____

4. 18, 24, 66, 120, 84

Common factors: ____________

Rule: ______________________

____

5. 18, 117, 27, 45, 90

Common factors: ____________

Rule: ______________________

____

6. Are all numbers that are divisible by 10 also divisible by 5?

Explain: ______________________

____

Name ______________________________

Visual Thinking

Imagine a square piece of paper, folded twice, as shown here.

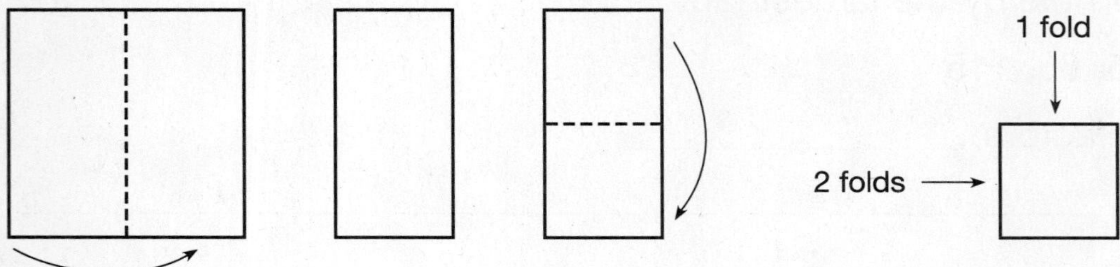

In each row, the picture on the left shows a folded square with one or more cuts in it. Circle the picture on the right that shows the unfolded square.

1.

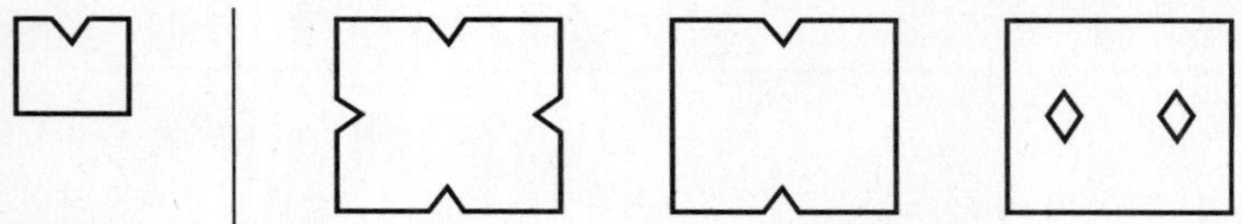

2.

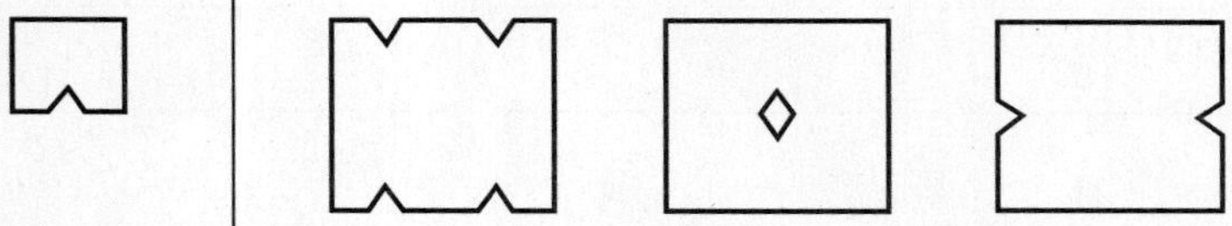

3.

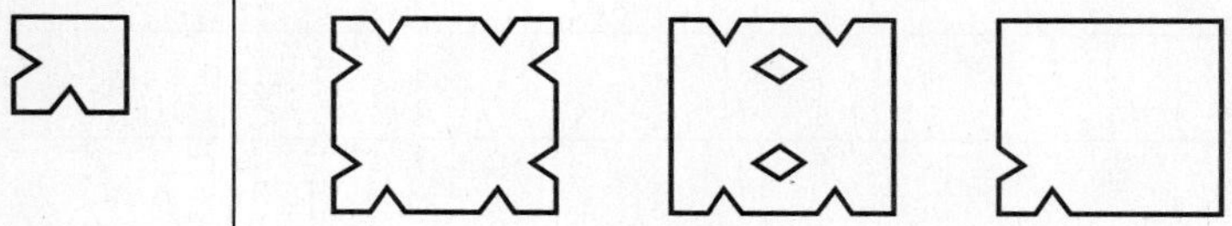

4.

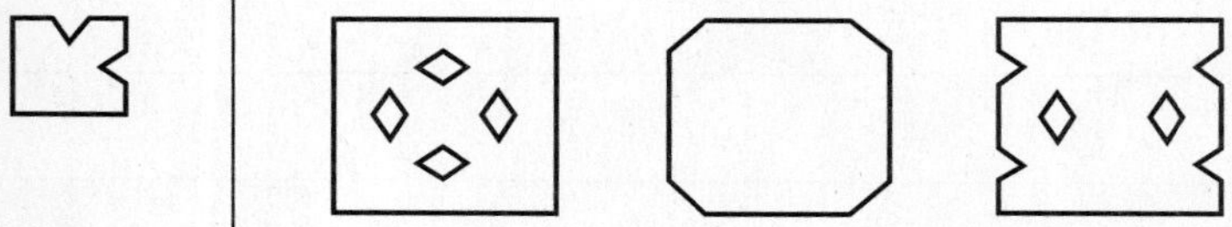

5.

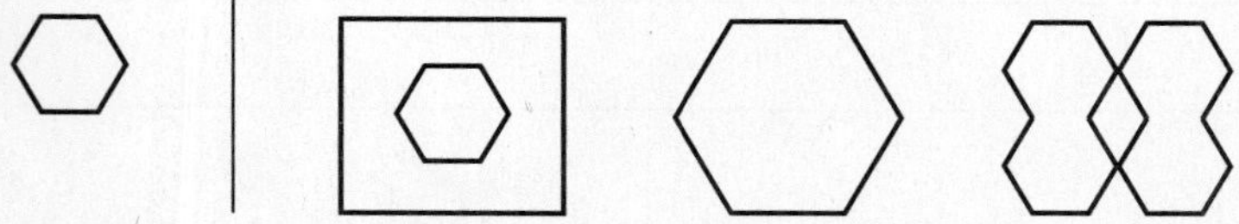

Name ____________________ **Extend Your Thinking 8-1**

Critical Thinking

Jan has filled her shopping cart with items that look like the solids you have studied. Here is a picture of her groceries.

1. **a.** How many items in the cart cannot roll? ________

   b. What are the items that cannot roll?

   ____

2. Most of the items in the cart are what solid shape? ________

3. What shape that you have studied is shown by only one item?

   ____

4. Name another cylinder-shaped item that can be bought in a supermarket.

   ____

5. The thermos is the most expensive item that she has purchased. It costs $3.50. The milk costs one half of this amount plus $0.06. How much does the milk cost?

   ____

6. If her purchases amount to $22.85 and she gives the cashier two ten-dollar bills and one five-dollar bill, how much change should Jan receive?

   ____

Name ______________________________ Extend Your Thinking 8-2

Patterns in Geometry

Look for a pattern. Draw the next two shapes to continue the pattern.

1.

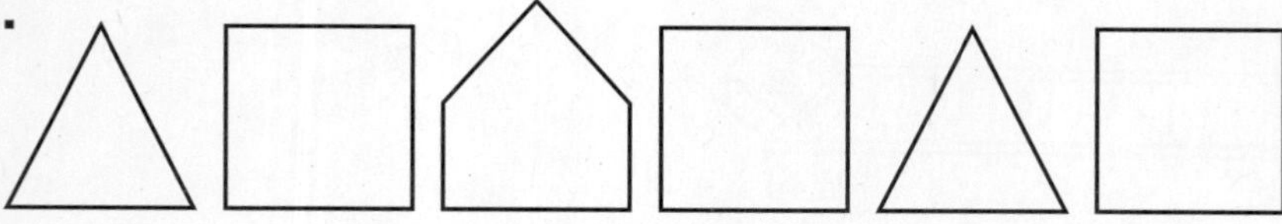

2.

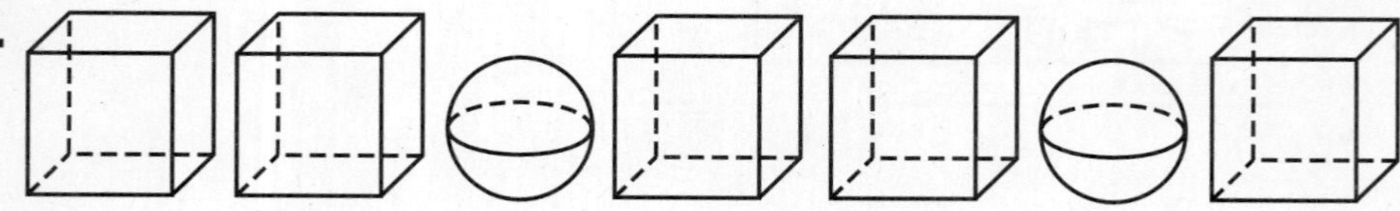

3.

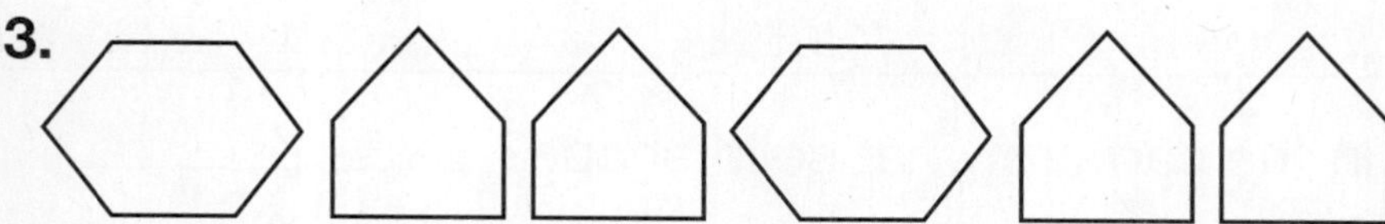

4.

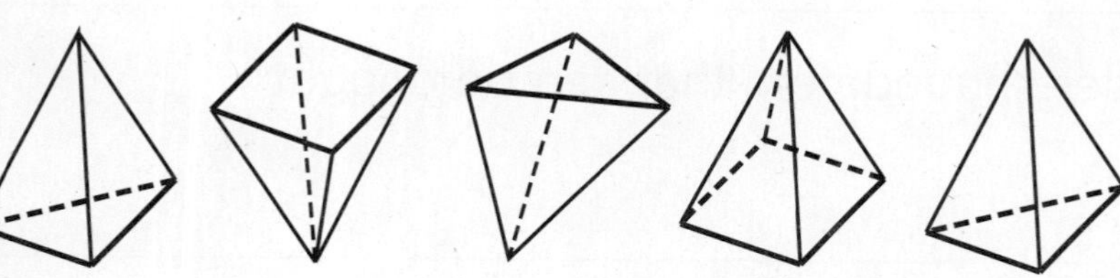

5.

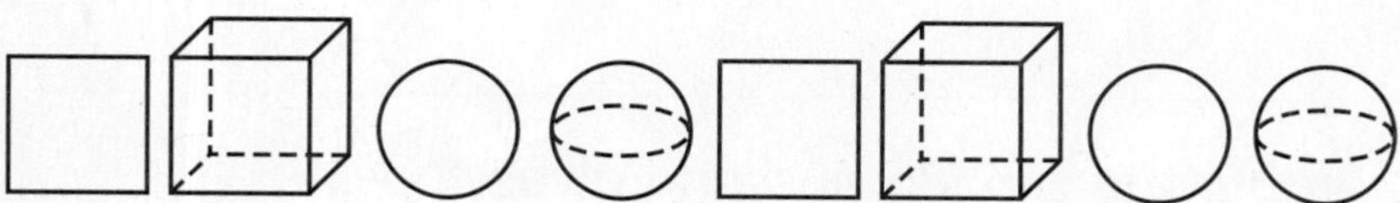

6.

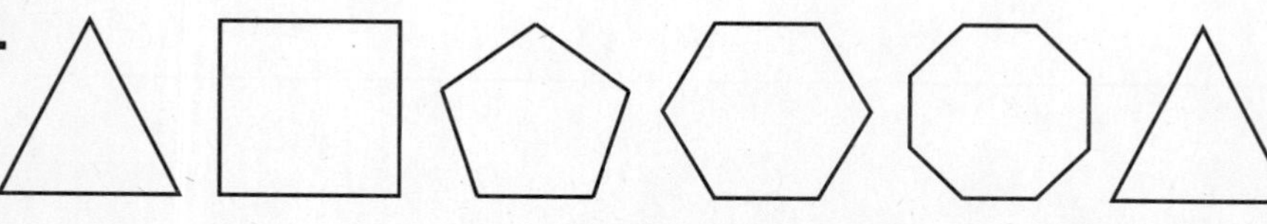

Name ______________________________

Visual Thinking

Look at each triangle. Is it equilateral, isoceles, or scalene? Label each one. Estimate the length of its sides in centimeters. Check your answer by measuring with a centimeter ruler.

1.

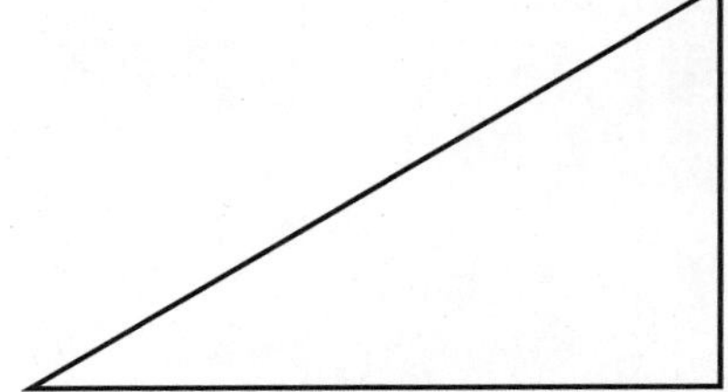

__________ triangle

guess ____ cm, ____ cm, ____ cm

check ____ cm, ____ cm, ____ cm

2.

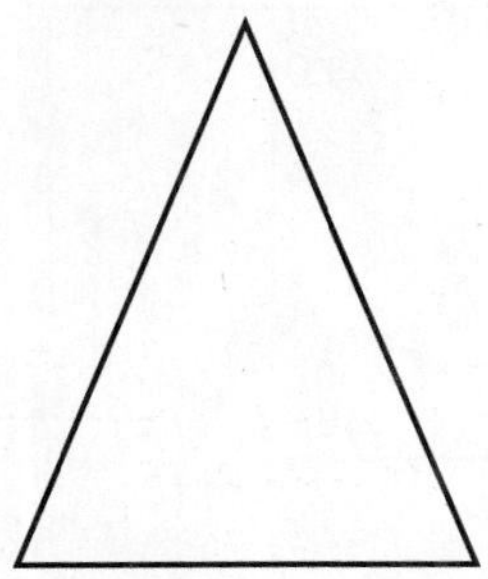

__________ triangle

guess ____ cm, ____ cm, ____ cm

check ____ cm, ____ cm, ____ cm

3.

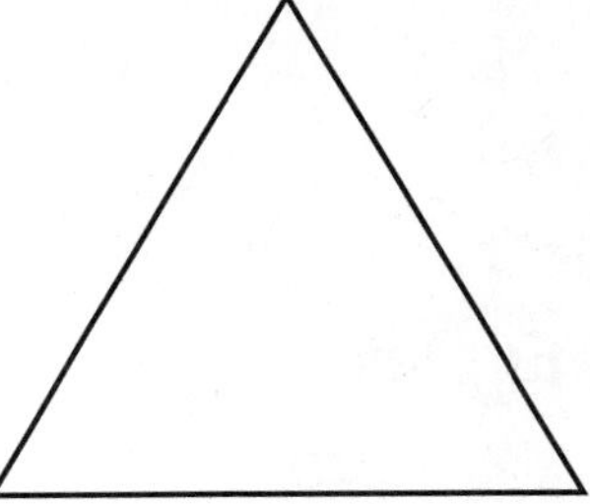

__________ triangle

guess ____ cm, ____ cm, ____ cm

check ____ cm, ____ cm, ____ cm

4.

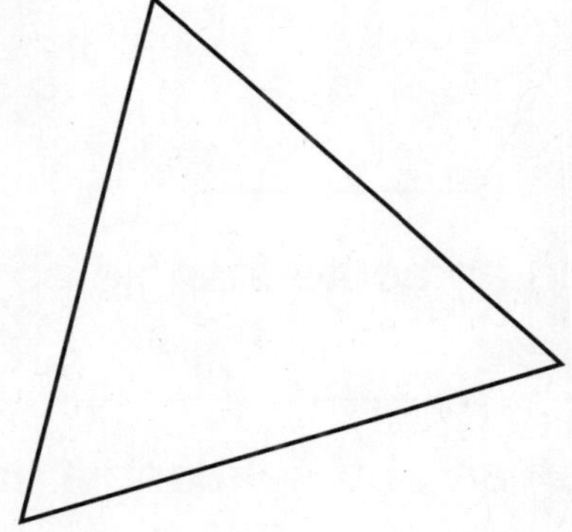

__________ triangle

guess ____ cm, ____ cm, ____ cm

check ____ cm, ____ cm, ____ cm

Name ______________________

Critical Thinking

Look at each angle below. Write the name of each angle. Then connect the two sides of each angle with one line. Circle the name of the triangle you make.

1. Angle ____________

equilateral
isosceles
scalene

2. Angle ____________

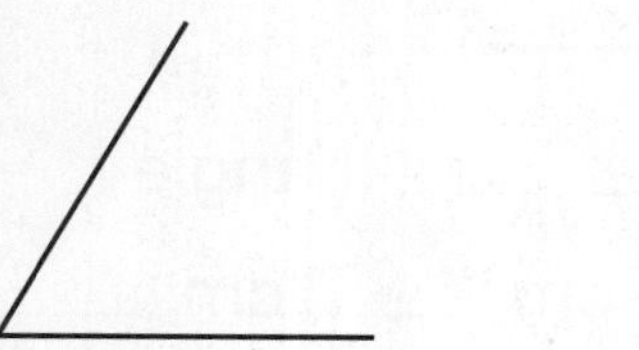

equilateral
isosceles
scalene

3. Angle ____________

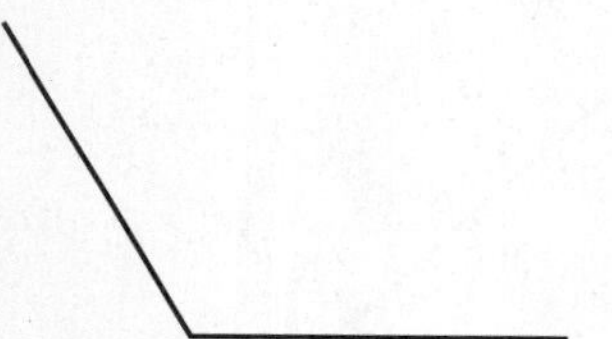

equilateral
isosceles
scalene

4. Can an acute triangle be an equilateral triangle? Explain.

____

5. Can an obtuse triangle have more than 1 acute angle? Explain.

____

____

Draw each of the following triangles.

6. right isosceles **7.** obtuse scalene **8.** obtuse isosceles

Name ____

Decision Making

Mr. Samatis, a carpenter, likes to make wooden toys for his children. He makes the toys using solid shapes. He can join them together with glue and nails.

Below is a list of some of the toys he has made for his children. Draw a sketch of the toy and label each solid that would be used.

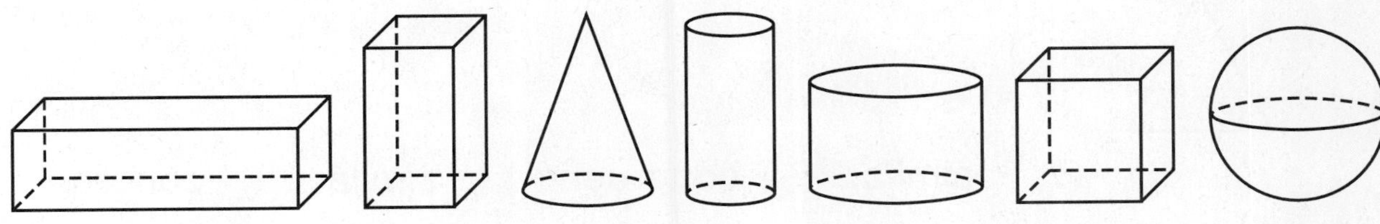

1. a toy truck

2. a doll-sized table

3. a see-saw

4. a wooden drum

5. a wooden doll

6. a top

Name ______________________________

Patterns in Geometry

(a.) Draw a pattern of shapes that are congruent with, similar to, or different from each figure shown, **(b.)** Then tell if the next shape should be congruent, similar or different.

1. a.

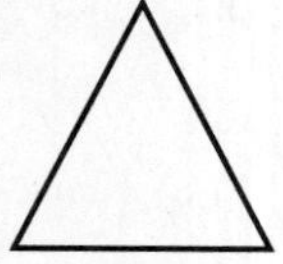

similar congruent similar congruent

b. ____________

2. a.

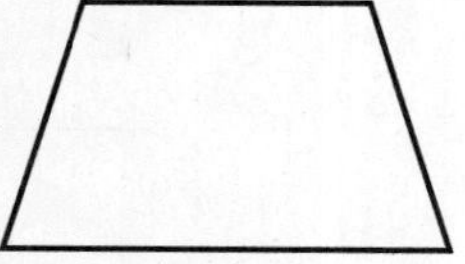

congruent different similar congruent

b. ____________

3. a.

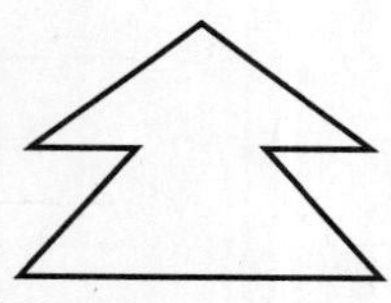

different different similar similar

b. ____________

4. a.

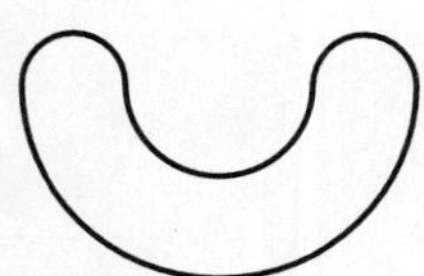

different congruent different congruent

b. ____________

Name ______________________________

Decision Making

There are 102 students in the science club. The club is trying to raise money for an overnight trip to Toronto, Canada, where they will visit a science center. They need to raise $500 for the trip. They have narrowed down their choices for ways to raise money.

Choice A: Hold a dance at school and charge $2.00 per ticket.

Choice B: Sell mail-order fruit baskets. Charge $5.00 per basket.

Choice C: Hold a raffle at school for a free trip to Toronto. Charge $1.00 per raffle ticket.

1. For Choice A, how many tickets to the dance will the club have to sell to meet their goal of raising $500? ______________

2. For Choice B, how many baskets will the club need to sell to meet their goal? ______________

3. For Choice C, how many raffle tickets will the club need to sell to raise $500? ______________

4. Write the advantages and disadvantages for each fundraising choice.

   Choice A: ______________________________

   ____

   Choice B: ______________________________

   ____

   Choice C: ______________________________

   ____

5. What do you think is the best fundraising choice for the science club? Explain.

   ____

   ____

   ____

   ____

Name ______________________________

Extend Your Thinking
8-8

Visual Thinking

Circle the figure on the right that shows half of the figure on the left.

1.

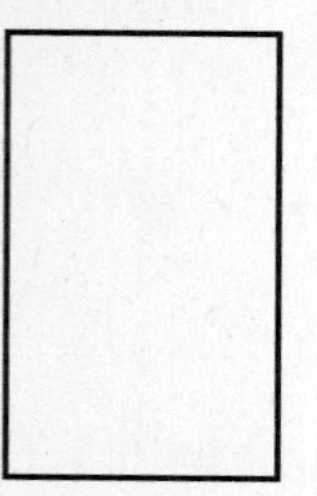

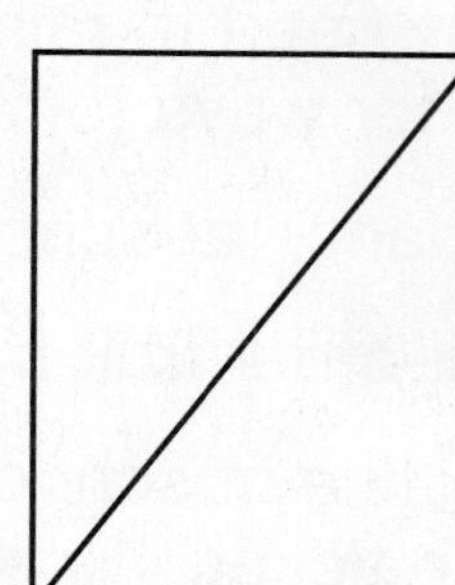

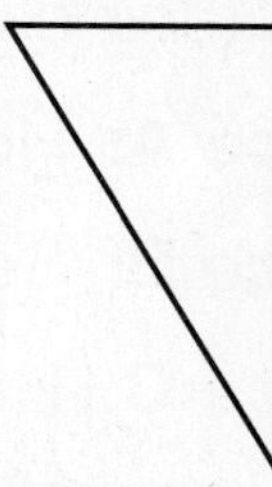

2.

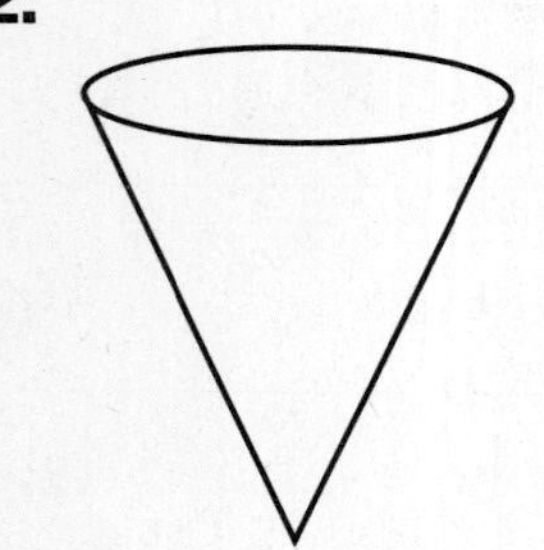

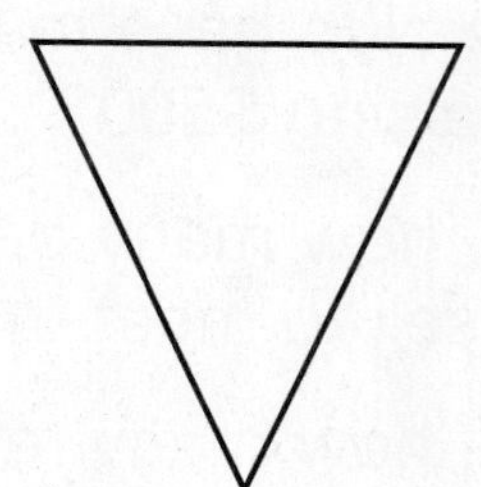

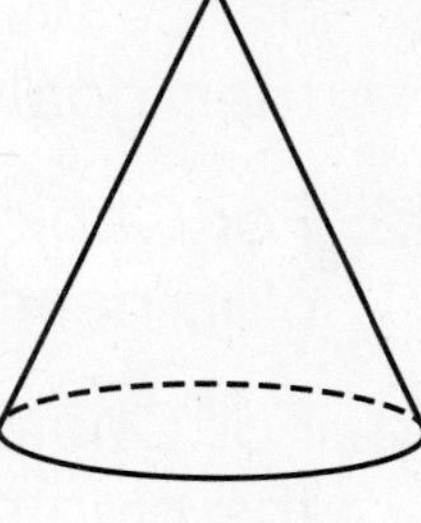

3.

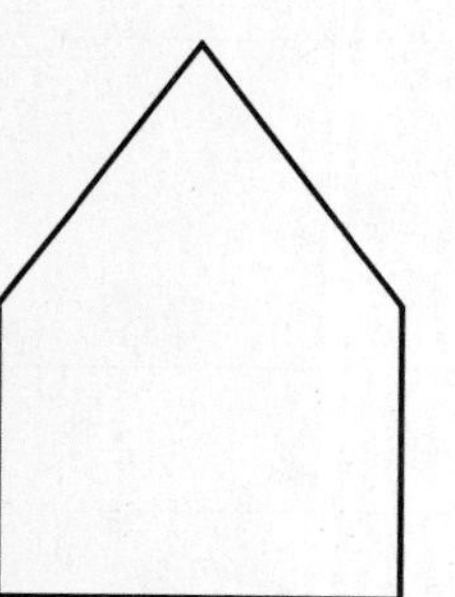

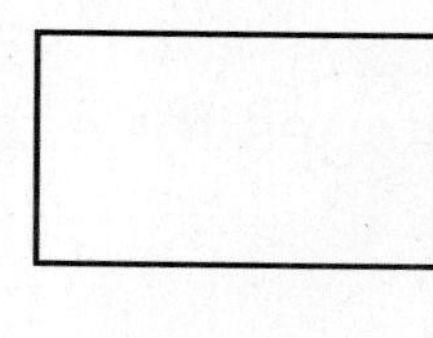

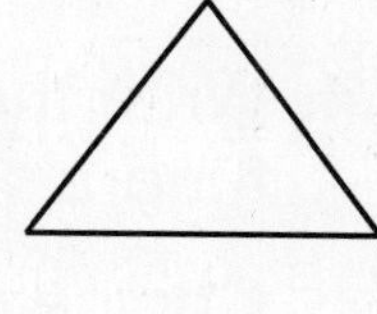

4.

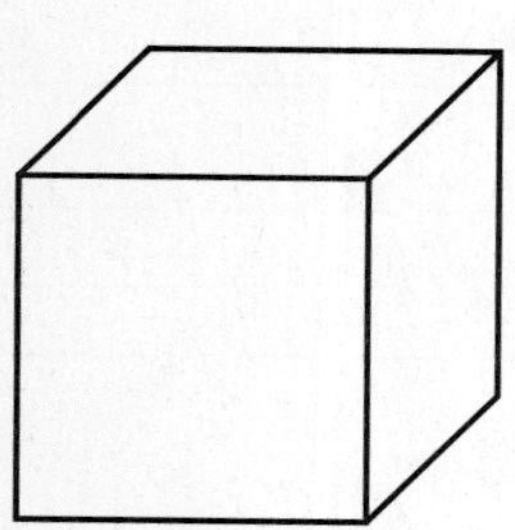

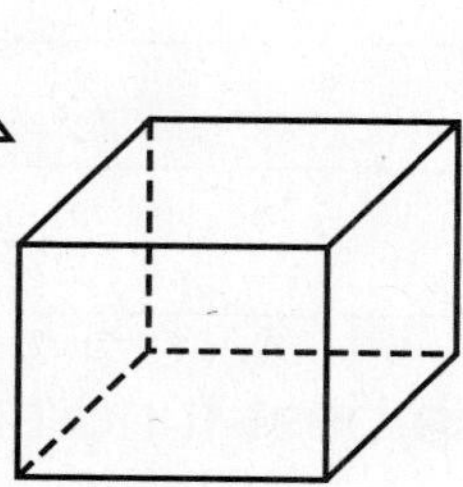

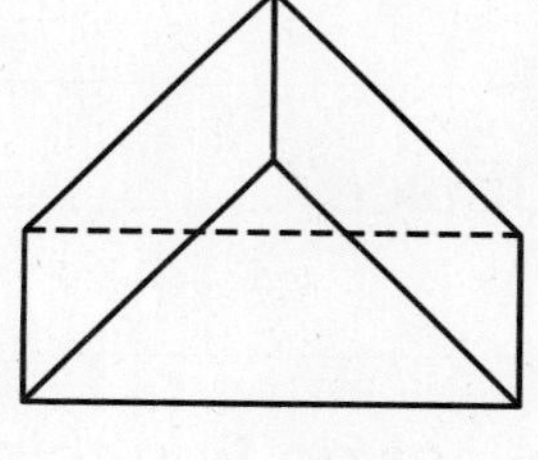

5.

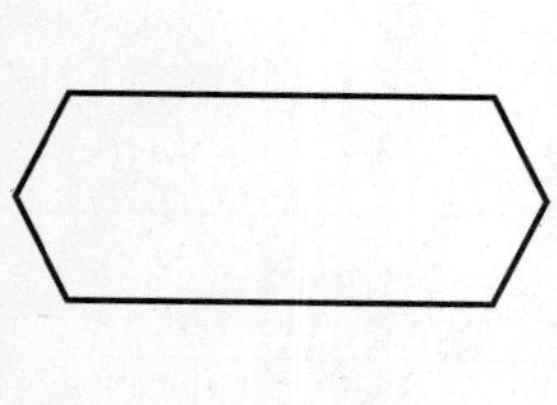

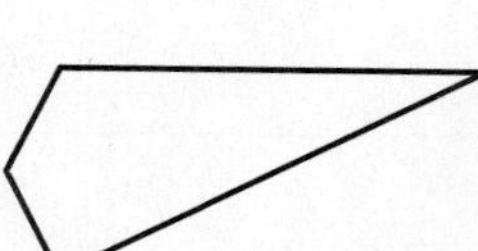

Name ______________________

Patterns in Algebra

Each shape represents a number. Write the number that each shape represents inside the shape.

1. (△ × 3) + 7 = 16
2. (⬠ × 5) + 11 = 36
3. (◯ × 6) + 4 = 64
4. (◯ × 7) + 3 = 59
5. (◯ × 4) + 18 = 54
6. (⬡ × 8) + 9 = 57
7. Describe how you solved **1–6**.

 ____

 ____

8. What do you notice about the number each shape represents?

 ____

Solve by using the pattern you found in **8.**

9. (△ × 6) + 11 = ______
10. (□ × 6) + 11 = ______
11. (⬠ × 6) + 11 = ______
12. (⬡ × 6) + 11 = ______
13. (◯ × 6) + 11 = ______
14. (◯ × 6) + 11 = ______
15. Describe the pattern you see in the answers for **9–14**.

 ____

 ____

Name ______________________________

Decision Making

Nicky can have a pet rabbit if she pays for its food and takes care of it. Each week, she earns $3 mowing lawns and earns $5 baby sitting. She spends $4 each week on things for school.

Here is what the rabbit eats each week.

Apple Slices	Carrots	Pellets	Hay
2 days per week	4 days per week	every day	every day
50¢ per week	50¢ per week	75¢ per week	75¢ per week

1. How much does the rabbit's food cost per week? __________

2. Can Nicky afford the cost of the rabbit food? Explain.

____

3. Every day Nicky must feed the rabbit, give it fresh water, and let it run outside. Every two days, she must change its litter. Nicky also does homework and chores, and takes gymnastics. She and her friends like to spend time together. Does she have enough money and time to care for the rabbit? Explain your reasoning.

____

____

____

4. Do you think that Nicky should get the rabbit? Explain.

____

____

5. If Nicky stopped mowing lawns to allow more time for school work, could she afford to have a rabbit? Explain.

____

Name ______________________________ **Extend Your Thinking 8-11**

Critical Thinking

Find the shape that doesn't belong in the group.

A.
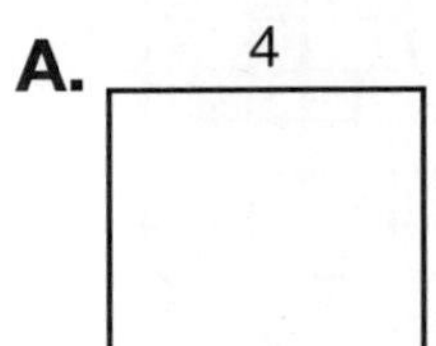

B. 1 7 **C.** 5 **D.** 3 5

1. ______ Explain your answer. ______________________________

A.
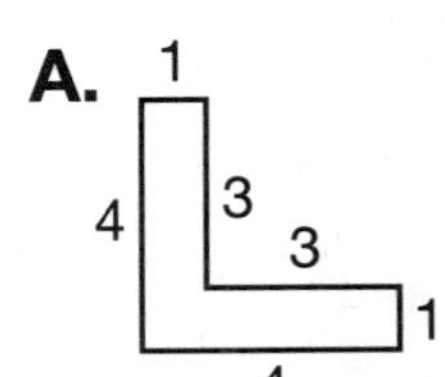

B. 7 4 **C.**
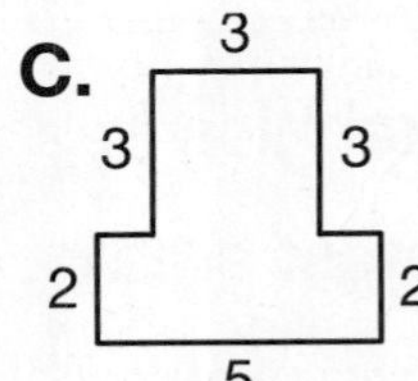

2. ______ Explain your answer. ______________________________

A.
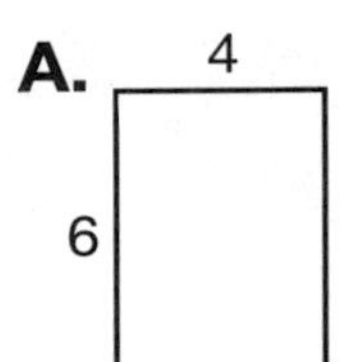

B. 2 8 **C.** 5 **D.** 2 12

3. ______ Explain your answer. ______________________________

A.
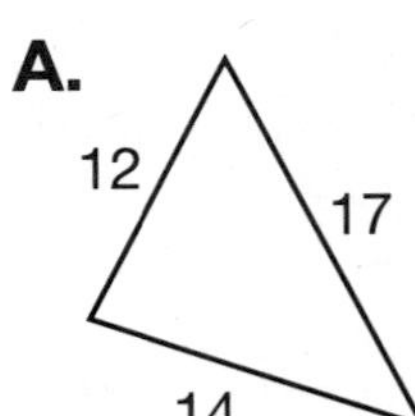

B. 13 19 **C.**
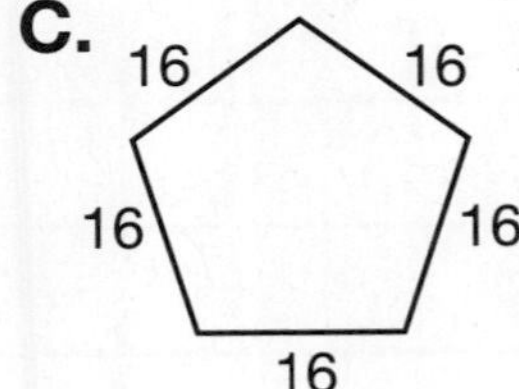

D. 1 9

4. ______ Explain your answer. ______________________________

A.
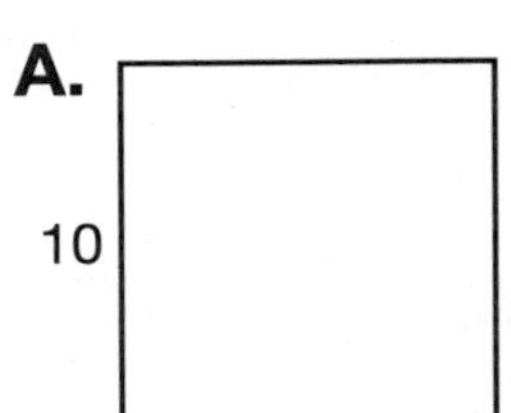

B. 20 30 **C.**
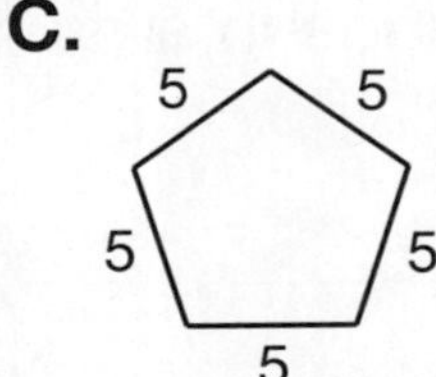

D. 30 20

5. ______ Explain your answer. ______________________________

Name ______________________________

Extend Your Thinking
8-12

Critical Thinking

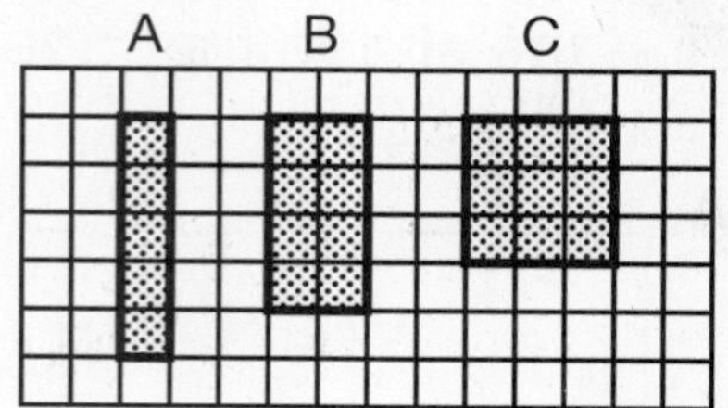

1. What is the perimeter of each of the three rectangles? ____________

2. What are the areas of each rectangle?

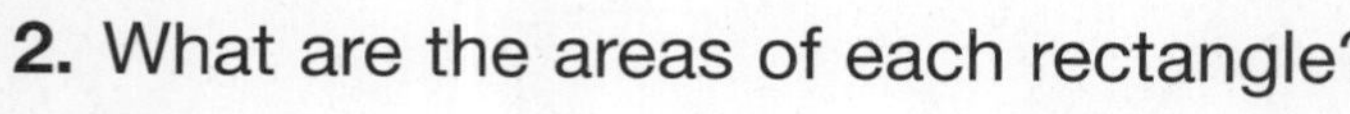

3. a. Draw on grid paper all possible rectangles with a perimeter of 16 units. Give the dimensions of each.

____

b. Which of these rectangles has the smallest area? ____________

c. Which has the greatest area? ____________

4. What conclusion can you make about the relationship between perimeter and area?

____

5. Use the information below to complete the table.
a. A rectangle has a length of 13 cm and a width of 7 cm.
b. Increase the width of rectangle **a** by 5 cm.
c. Increase the length of rectangle **b** by 5 cm.

Length	Width	Perimeter	Area	Change in Perimeter	Change in Area
a. 13 cm	7 cm				
b. 13 cm					
c.					

e. What is the overall change in perimeter and area?

____

f. Why is the change in area so much greater than the change in perimeter?

____

____

Name ______________________________

Visual Thinking

1. What is the volume of this shape in cubic units? ____________
2. On how many cubes do you see 3 faces? ____________
3. On how many cubes do you see 2 faces? ____________
4. How many show only 1 face? ____________
5. How many are hidden from view? ____________
6. Write a number sentence using the answers from **1–4** to find the answer to **5.**

____

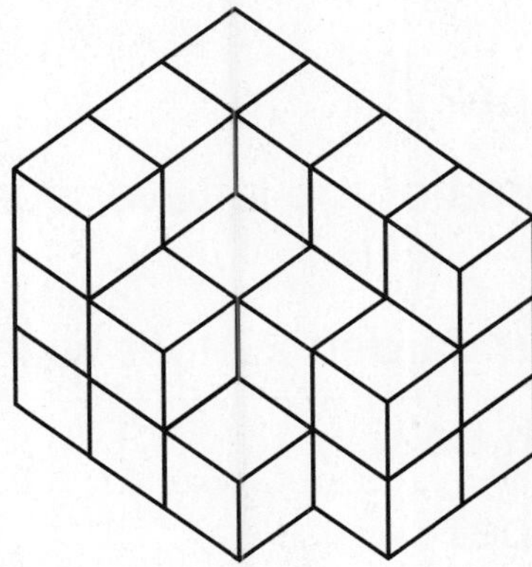

7. On how many cubes do you see 3 faces? ____________
8. On how many cubes do you see 2 faces? ____________
9. How many show only 1 face? ____________
10. How many cubes are hidden from view? ____________
11. What is the volume of this shape in cubic units? ____________

Name ______________________

Extend Your Thinking
8-14

Decision Making

Suppose you are building a fence for a garden in your yard. Your yard is 50 ft wide and has an area of 500 square ft.

Your father has 88 ft of garden fencing, so your garden has to have a perimeter of 88 feet. How big an area would you set aside for your garden?

1. Suppose you made your garden 5 feet wide.
   - **a.** What would its length be? ______
   - **b.** What would its area be? ______
   - **c.** What would be the area of the leftover space in the yard? ______
2. Suppose you made your garden 10 feet wide.
   - **a.** What would its length be? ______
   - **b.** What would its area be? ______
   - **c.** What would be the area of the leftover space in the yard? ______
3. Suppose you made your garden 15 feet wide.
   - **a.** What would its length be? ______
   - **b.** What would its area be? ______
   - **c.** What would be the area of the leftover space in the yard? ______
4. Suppose you made your garden 22 feet wide.
   - **a.** What would its length be? ______
   - **b.** What would its area be? ______
   - **c.** What would be the area of the leftover space in the yard? ______
5. About how wide would you make your garden? Explain your reasoning.

____

____

Name ____

Extend Your Thinking
9-1

Visual Thinking

Imagine a rectangular piece of paper folded in half once, as shown here.

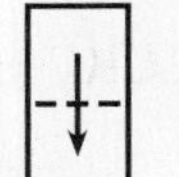

In each row, the picture on the left shows the folded rectangle, exactly as above, but with one or more cuts in it. Ring the picture on the right that shows the same rectangle unfolded.

1.

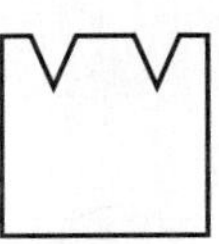

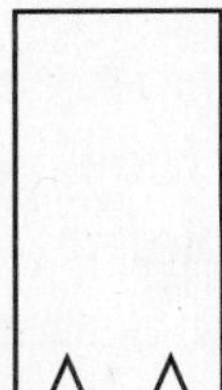

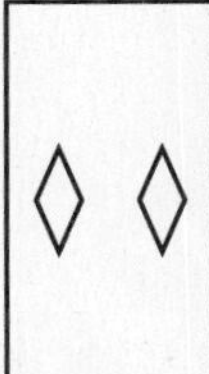

2.

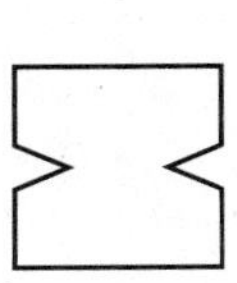

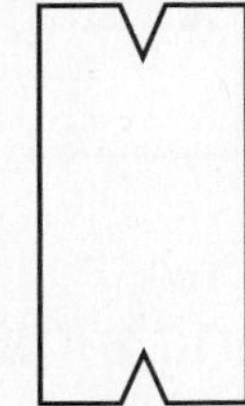

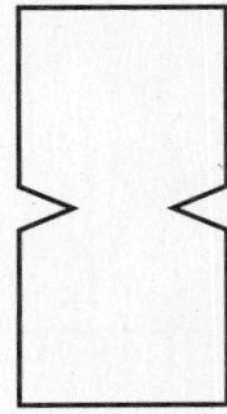

3.

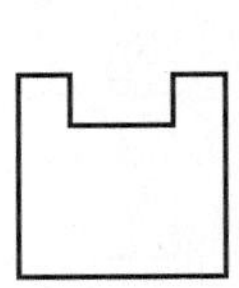

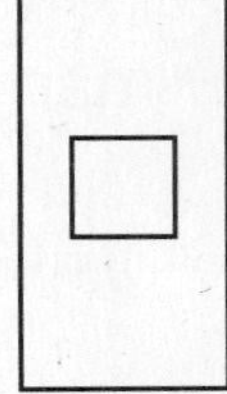

4.

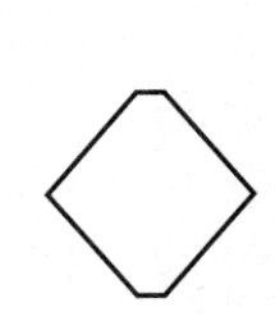

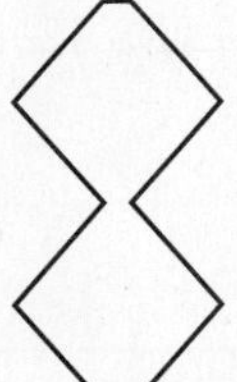

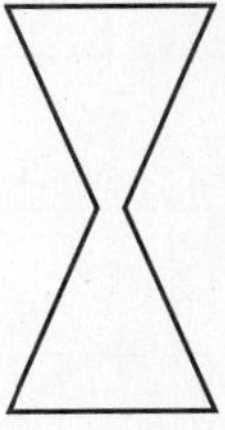

5.

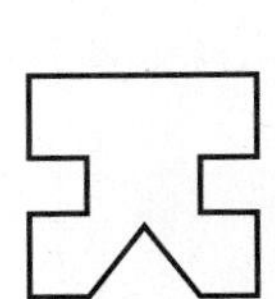

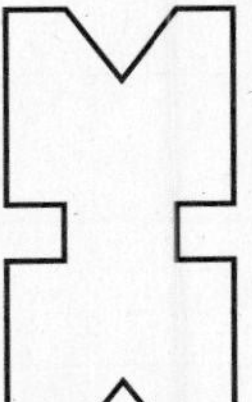

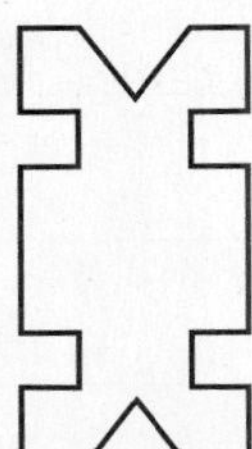

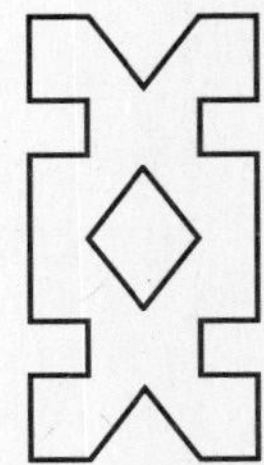

Name ______________________

Critical Thinking

Anna has a garden in her backyard. Here is a list of the plants in her garden.

Plants	Number
tomatoes	4
lettuce	5
violets	7
cabbages	2
roses	5
daisies	4
cucumbers	6

1. What fraction of Anna's garden are tomatoes? ________

2. What fraction of Anna's garden are roses? ________

3. How many of the plants in the garden are flowers? ________

4. What fraction of Anna's garden are vegetables? ________

5. What fraction of the flowers are violets? Explain.

____

____

____

6. What fraction of the vegetables are cabbages? Explain.

____

____

____

Name ______________________________ Extend Your Thinking 9-3

Decision Making

Ms. Monroe, a gym teacher at Debbie's school, gave out surveys to find out how 100 students spend their free time from 3:00 P.M. to 5:00 P.M. She is thinking about creating an after-school sports program, and wants to find out how students spend their time after school.

The survey showed that 25 students go to the park, 45 students read or spend time with friends, 10 students do chores, and 20 students do homework.

1. Use the data from the survey to answer the following questions.
   a. What fraction of the students surveyed do homework from 3:00 P.M. to 5:00 P.M.? ____________
   b. What fraction of the students surveyed go to the park after school? ____________
   c. What fraction of the students surveyed do chores? ____________
   d. What fraction of the students read or spend time with friends? ____________
2. From the survey results, do you think that there would be many students who could participate in an after-school sports program? Explain.

   ____

   ____

   ____
3. If Ms. Monroe decides to start an after-school sports program, she might do another survey asking students about their favorite sports. Do you think this is a good idea? Why or why not?

   ____

   ____

   ____

Name ______________________________

Extend Your Thinking
9-4

Patterns in Numbers

Write the next three numbers in each pattern.
Give each rule.

1. 1, $1\frac{1}{2}$, 2, $2\frac{1}{2}$, ________, ________, ________

Rule: ______________________________

2. $\frac{3}{5}$, $\frac{4}{5}$, 1, $\frac{6}{5}$, $\frac{7}{5}$, $\frac{8}{5}$, ________, ________, ________

Rule: ______________________________

3. $\frac{1}{3}$, $\frac{2}{3}$, 1, $1\frac{1}{3}$, $1\frac{2}{3}$, ________, ________, ________

Rule: ______________________________

4. 3, $\frac{7}{2}$, 4, $\frac{9}{2}$, ________, ________, ________

Rule: ______________________________

5. 1, $1\frac{1}{7}$, $1\frac{2}{7}$, $1\frac{3}{7}$, $1\frac{4}{7}$, ________, ________, ________

Rule: ______________________________

6. 1, $\frac{12}{11}$, $\frac{13}{11}$, $\frac{14}{11}$, $\frac{15}{11}$, $\frac{16}{11}$, $\frac{17}{11}$, $\frac{18}{11}$, $\frac{19}{11}$, ________, ________, ________

Rule: ______________________________

7. $2\frac{1}{5}$, $\frac{12}{5}$, $2\frac{3}{5}$, $\frac{14}{5}$, ________, ________, ________

Rule: ______________________________

Name ______________________________

Visual Thinking

Look at each solid figure on the left. Circle each shape on the right that is used to make each solid. Cross out any unused shapes.

1. 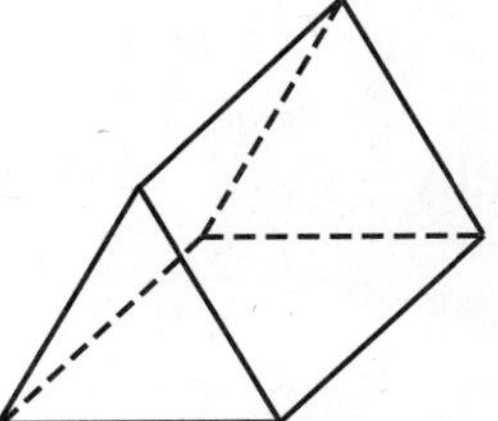 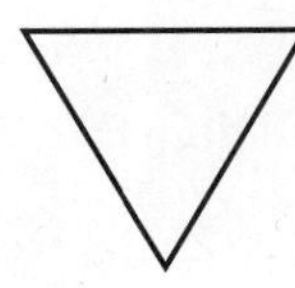 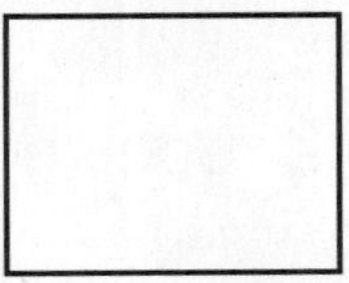 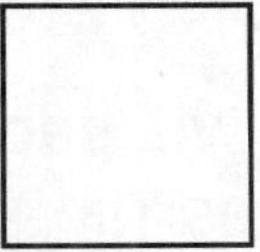 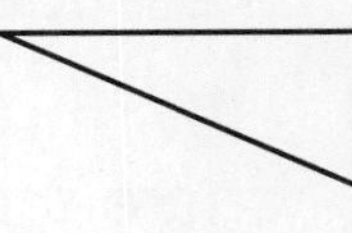

2. 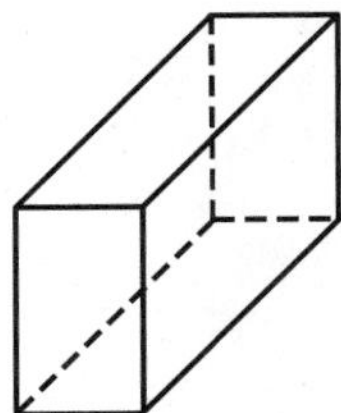 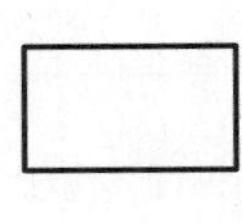 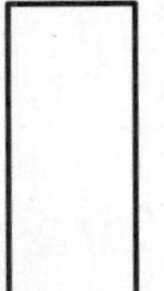 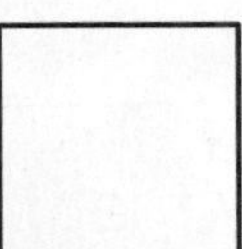 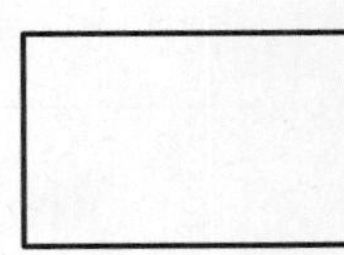

3. 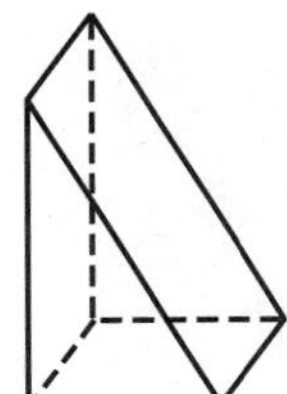 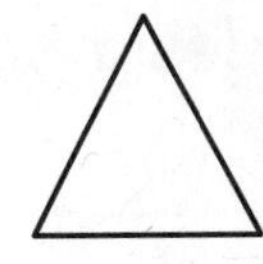 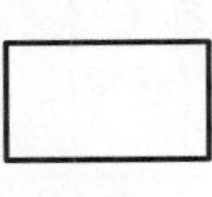 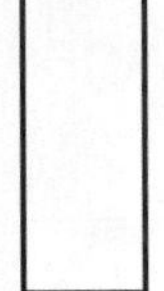 

4. 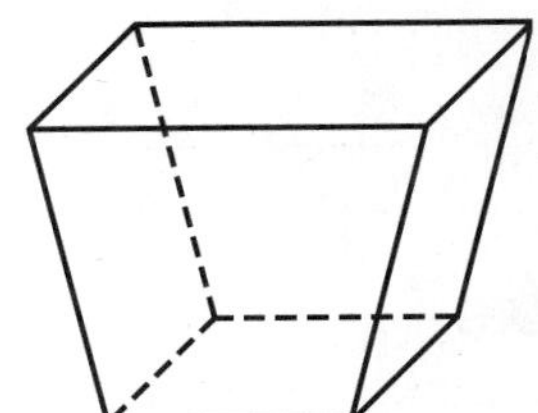 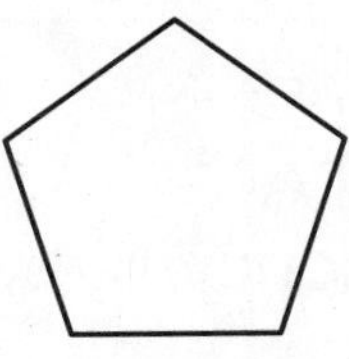 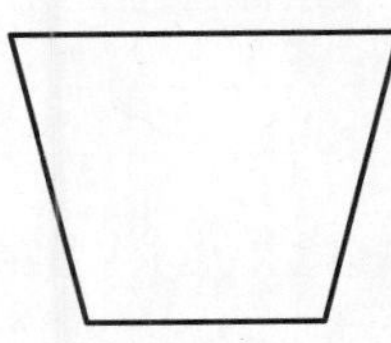 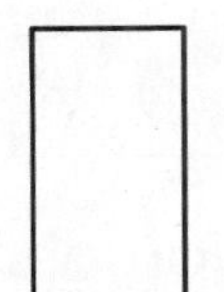 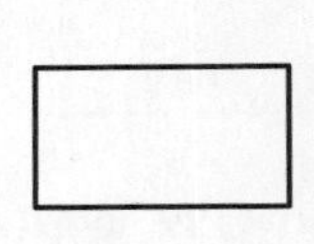

5. 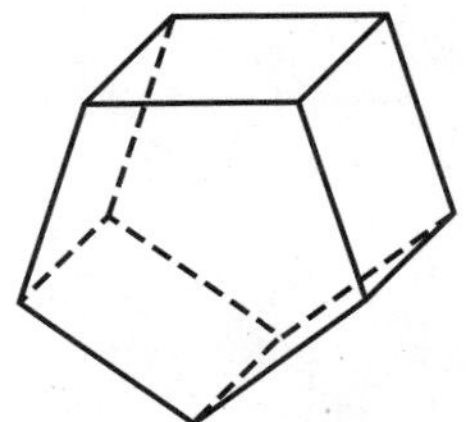 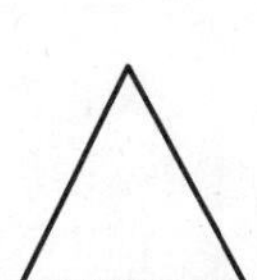 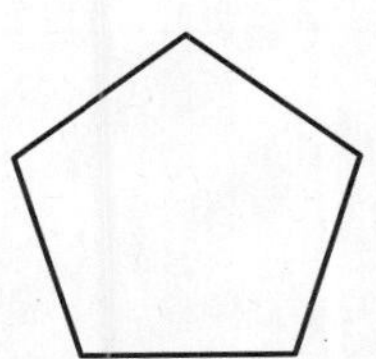 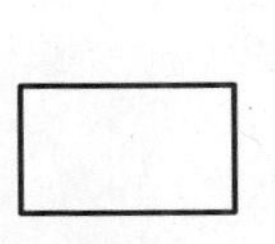 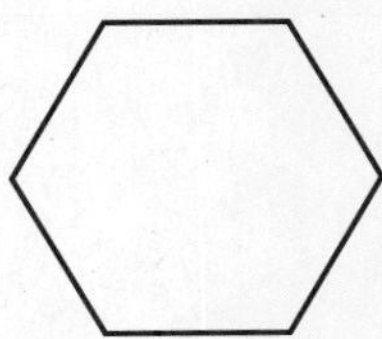

Name ______________________________

Extend Your Thinking
9-6

Decision Making

Mrs. Jackson's four children completed chores to earn a total of $22.00. She told them that they could decide how to split the money among themselves. Her children are Alonso—age 14, Greta—age 16, Luis—age 10, and Angela—age 8.

1. How much will each one receive if the children equally share their earnings? ________
2. Describe how the children could equally share whole dollar amounts.

____

____

3. List another way that the children could split the money.

____

____

4. List the advantages for the three choices described in **1–3**.

____

____

____

____

____

5. How would you choose to divide the money by whole-dollar amounts? Explain.

____

____

Name ________________________________ **Extend Your Thinking 9-7**

Visual Thinking

Write the fraction for the shaded part of each figure below. Then write if the two fractions are equivalent or not equivalent.

1.

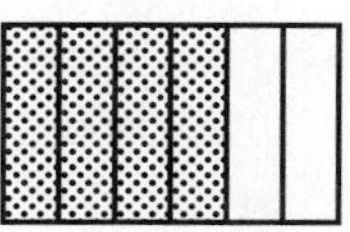

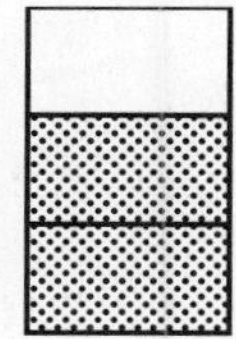

________ ________ ________________

2.

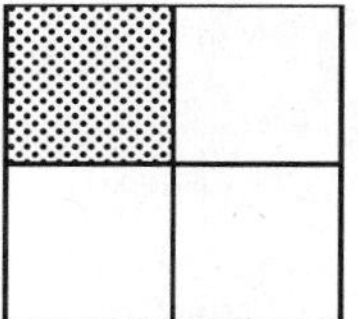

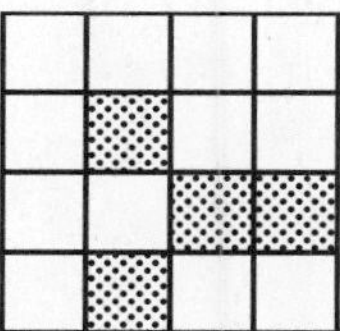

________ ________ ________________

3.

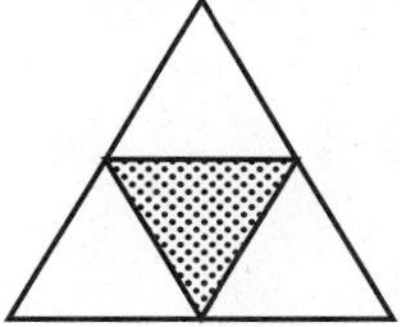

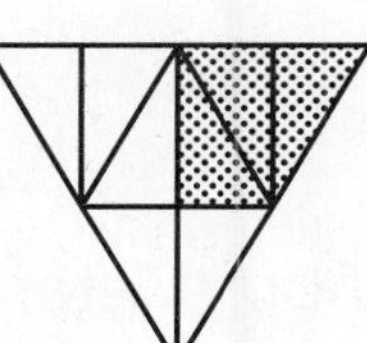

________ ________ ________________

4.

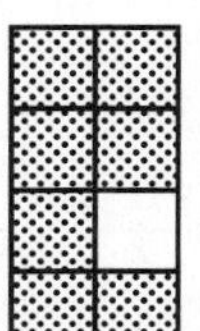

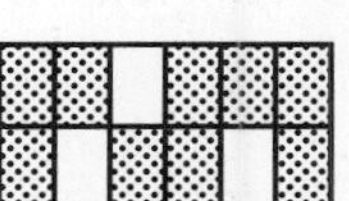

________ ________ ________________

5.

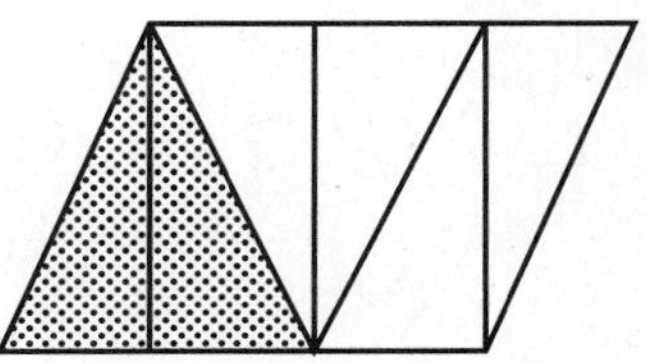

________ ________ ________________

Name ___________________________________

Critical Thinking

Did you know that the hour of the day depends on where you are in the world? When New York City students are opening up their schoolbooks, San Francisco students are still fast asleep. The mainland United States is divided into 4 time zones.

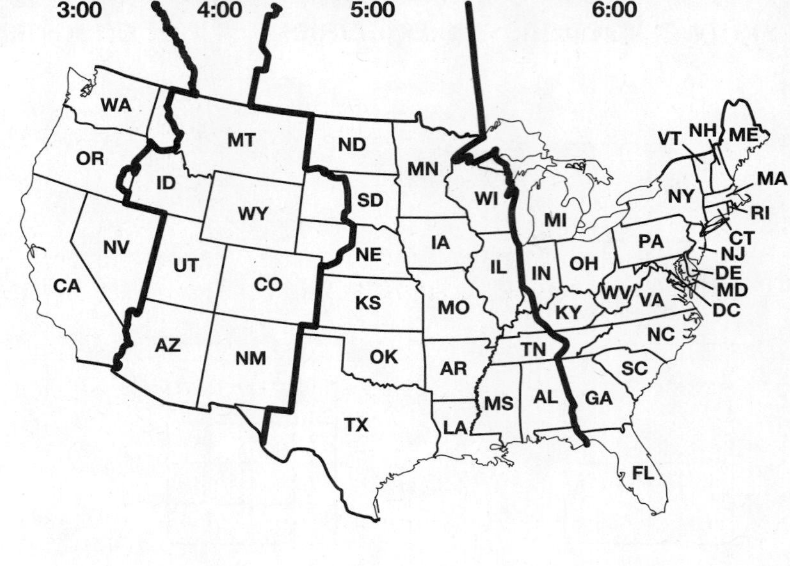

Use the map to find the time. Label the time A.M. or P.M.

1. It is 4:00 P.M. in Pennsylvania. What time is it in Mississippi?

____

2. It is 11:00 A.M. in Nevada. What time is it in Colorado?

____

3. The time in Dublin, Ireland is 5 hours later than the time in New York City. When it's 12:00 P.M. in Missouri, what time is it in Dublin? _______________

4. Mike, who lives in Illinois, starts his paper route at 3:30 P.M. He arrives back home 43 minutes later and immediately calls a friend who lives in Utah. When he calls, what time is it in Utah? _______________

5. a. Mr. Inverso leaves work on the east side of Nebraska at 5:12 P.M. He drives to a convenience store, arriving at 5:27 P.M. He spends 6 minutes in the store. It takes him another 13 minutes to drive home to the west side of Nebraska. What time is it when he arrives home? _______________

b. Describe how you solved the problem.

____

____

Name ______________________

Decision Making

Make some gifts! Fifi's Fabric Shop has fabric for simple projects like making dinner napkins or pillow covers.

Amount of fabric	Cotton prints 45 in. wide $5.95 per yard	Linen solids 60 in. wide $12.95 per yard
$\frac{7}{8}$ yard	Enough for 6 napkins or 3 pillow covers	Enough for 8 napkins or 4 pillow covers
$\frac{1}{2}$ yard	Enough for 3 napkins or $1\frac{1}{2}$ pillow covers	Enough for 4 napkins or 2 pillow covers

A pillow cover has two separate pieces of the same size that are sewn together.

1. a. Which fabric costs more per yard? ______________________

b. How much more? ______________________

2. Suppose you want to make solid blue napkins. Which fabric should you choose? Why?

____

3. a. You want to make 4 pillow covers, each with one solid pink side and one flowered side. What fabric should you buy?

____

b. Will there be enough leftover fabric to make another pillow cover? If so, what kind of pillow cover would it be?

____

4. Suppose you have $15 to buy fabric.

a. What fabric will you buy? ______________________

b. What will you make?

____

c. How much of it will you need? ______________________

Name ______________________

Extend Your Thinking
9-10

Visual Thinking

These shapes have been made by joining together letters of the alphabet. All of the letters are upper-case. Some of the letters may have been flipped. Write the two letters which have been joined.

1.  ________

2.  ________

3.  ________

4.  ________

You can solve messages in code by drawing the missing half of each letter. Decode these words.

5.  ________

6.  ________

7.  ________

Name ______________________

Decision Making

The community bulletin board has ads for two jobs that are available right now.

	Baby Sitting	Yard Work
Duties	Make sure children are safe. Feed dinner to children. Do dishes. Entertain children. Put children to bed.	Mow and weed lawn. Trim bushes. Do edging around sidewalks. Rake leaves. Add yard waste to compost heap. Shovel snow in winter.
Hours	Fridays & Saturdays 6:00 P.M.–10:30 P.M.	Saturdays 10:00 A.M.–3:00 P.M.
Pay	$5.25 per hour	$7.50 per hour

1. a. Which job pays more per hour? ______________

b. How much more? ______________

2. a. Which job pays more per week? ______________

b. How much more? ______________

3. Which job would allow you to read or do homework and still get paid for your time? ______________

4. Why might someone choose baby sitting?

____

____

5. Why might someone choose yard work?

____

____

6. Make a decision. Which job will you choose? Explain your reasoning.

____

____

Name ______________________________ **Extend Your Thinking 9-12**

Visual Thinking

Draw the next shape in the sequence.

Look for patterns.

1.

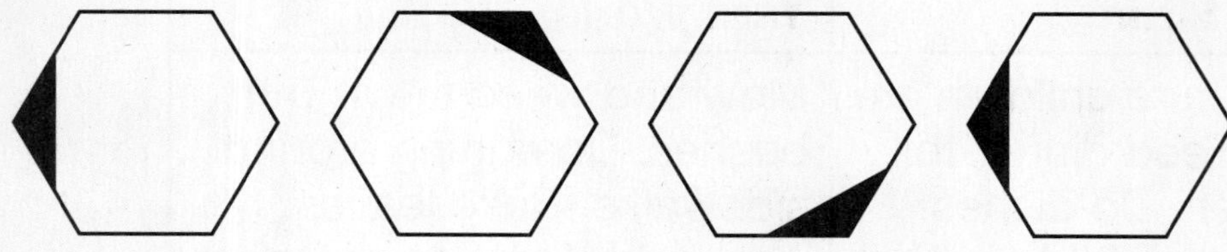

2.

3.

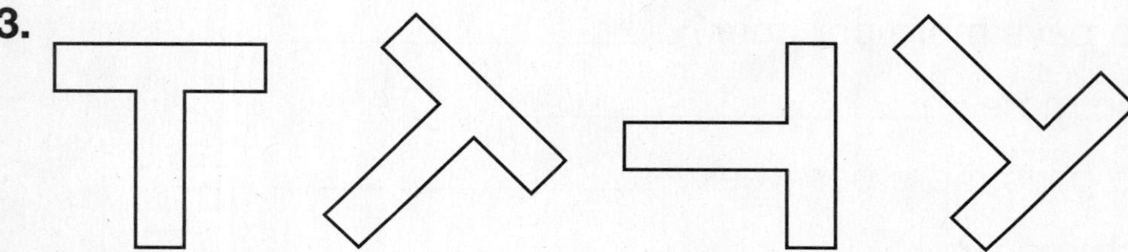

4.

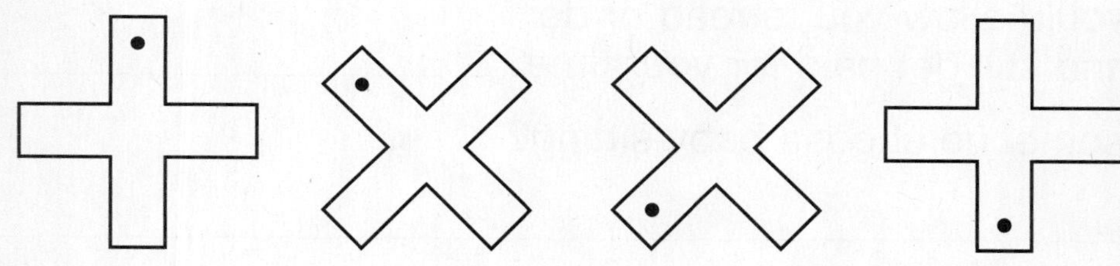

5.

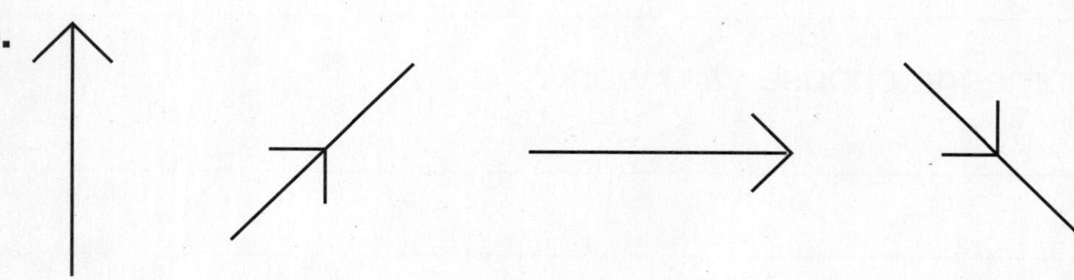

Name ____________________

Critical Thinking

Choose a method to solve these problems about feet, yards, and miles.

1. The Boston Marathon race takes place in the streets of greater Boston every spring and covers a distance of 26 miles 385 yards. When it was first run in 1897, the course covered a distance of 24 miles 1,232 yards. How much farther do participants have to run today than in 1897? Explain how you found the solution.

2. The world record for stacking dominoes is held by Aleksandr Bendikov of Belarus, who stacked 522 dominoes on a single supporting domino. The dominoes were stacked flat, one on top of another. If 4 dominoes equals 1 inch, about how many feet high was the stack? Explain how you found your solution.

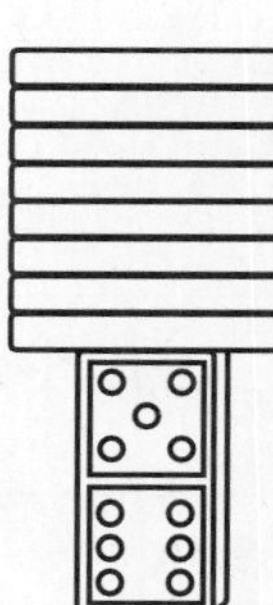

3. The staircase in the Empire State Building in New York City has 1,575 steps. If each step is 8 inches tall, how many feet would you climb if you walked up the staircase? Explain your method of solving the problem.

Name ______________________________ **Extend Your Thinking 9-14**

Patterns in Numbers

Marco is planning a two-week summer vacation trip to San Antonio. He wants to save $160 for the trip. He has exactly 10 weeks before he leaves for Texas. He wants to save $1 the first week, $3 more the second week, $6 more the third week, $10 more the fourth week, and so on, continuing this pattern.

1. What is the total amount of money Marco will have in the first week?

   ________ the second week? ________ the third week? ________

2. How much money does Marco want to save? ________

3. What is the total amount of money Marco will have after 5 weeks?

   ____

4. Continue this pattern to show how much Marco will save each week for 10 weeks.

   1, 3, 6, 10, ______, ______, ______, ______, ______, ______

5. Describe this pattern.

   ____

6. Complete this table using Marco's saving pattern.

Week	1	2	3	4	5	6	7	8	9	10
Amount saved	$1	$3	$6	$10				$36	$45	$55
Total savings	$1	$4								

7. How much money will he have saved after the 10 weeks?

   ____

8. How much over or under the total amount that he wanted to save will Marco save in 10 weeks? ________

Solve. Make a table to help.

9. Marco's brother Paul wants to save $80 in 6 weeks. He saves nothing the first week, $2 the second, $6 the third, $12 the fourth and so on. If he continues this pattern, will he have reached his goal after the sixth week?

   ____

Name ______________________

Extend Your Thinking
10-1

Patterns in Numbers

Write the next two numbers to continue the pattern. Then write the rule.

1. $\frac{1}{9}$, $\frac{2}{9}$, $\frac{3}{9}$, $\frac{4}{9}$, ___, ___

Rule: ______________________

2. $\frac{11}{12}$, $\frac{5}{6}$, $\frac{3}{4}$, $\frac{2}{3}$, ___, ___

Rule: ______________________

3. $\frac{2}{15}$, $\frac{4}{15}$, $\frac{2}{5}$, $\frac{8}{15}$, ___, ___

Rule: ______________________

4. $\frac{15}{16}$, $\frac{13}{16}$, $\frac{11}{16}$, $\frac{9}{16}$, ___, ___

Rule: ______________________

5. $\frac{1}{2}$, $\frac{1}{2}$, $\frac{1}{3}$, $\frac{1}{3}$, $\frac{1}{3}$, $\frac{1}{4}$, $\frac{1}{4}$, ___, ___

Rule: ______________________

6. 0, $\frac{1}{24}$, $\frac{1}{8}$, $\frac{1}{4}$, ___, ___

Rule: ______________________

Make up your own number patterns with fractions. Leave some blank spaces. Give them to a classmate to solve.

7. ________, ________, ________, ________, ________

8. ________, ________, ________, ________, ________

Name ______________________________

Extend Your Thinking
10-2

Visual Thinking

Look at each figure on the left. Then circle the fractional piece on the right that would complete the circle.

1. 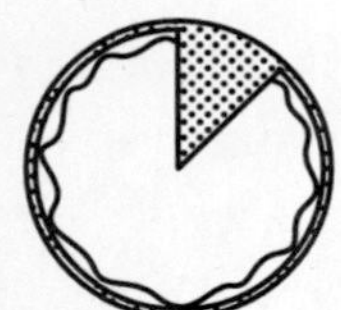  

2. 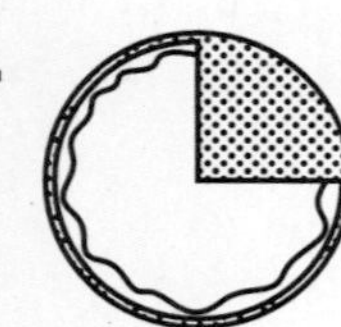   

3. 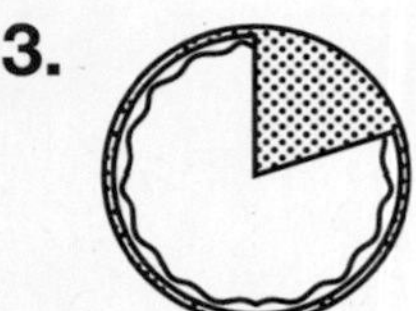 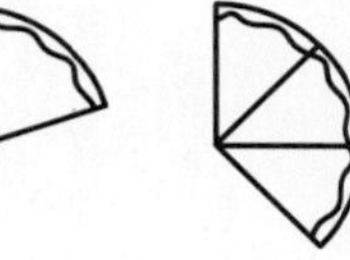 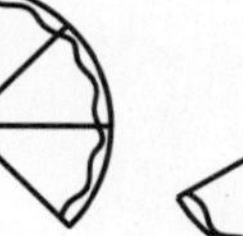  

4. 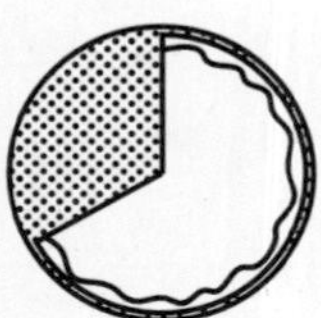  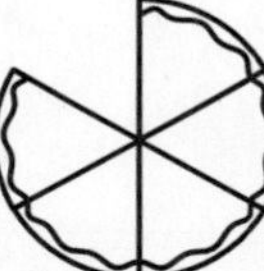 

5. 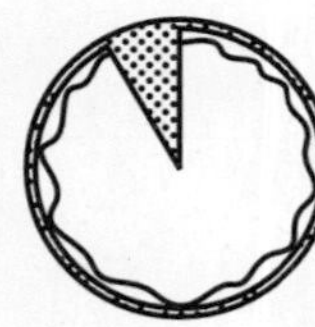   

6. 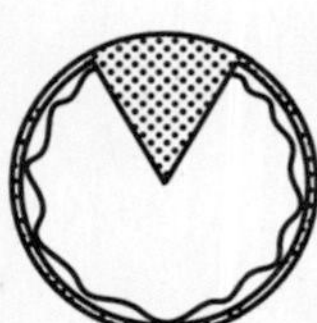 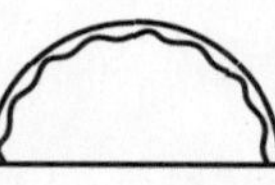  

 Use with pages 434–435.

Name ______________________

Extend Your Thinking
10-3

Visual Thinking

Add each pair of fractions. Then circle the shape with the shading that best represents the answer.

1. $\frac{1}{3} + \frac{1}{3} =$ ____________

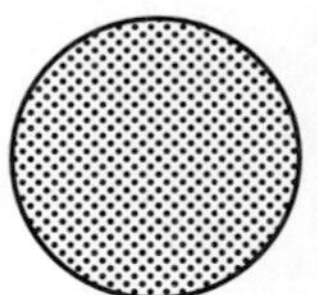
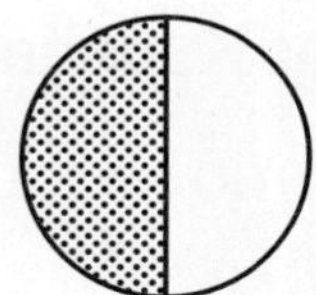
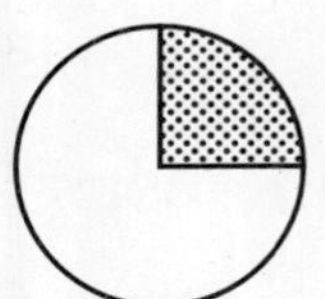
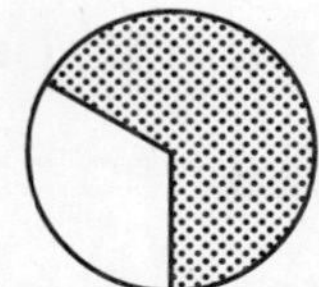

2. $\frac{5}{6} + \frac{1}{6} =$ ____________

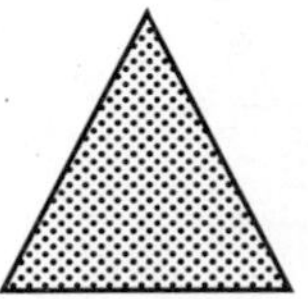
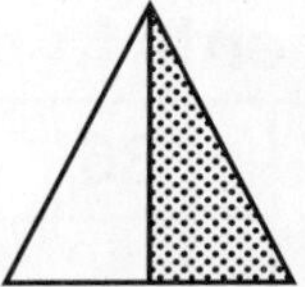
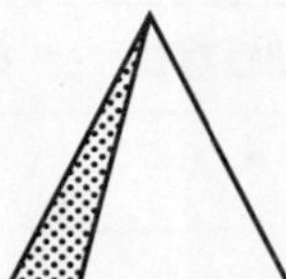
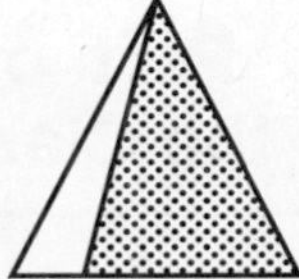

3. $\frac{1}{12} + \frac{1}{6} =$ ____________

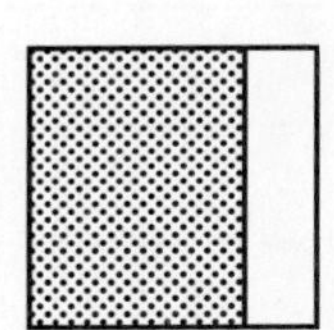
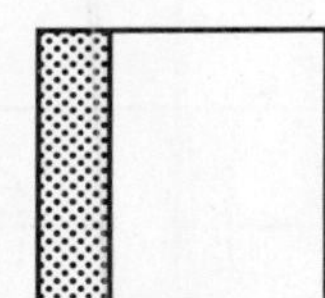

4. $\frac{1}{5} + \frac{3}{10} =$ ____________

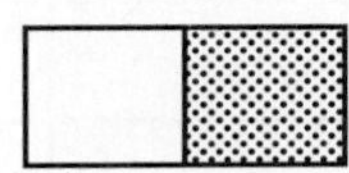
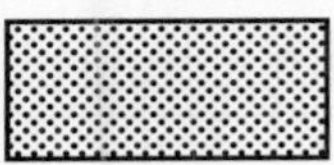

5. $\frac{3}{8} + \frac{1}{4} =$ ____________

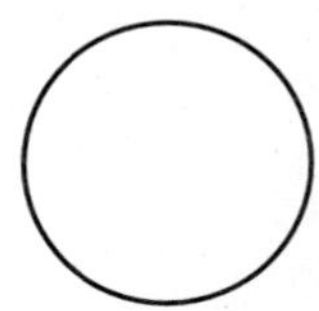
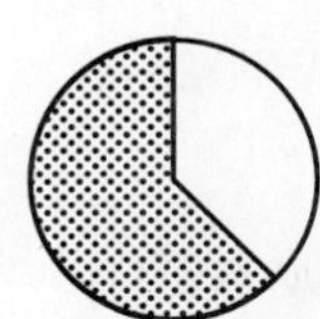
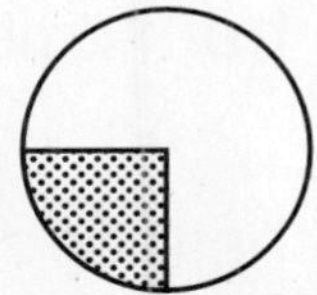

Name ________________________________ Extend Your Thinking 10-4

Critical Thinking

A group of 4th-grade students was studying the state of Missouri. They took a survey to find out how many classmates had ever visited Kansas City or St. Louis.

Here is what they found out:

- $\frac{1}{2}$ of the class had been to St. Louis but not Kansas City.
- $\frac{1}{6}$ of the class had been to Kansas City but not St. Louis.
- $\frac{1}{4}$ of the class had been to neither city.
- $\frac{1}{12}$ of the class had been to both cities.

Use patterns to complete the table. Then use it to answer the questions.

Part of the Class	Number of Students in the Class			
	12	24	36	48
$\frac{1}{12}$	1	2		
$\frac{2}{12}$	2	4	6	
$\frac{3}{12}$		6	9	12
$\frac{4}{12}$			12	16
$\frac{5}{12}$	5			
$\frac{6}{12}$		12		
$\frac{7}{12}$			21	
$\frac{8}{12}$				32
$\frac{9}{12}$			27	
$\frac{10}{12}$		20		
$\frac{11}{12}$	11			
$\frac{12}{12}$			36	

1. If there are 24 students in the class, how many have been to neither city? ________
2. If 4 students have been to both cities, how many students are in the class? ________
3. If 6 students have been to neither city, how many students have been to both cities? ________

Tim 11
Bob 3
Jane 5
Sue 5
Jill 8

Mike 9
John 10
Tom 10
Beth 7
Kelly 3
Sally 10

Name ________________________________

Decision Making

Today is Saturday. The roller-skating rink is open from 9:00 A.M. to 9:00 P.M.! You have a party to go to at 3:30 P.M., but there's time to fit in some skating before you go.

Full day	$6.00
6 hours	$4.00
3 hours	$3.00
2 hours	$2.00

1. Zeke and Kye want to skate from 9:00 A.M. to noon, take a lunch break for an hour, and then skate until 3:00 P.M. Should each buy a full-day ticket or separate tickets for the morning and the afternoon? Explain.

   ____

2. Suppose you have $4.00 to spend, Zeke has $2.00, and Kye has $3.00.

   a. How much more time could you skate than Zeke? ____________

   b. How much more time could you skate than Kye? ____________

   c. If you pooled your money, could you all skate for the same amount of time? Explain.

   ____

3. If you went skating at 12:00 noon and paid $3.00, would you have enough time to get to the party if it is a 15-minute walk away? Explain.

   ____

4. Which hours would you choose to skate? How much would it cost?

   ____

   ____

   ____

Name ______________________________ Extend Your Thinking **10-6**

Critical Thinking

Classify the fractions.

Write the letter of the can where each fraction could be placed. There will be an equal number of fractions for each can.

A. Less than $\frac{1}{2}$ **B.** Equal to $\frac{1}{2}$ **C.** Greater than $\frac{1}{2}$

1. $\frac{1}{4}$ ______	**2.** $\frac{5}{8}$ ______	**3.** $\frac{5}{10}$ ______	**4.** $\frac{3}{4}$ ______
5. $\frac{3}{8}$ ______	**6.** $\frac{5}{9}$ ______	**7.** $\frac{6}{12}$ ______	**8.** $\frac{3}{7}$ ______
9. $\frac{11}{20}$ ______	**10.** $\frac{3}{5}$ ______	**11.** $\frac{13}{24}$ ______	**12.** $\frac{2}{3}$ ______
13. $\frac{7}{12}$ ______	**14.** $\frac{4}{10}$ ______	**15.** $\frac{9}{18}$ ______	**16.** $\frac{7}{20}$ ______
17. $\frac{7}{14}$ ______	**18.** $\frac{2}{4}$ ______	**19.** $\frac{8}{16}$ ______	**20.** $\frac{1}{3}$ ______
21. $\frac{12}{24}$ ______	**22.** $\frac{5}{14}$ ______	**23.** $\frac{3}{6}$ ______	**24.** $\frac{9}{20}$ ______

25. Describe the patterns you see in the fractions in each category.

____

____

____

____

Name ______________________

Critical Thinking

The graph shows changes in the size of the average farm from 1940 to 1990.

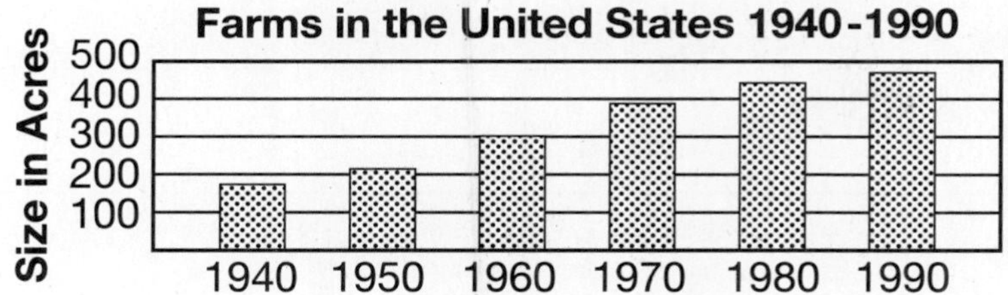

You want to buy a farm. Before you make a decision about which farm to buy, you decide to find out some facts about the size of farms.

1. Based on the graph, how has the average size of a farm changed from 1940 to 1990?

   ____

2. About how much larger was an average farm in 1980 than an average farm in 1950?

   ____

   ____

3. If you bought a farm that was double the size of an average farm in 1940, would your farm be as large as the average farm in 1990? Explain.

   ____

   ____

4. Suppose you buy a 400-acre farm.

   a. What year's average farm size is your farm closest to in size? __________

   b. About what fractional part of your farm is represented by an average farm in 1960?

   ____

   c. Predict how the size of an average farm in the year 2000 will compare to the size of your farm. Give reasons for your prediction.

   ____

   ____

Name ______________________________

Extend Your Thinking
10-8

Patterns in Numbers

Follow the pattern to find the next three weights. Tell what rule was used to make the pattern.

1. 75 oz, 69 oz, 63 oz, 57 oz, ________, ________, ________

Rule: ______________________________

2. 5 oz, 21 oz, 37 oz, 53 oz, ________, ________, ________

Rule: ______________________________

3. 8 lb; 2 T 20 lb, 4 T 32 lb, 6 T 44 lb, ________, ________, ________

Rule: ______________________________

4. 8 T 1,300 lb; 7 T 1,800; 7 T 300 lb; 6 T 800 lb;

________, ________, ________

Rule: ______________________________

5. 13 oz, 2 lb 5 oz, 3 lb 13 oz, 5 lb 5 oz

________, ________, ________

Rule: ______________________________

6. 432 oz, 384 oz, 336 oz, 288 oz, ________, ________, ________

Rule: ______________________________

7. 34 oz, 50 oz, 82 oz, 130 oz, ________, ________, ________

Rule: ______________________________

Name ______________________________

Decision Making

Sam's Market offers foods in various amounts.

	1 cup	1 pint	1 quart	1 gallon
apple juice	$0.56	$0.96	$1.79	$6.89
ice cream	$1.49	$2.49	$3.98	$7.59
carrot juice	$0.89	$1.69	$2.99	$9.49
milk	$0.65	$0.89	$1.79	$3.79
orange juice	$1.89	$3.49	$5.99	not available

- The orange juice and carrot juice are freshly made and must be used within 3 days.
- Cups and pints of ice cream come in 5 flavors. Quarts and gallons come in 15 flavors.
- The apple juice comes only in glass containers.

1. What are the advantages of buying by the cup or pint?

____

2. What are the disadvantages of buying by the cup or pint?

____

3. What are the advantages of buying by the quart or gallon?

____

4. What are the disadvantages of buying by the quart or gallon?

____

____

5. Why might someone buy carrot juice by the gallon?

____

6. Why might someone buy milk by the cup?

____

7. Make a decision. If you had $20, what would you buy? Explain.

____

____

Name ______________________________

Visual Thinking

Similar figures have the same shape but not the same size. Look at each figure on the left. Circle the similar figure on the right.

1. 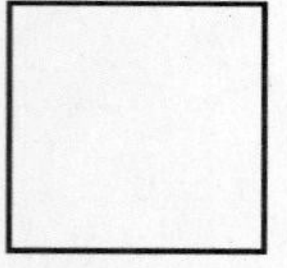

2. 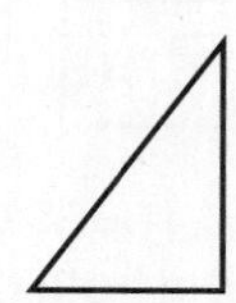  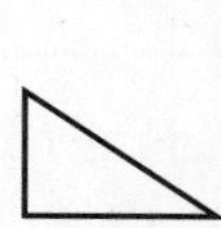 

3. 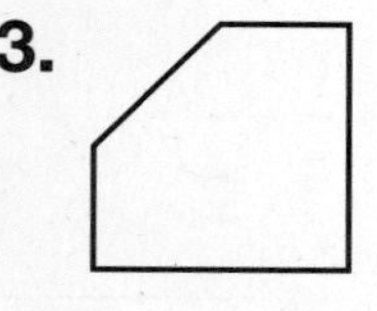 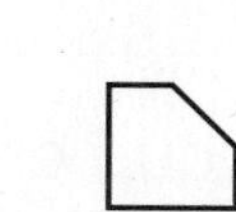 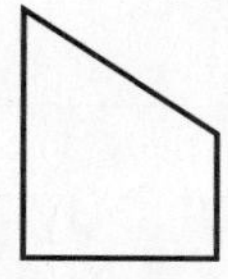 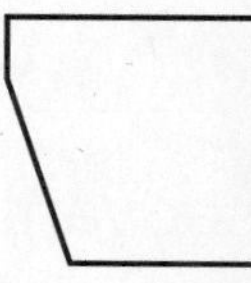 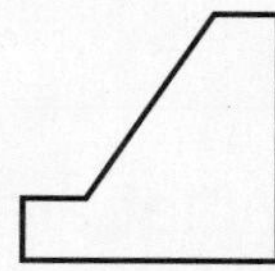

4. 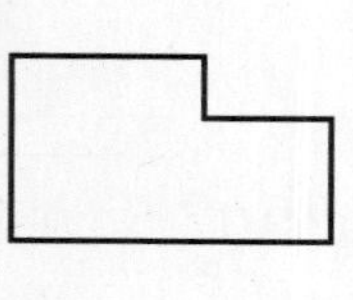 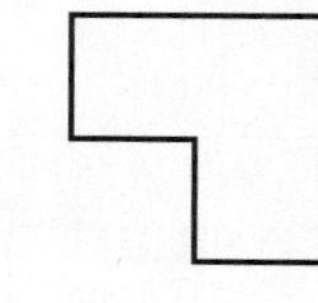 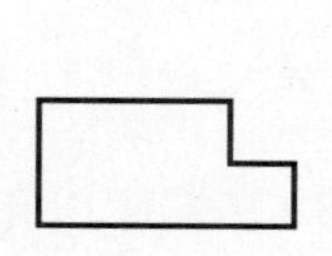 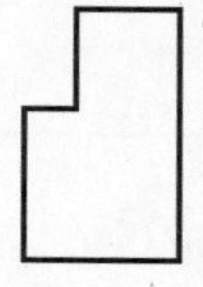 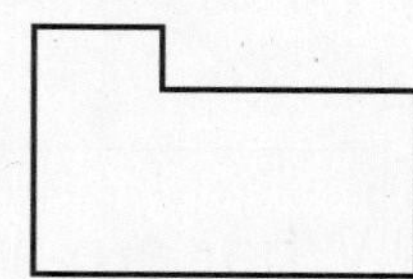

5. 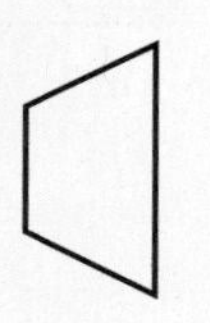 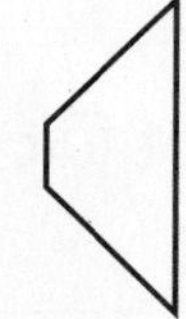 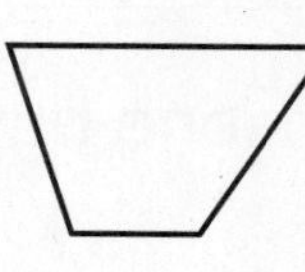 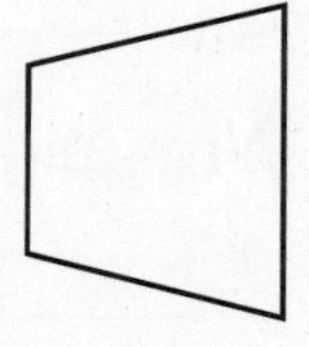

6. 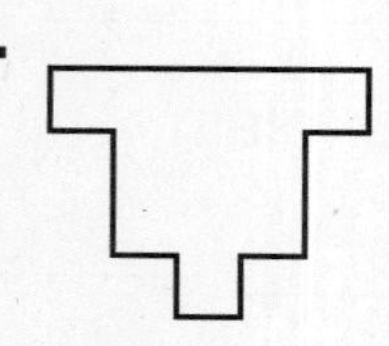 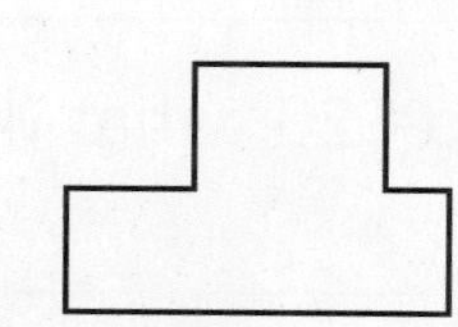 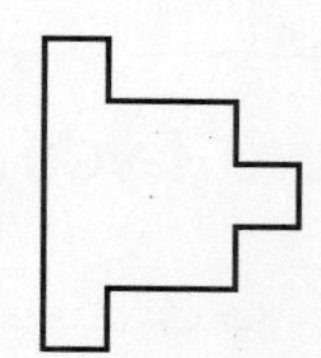 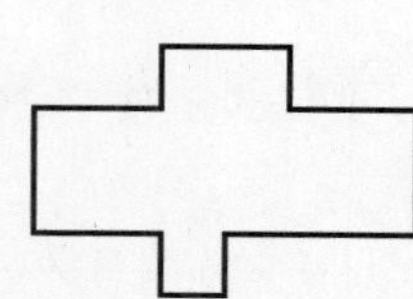

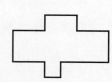

Name ______________________________

Patterns in Numbers

Give the next three numbers. Write the rule used to form the pattern.

1. 144, 180, 216, 252, ________, ________, ________

Rule: ______________________________

2. 450, 432, 414, 396, ________, ________, ________

Rule: ______________________________

3. 67, 78, 100, 133, ________, ________, ________

Rule: ______________________________

4. 29, 46, 80, 131, ________, ________, ________

Rule: ______________________________

5. 812, 787, 737, 662, ________, ________, ________

Rule: ______________________________

6. 28, 41, 67, 106, ________, ________, ________

Rule: ______________________________

7. 517, 511, 499, 481, ________, ________, ________

Rule: ______________________________

8. 3, 6, 12, 24, ________, ________, ________

Rule: ______________________________

Name ____________________

Critical Thinking

The Food Pyramid shows how much of each type of food you should eat each day. Use it to help you answer the questions.

1. Kari eats equal numbers of servings of bread, cereal, rice, and pasta, and she stays within the guidelines. How many servings of each does she have? ____________

2. For breakfast, Kari had one serving of cereal and 1 serving of fruit. What is the minimum amount of fruit she needs during the rest of the day?

   ____________ The maximum? ____________

3. At lunch, Kari had one serving each of green beans, peas, and carrots. She likes vegetables and wants to eat the maximum recommended amount. How many servings can she have at dinner? ____________

4. Kari had one serving of milk with her breakfast cereal. She had milk and yogurt at lunch. Should she have cheese with dinner? Explain.

   ____

5. Phil had an egg salad sandwich at lunch. With his egg salad sandwich, Phil had a salad and carrot sticks. Does he need to have another serving of vegetables for dinner? Explain.

   ____

Name ______________________________ **Extend Your Thinking 11-1**

Visual Thinking

Circle the shape on the right that belongs in the group on the left.

1. 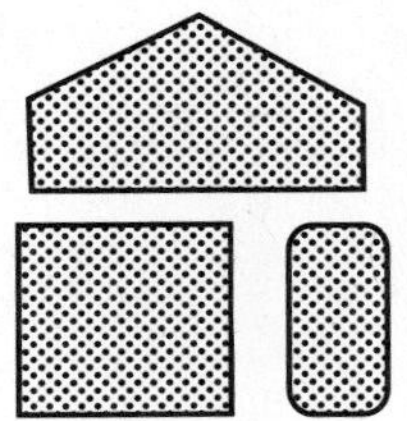

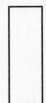

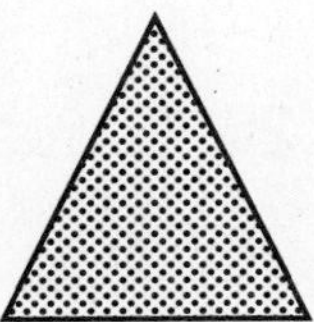

2. 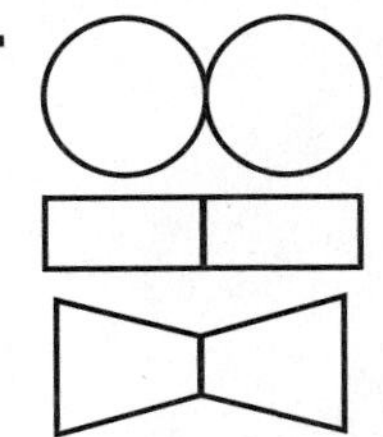

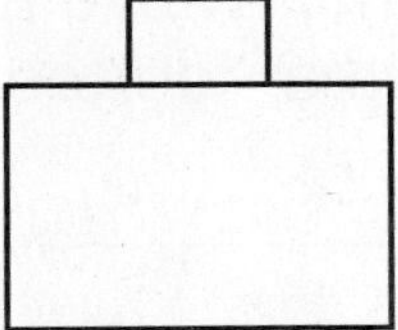

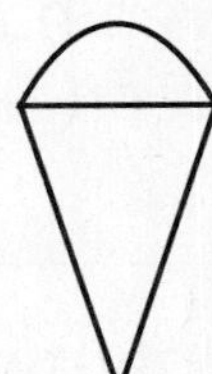

3. 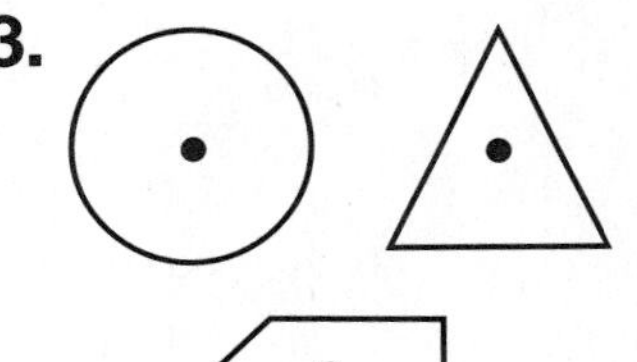

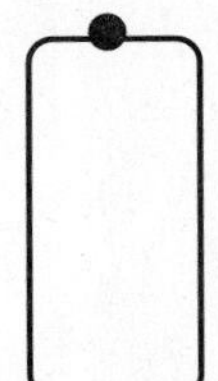

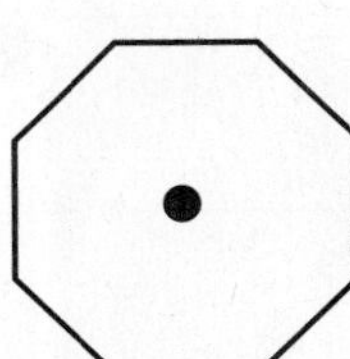

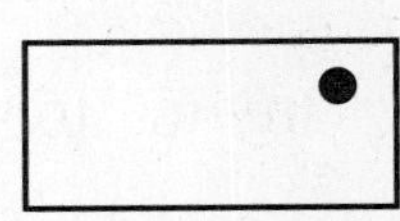

4. 

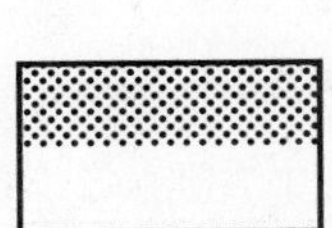

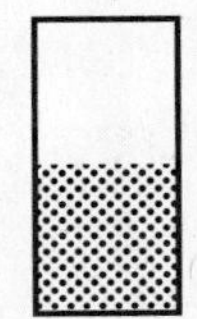

5. 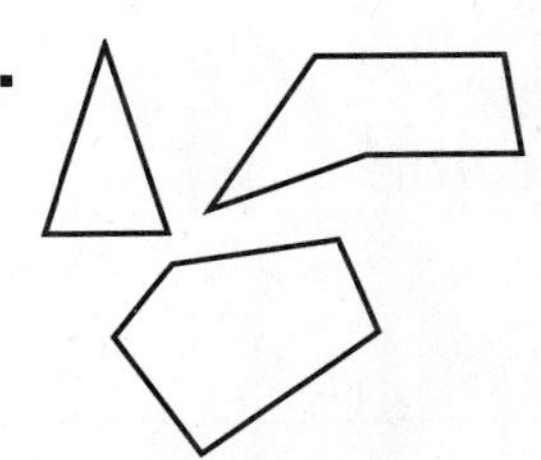

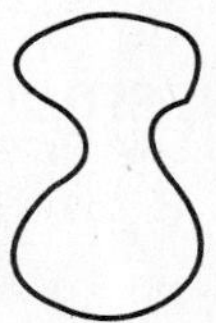

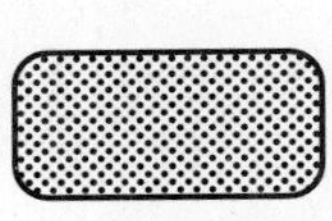

Name ______________________________

Extend Your Thinking
11-2

Patterns in Numbers

Write the next two numbers in each pattern.

1. 0.1, 0.2, 0.3, 0.4, ________, ________

2. 1.1, 0.9, 0.7, ________, ________

3. 0.23, 0.24, 0.25, 0.26, ________, ________

4. 0.09, 0.08, 0.07, 0.06, ________, ________

5. three tenths, four tenths, five tenths, six tenths,

________________, ________________

6. eleven hundredths, twelve hundredths, thirteen hundredths, fourteen hundredths,

________________, ________________

7. twenty-two hundredths, twenty hundredths, eighteen hundredths, sixteen hundredths,

________________, ________________

8. $\frac{4}{10}$, $\frac{5}{10}$, $\frac{6}{10}$, $\frac{7}{10}$, ________, ________

9. $\frac{62}{100}$, $\frac{63}{100}$, $\frac{64}{100}$, $\frac{65}{100}$, ________, ________

10. 0.10, 0.1, 0.20, 0.2, 0.30, 0.3, ________, ________

11. 0.9, 0.90, 0.8, 0.80, 0.7, 0.70, ________, ________

12. eight tenths, eighty hundredths, seven tenths, seventy hundredths, six tenths, sixty hundredths,

________________, ________________

13. 0.67, 0.68, 0.69, 0.7, 0.71, 0.72, 0.73, 0.74, 0.75, 0.76, 0.77, 0.78,

________, ________

14. Write your own pattern and have a classmate write in the next two numbers.

____

____

Name ______________________________ **Extend Your Thinking 11-3**

Critical Thinking

Tony has collected $5.17 worth of coins.

1. What is the fewest number of coins that Tony could have? What are they? Explain how you found the answer.

____

____

____

____

____

2. What is the greatest number of coins Tony could have? What are they?

____

3. Suppose Tony bought a bottle of juice with his coins. He has nine quarters, eleven dimes, seven nickels, and twenty-one pennies left.

   a. How much did the juice cost? __________

   b. What coins could Tony have used to buy the juice?

   ____

4. If Tony only had dimes and pennies in his collection, could he have an equal number of dimes and pennies? Explain. What strategy did you use to find the answer?

____

____

5. If Tony had only 13 quarters in his collection, what could the other coins be?

____

Name ______________________________

Extend Your Thinking
11-4

Decision Making

There are seven sprinters on the high school track team. Only three of the sprinters can run the 100-meter sprint in the upcoming meet. The seven runners ran three races to help decide who should be selected to run in the meet.

	Time		
Runner	**Race 1**	**Race 2**	**Race 3**
Heather	17.9	18.12	18.10
Keisha	17.87	17.80	17.99
Darcy	17.82	17.97	17.81
Angelina	17.89	18.10	17.8
Tamara	18.14	17.86	18.12
Marisa	17.91	17.84	17.93
Ming	17.90	17.9	17.88

1. Who were the top 3 finishers in Race 1? Write the runners' names and their times in order, from 1st to 3rd.

____

2. Did any of the runners in Race 1 finish the race at the same time? How do you know?

____

3. Who were the top 3 finishers in Race 2? Write the runners' names and their times in order, from 1st to 3rd.

____

4. Who were the top 3 finishers in Race 3? Order their names and times.

____

5. Which three runners do you think should run in the meet? Explain.

____

____

Name ____

Visual Thinking

Circle the two figures in each row that are alike.

1.     

2. 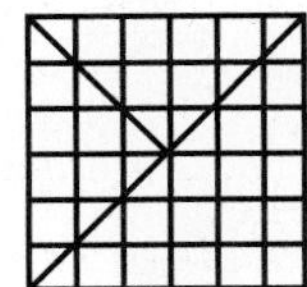 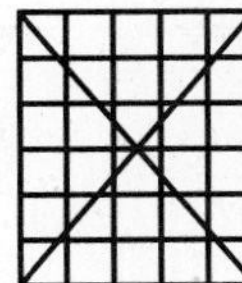 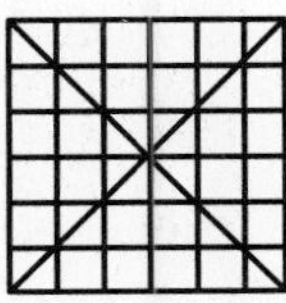  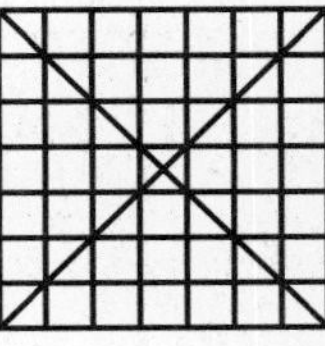

3. 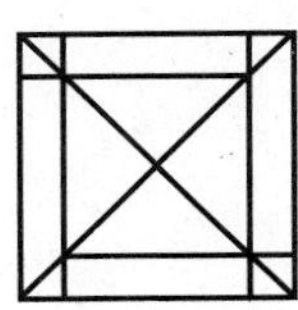 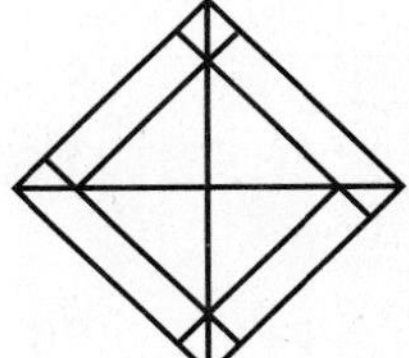 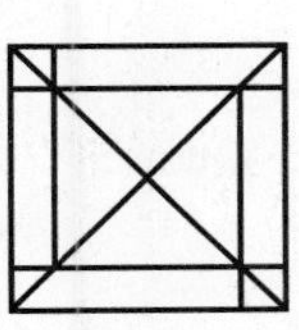 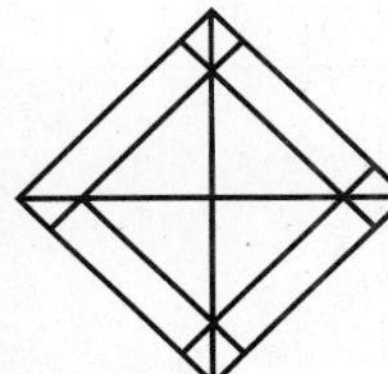 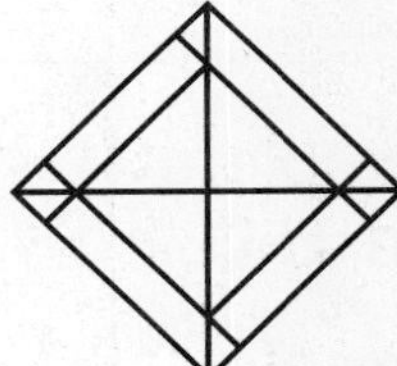

4.     

5. 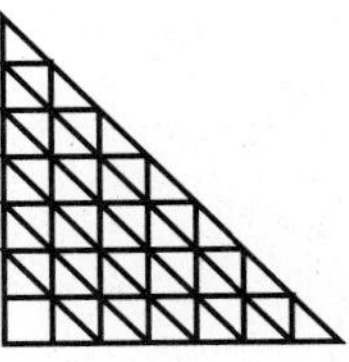 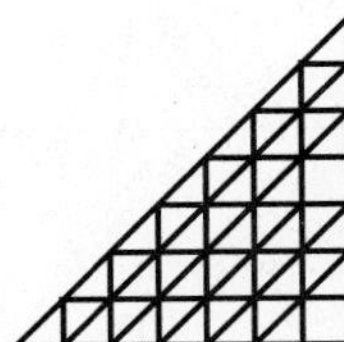 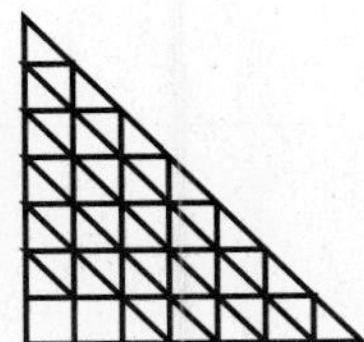 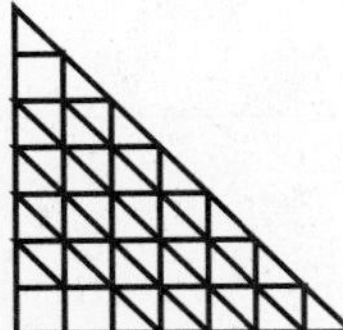 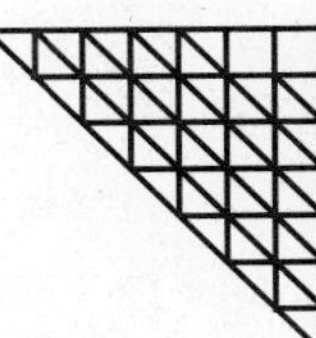

Name ______________________________

Extend Your Thinking
11-6

Patterns in Numbers

Complete **1–8** using the same pattern used in samples **A** and **B**.

Sample A $\frac{1}{2}$, $\frac{5}{10}$, $\frac{5}{1}$, 5

Sample B $\frac{6}{5}$, $\frac{12}{10}$, $\frac{12}{1}$, 12

1. $\frac{1}{5}$, ______, ______, ______

2. $\frac{3}{5}$, ______, ______, ______

3. $\frac{4}{5}$, ______, ______, ______

4. $\frac{1}{10}$, ______, ______, ______

5. $\frac{2}{2}$, ______, ______, ______

6. $\frac{8}{5}$, ______, ______, ______

7. $\frac{3}{2}$, ______, ______, ______

8. $\frac{7}{5}$, ______, ______, ______

9. Describe the pattern.

____

____

Complete **10–15** using the same pattern used in samples **C** and **D**.

Sample C $\frac{1}{4}$, $\frac{25}{100}$, $\frac{25}{10}$, 2.5

Sample D $\frac{7}{10}$, $\frac{70}{100}$, $\frac{70}{10}$, 7.0

10. $\frac{3}{4}$, ______, ______, ______

11. $\frac{4}{10}$, ______, ______, ______

12. $\frac{9}{25}$, ______, ______, ______

13. $\frac{3}{20}$, ______, ______, ______

14. $\frac{27}{25}$, ______, ______, ______

15. $\frac{37}{20}$, ______, ______, ______

16. Describe the pattern.

____

____

Name ______________________________

Visual Thinking

For each shape, write the letter of the sentence that describes the shape. Some shapes may fit more than one description.

a. This shape has no right angles.

b. This shape has only one right angle.

c. This shape has 4 right angles.

d. This shape has 2 sets of parallel sides.

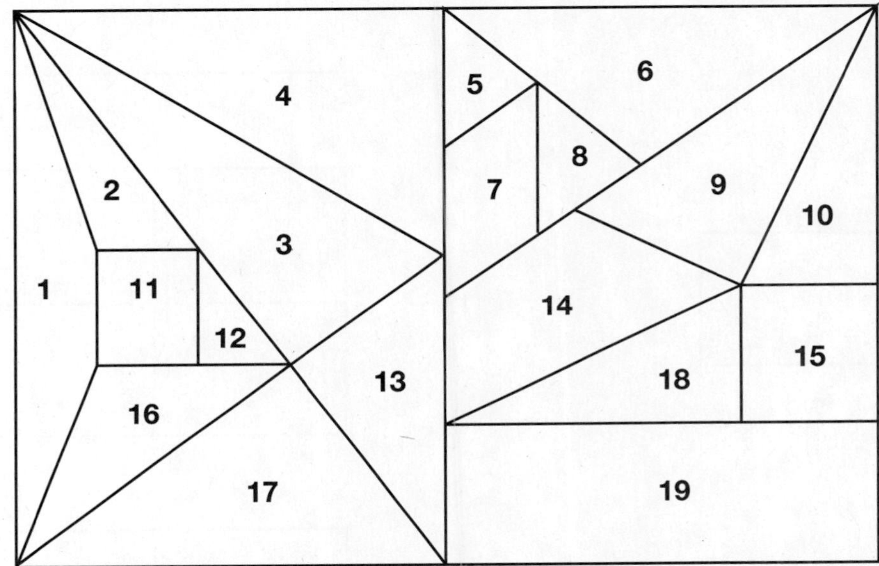

1. ______ **2.** ______ **3.** ______

4. ______ **5.** ______ **6.** ______

7. ______ **8.** ______ **9.** ______

10. ______ **11.** ______ **12.** ______

13. ______ **14.** ______ **15.** ______

16. ______ **17.** ______ **18.** ______

19. ______

Name ____________________

Extend Your Thinking
11-8

Visual Thinking

The rectangles in the first column are sheets of paper that have been folded in fourths. A hole has been punched out of each rectangle. The designs in column 2 show the sheets of paper after they have been opened up. The dashed lines represent the fold lines. Draw a line from each folded rectangle to its matching design.

1. 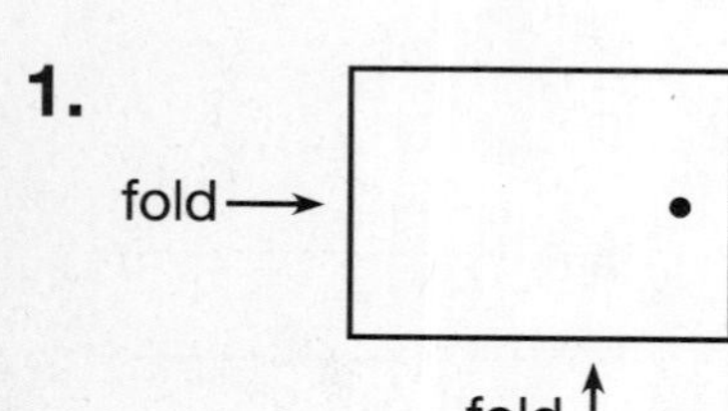

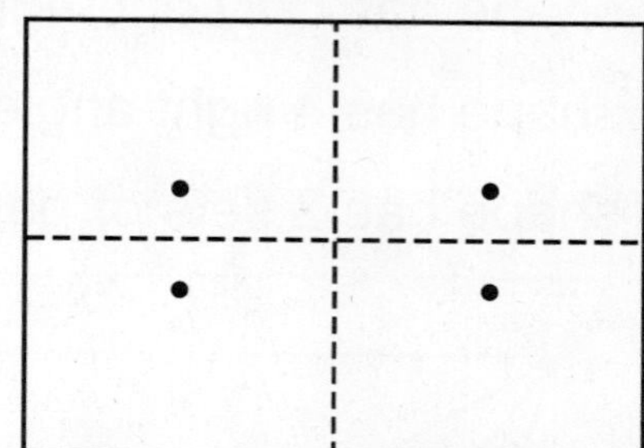

2. 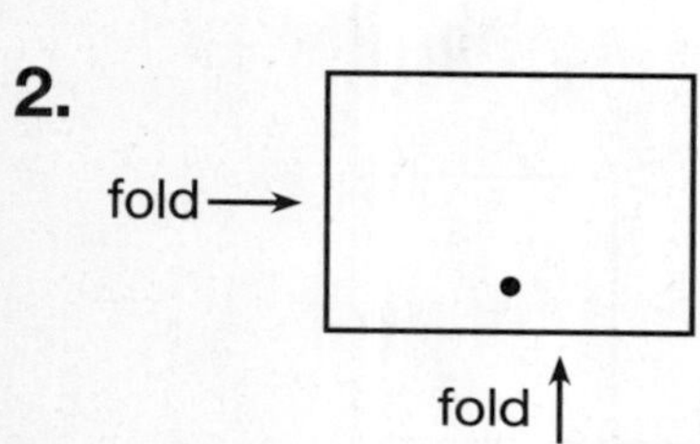

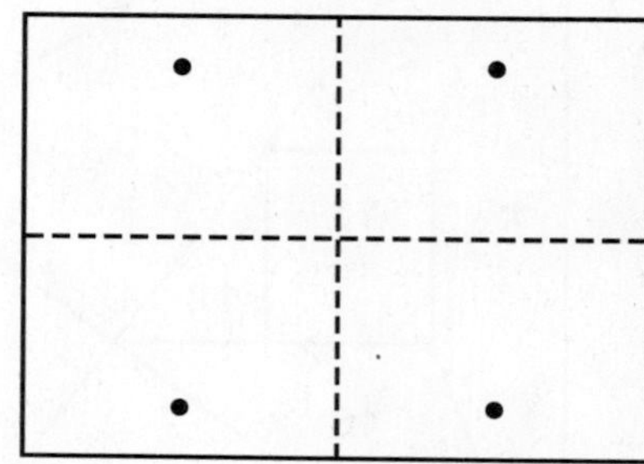

3. 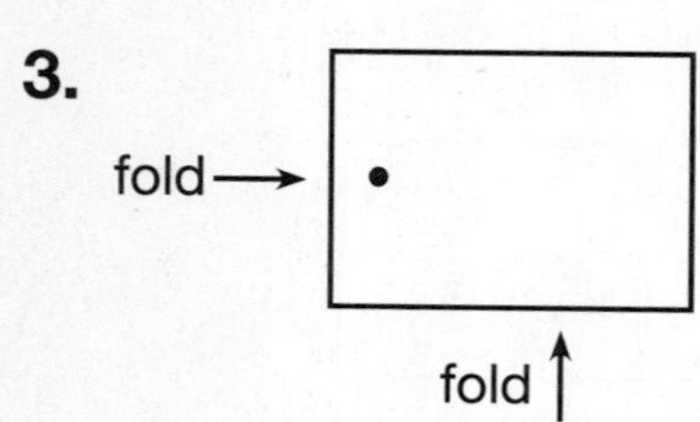

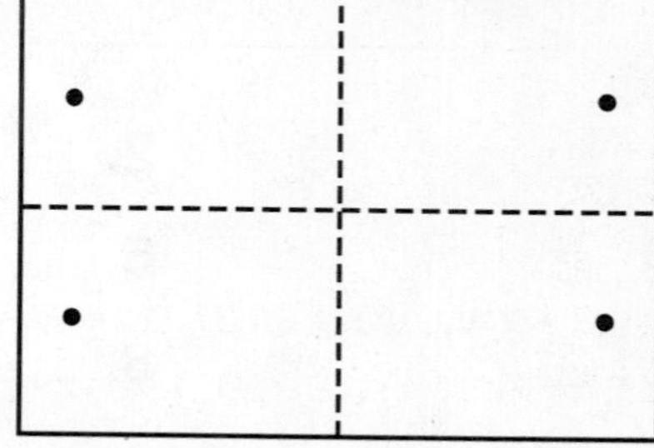

4. 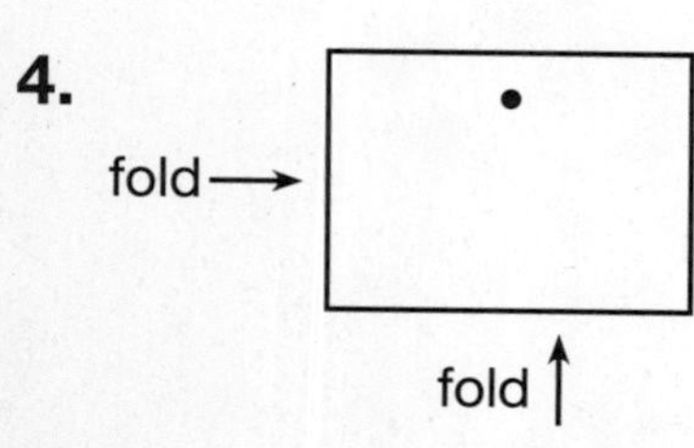

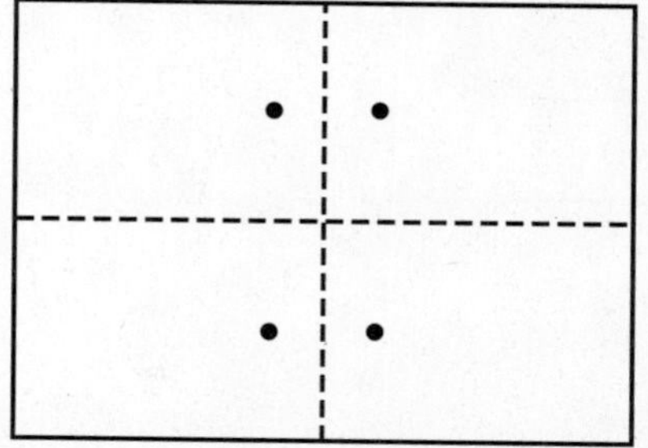

Name ______________________________

Critical Thinking

1. Write four pairs of decimals to complete each column in the table.

Sums			Differences		
greater than 1	equal to 1	less than 1	greater than 1	equal to 1	less than 1
0.34, 0.89			6.9, 0.7		

2. Explain how you can tell whether the sum of two decimals is greater than 1 or less than 1.

____

____

____

____

3. Explain how you can tell whether the sum of two decimals is equal to 1.

____

____

4. Explain how you can tell whether the difference of two decimals is equal to 1.

____

____

Name ______________________

Decision Making

Rasheed is building rectangular picture frames. He can build frames with these dimensions:

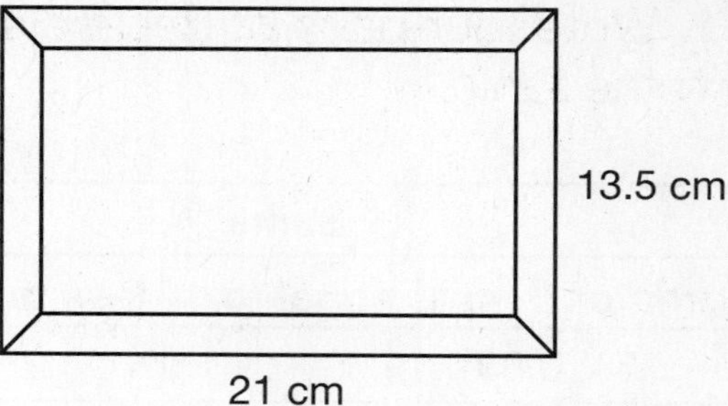

13.5 cm by 21 cm

19.25 cm by 25 cm

26.5 cm by 34 cm

He has 2.5 m of wood. How can he best use the wood?

1. What is the perimeter of a 13.5 cm by 21 cm frame? ______
2. What is the perimeter of a 19.25 cm by 25 cm frame? ______
3. What is the perimeter of a 26.5 cm by 34 cm frame? ______
4. a. How much wood does Rasheed need to build one of each frame? ______

   b. Can he build one of each frame with 2.5 m of wood? Explain.

   ____

5. If Rasheed decided to buy 0.75 m more wood, would he have enough to build each frame? Explain.

   ____

   ____

6. Using 2.5 m of wood, how many of each size frame should Rasheed build? Explain.

   ____

   ____

   ____

Name ______________________

Extend Your Thinking 11-11

Patterns in Numbers

Tell what rule was used to make the pattern. What are the next three numbers?

1. 0.4, 4, 40, ________, ________, ________

Rule: ______________________

2. 0.12, 1.2, 12, ________, ________, ________

Rule: ______________________

3. 0.6, 0.8, 1.0, ________, ________, ________

Rule: ______________________

4. 0.4, 0.8, 1.6, ________, ________, ________

Rule: ______________________

5. 20,000; 2,000; 200; ________; ________; ________

Rule: ______________________

6. 6, 12, 18, ________, ________, ________

Rule: ______________________

7. 130,000; 13,000; 1,300; ________; ________; ________

Rule: ______________________

8. 3.6, 3.3, 3.0, ________, ________, ________

Rule: ______________________

9. 0.3, 1.5, 7.5, ________, ________, ________

Rule: ______________________

10. 0.32, 0.16, 0.08, ________, ________, ________

Rule: ______________________

Name ______________________________ **Extend Your Thinking 11-12**

Critical Thinking

Write >, <, or = in each circle to make a true metric sentence.

1. 5 m ◯ 50 cm

2. 2.46 cm ◯ 0.0246 m

3. 0.23 m ◯ 2.3 cm

4. 39.9 cm ◯ 0.0399 m

5. 89 m ◯ 890 cm

6. 37.2 cm ◯ 0.372 m

7. 3820 cm ◯ 3.82 m

8. 1.12 m ◯ 11.2 cm

Arrange the five numbers in the box from greatest to least. Write the numbers on the lines.

9. a. ______________

b. ______________

c. ______________

d. ______________

e. ______________

48.7 cm	487 cm	0.0487 m	487 m	48.7 m

10. If you had a strip of paper one meter long, how could you show how long a centimeter is? Explain.

____

____

11. Jan said, "I am 1.2 meters tall." Stan said, "No, you're not. You are 120 centimeters tall." Explain why both of them are correct.

____

12. Kelly said, "I'd like to measure the thickness of this book in meters." Jerome said, "You should measure it in centimeters instead." Who is right? Explain.

____

____

Name ______________________________ Extend Your Thinking 11-13

Visual Thinking

Complete 1–6 using the same pattern used in Samples **A** and **B**.

Sample A

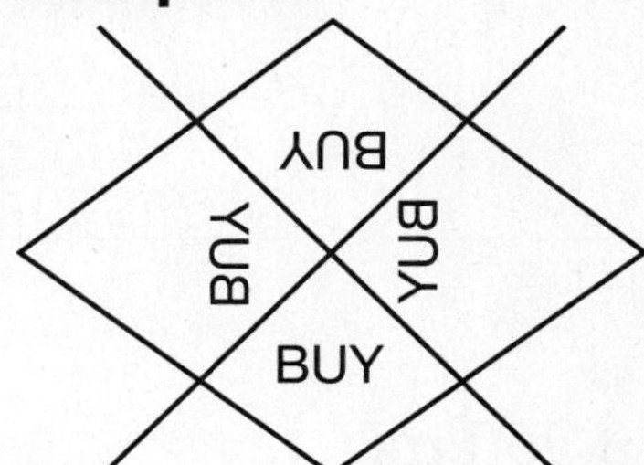

Sample B

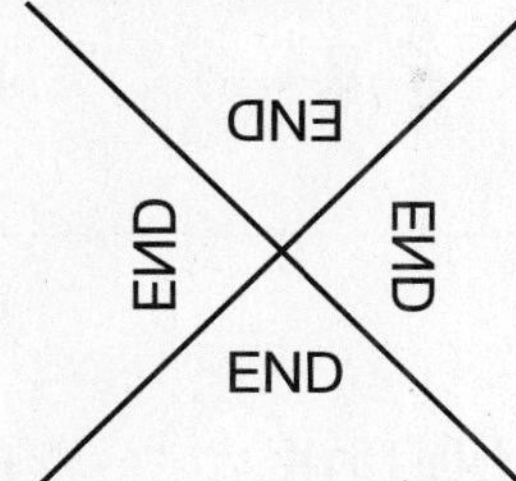

1.

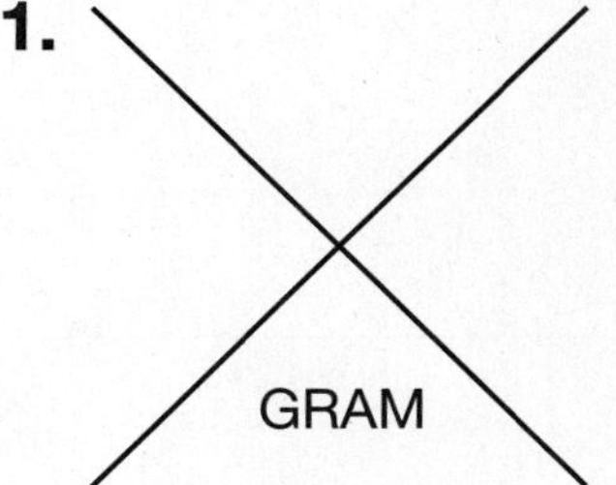

2.

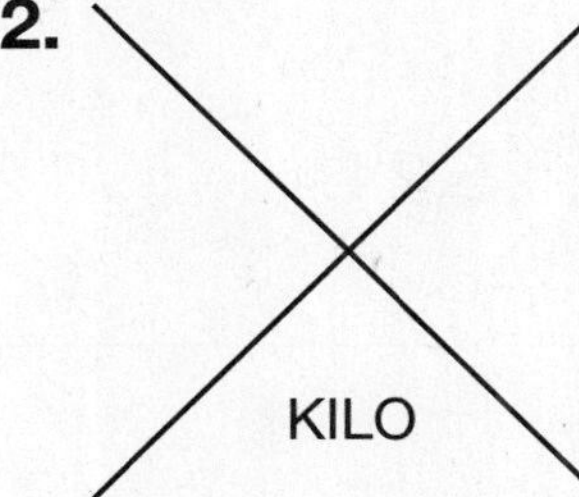

3.

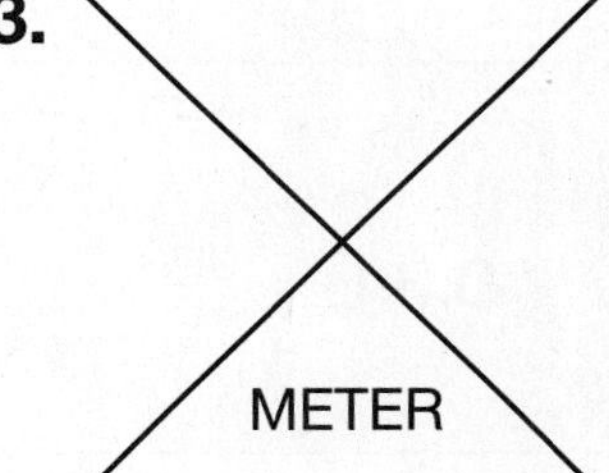

4.

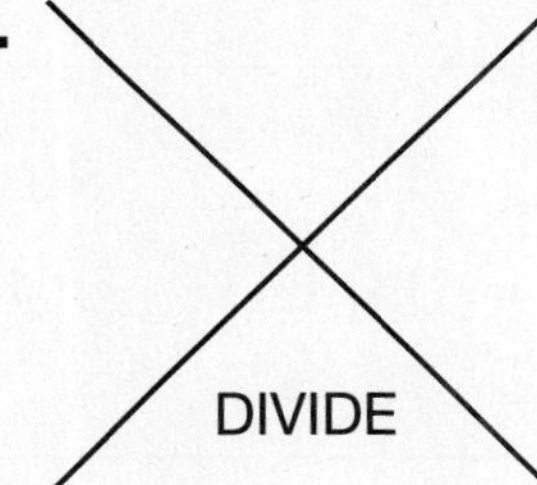

5.

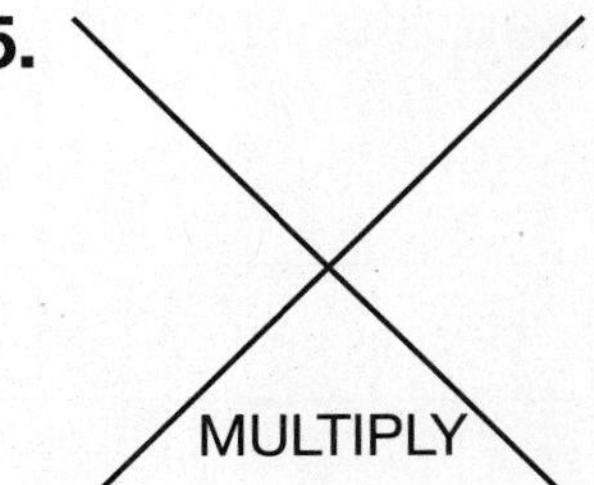

6.

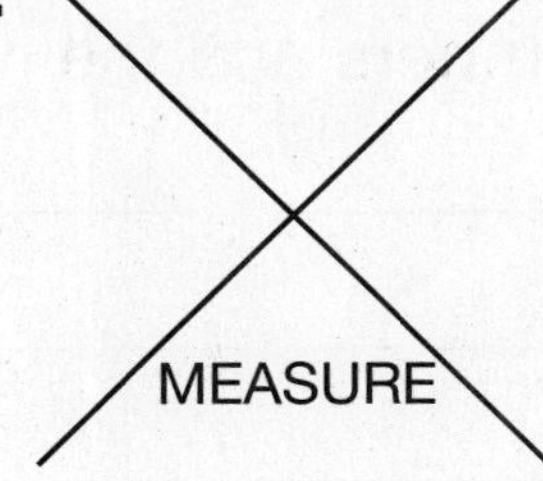

Name ______________________________ **Extend Your Thinking 11-14**

Patterns in Numbers

Complete the pattern. Then write the rule.

1. 3,000 mL 3.2 L 3,400 mL 3.6 L ____________

Rule: ______________________________

2. 5 L 5,500 mL 6 L 6,500 mL ____________

Rule: ______________________________

3. 4,200 mL 5.2 L 6,200 mL 7.2 L ____________

Rule: ______________________________

4. 3 L 2,400 mL 1.8 L 1,200 mL ____________

Rule: ______________________________

5. 750 mL 0.6 L 450 mL 0.3 L ____________

Rule: ______________________________

Write your own mL or L patterns. Have a classmate write in the next two numbers and the rule.

6. ______ ______ ______ ______ ______ ______

Rule: ______________________________

7. ______ ______ ______ ______ ______ ______

Rule: ______________________________

8. ______ ______ ______ ______ ______ ______

Rule: ______________________________

Name ______________________________ **Extend Your Thinking 11-15**

Critical Thinking

Complete each sentence with the correct measure. Use g, kg, L, mL, m, cm, °C, or °F.

1. The basketball player was 208 ________ tall.
2. The cat weighs about 6 ________.
3. The living room was a comfortable room temperature of 20 ________.
4. The flower vase held about 100 ________ of water.
5. The house key was 4 ________ long.
6. The horse weighs about 425 ________.
7. The jug held 2 ________ of water.
8. The gas tank held 60 ________ of gasoline.
9. A can of tuna weighed 173 ________.
10. In the 1996 Summer Olympics, Michael Johnson ran a 400 ________ run in a little more than 43 seconds.
11. The inside temperature of the refrigerator was 5 ________.
12. The hot soup was 120 ________.
13. The can of soup weighed 300 ________.
14. The baseball bat is 1 ________ long.
15. A jar of honey holds about 600 ________.
16. Swimming is comfortable at 37 ________.

Write a sentence for each unit of measure.

17. kilogram ______________________________
18. °C ______________________________
19. liter ______________________________
20. meter ______________________________
21. °F ______________________________

Name ____________________ Extend Your Thinking 11-16

Critical Thinking

How many stars are there:

1. In the rectangle? ________
2. In the circle? ________
3. In the larger triangle? ________
4. In the circle but not in the rectangle or larger triangle? ________
5. In the rectangle but not in the circle or larger triangle? ________
6. In the larger triangle but not in the rectangle or circle? ________
7. In common to the rectangle and larger triangle but not the circle?

   ____

8. In common to the circle and larger triangle but not the rectangle?

   ____

9. In common to the rectangle and circle but not the larger triangle?

   ____

10. All together in the rectangle and circle? ________
11. All together in the circle and the larger triangle? ________
12. All together in the rectangle and the larger triangle? ________
13. All together in the circle, larger triangle, and rectangle? ________
14. Draw a diagram using a square and a circle. There should be 8 stars in the square, 12 in the circle and 4 in common to both. What is the total number of stars?

    ____

Name ______________________

Extend Your Thinking
12-1

Patterns in Division

Find each quotient. Tell what rule was used to make the pattern. What are the next two division problems and quotients?

1. 640 ÷ 8, 560 ÷ 8, 480 ÷ 8, __________, __________

Quotients: ______, ______, ______, ______, ______

Rule: ______________________

2. 280 ÷ 7, 350 ÷ 7, 420 ÷ 7, __________, __________

Quotients: ______, ______, ______, ______, ______

Rule: ______________________

3. 18 ÷ 9, 36 ÷ 9, 54 ÷ 9, __________, __________

Quotients: ______, ______, ______, ______, ______

Rule: ______________________

4. 121 ÷ 11, 99 ÷ 11, 77 ÷ 11, __________, __________

Quotients: ______, ______, ______, ______, ______

Rule: ______________________

5. 240 ÷ 2, 240 ÷ 4, 240 ÷ 6, __________, __________

Quotients: ______, ______, ______, ______, ______

Rule: ______________________

6. 600 ÷ 60, 500 ÷ 50, 400 ÷ 40, __________, __________

Quotients: ______, ______, ______, ______, ______

Rule: ______________________

7. Make up your own division patterns. Leave some blank spaces. Give them to a classmate to solve.

____

Name ______________________

Extend Your Thinking
12-2

Patterns in Numbers

Write the next three numbers to continue the pattern. Then give the greatest number that evenly divides all of the numbers in the pattern.

1. 7, 14, 21, 28, ________, ________, ________

____

2. 5, 10, 15, 20, ________, ________, ________

____

3. 90, 81, 72, 63, ________, ________, ________

____

4. 220, 209, 198, 187, ________, ________, ________

____

5. 25, 50, 75, 100, ________, ________, ________

____

6. 20, 30, 40, ________, ________, ________

____

7. 8, 16, 24, 32, ________, ________, ________

____

8. 108, 120, 132, 144, ________, ________, ________

____

Name ________________________________

Visual Thinking

Find the pattern in each row. Draw the next picture to continue the pattern.

1.     

2. 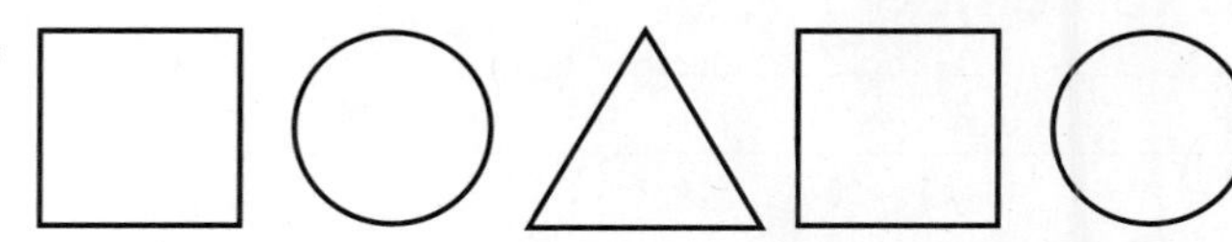

3. 

4. 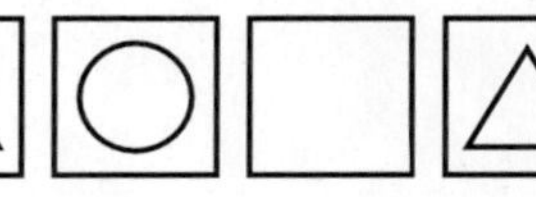   

5. 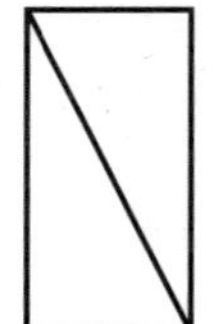  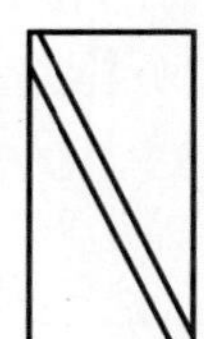  

6. 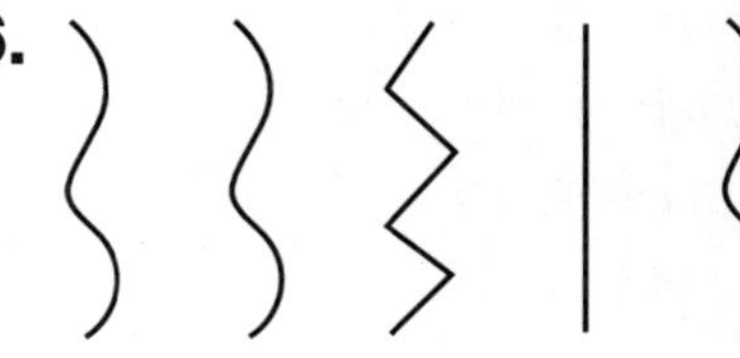 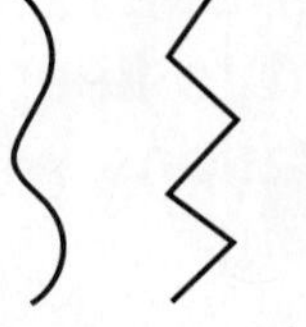

Name ______________________

Critical Thinking

Solve each problem. Explain your reasoning.

1. What is the least number you can divide by 63 and have a 1-digit quotient with no remainder?

____

2. What is the greatest number you can divide by 36 and have a 1-digit quotient with no remainder?

____

3. What is the greatest number you can divide by 18 and have a 2-digit quotient under 20 with no remainder?

____

____

4. What is the least number you can divide by 72 and have a 2-digit quotient with no remainder?

____

5. You have 313 fresh carnations from your garden. You want your friends to take 2 dozen each. You want to pin 1 carnation on your jacket. You don't want any flowers to be wasted. How many friends will have to take flowers?

____

____

6. You want to give an equal number of 222 origami decorations to 8 friends. You want to keep 5 and give 9 to your sister. How many decorations will each friend get?

____

____

Name ________________________________

Decision Making

The fair is in town! If you had $20, and the fair was closing in 3 hours, what would you do?

Ride	Cost in Tickets	Average Time in Line
Ferris Wheel	5	15 minutes
Fun House	3	5 minutes
The Hammer	6	16 minutes
The Chute	4	10 minutes
The Thrill-a-Minute	7	18 minutes
Roller Coaster	9	22 minutes

Food Item	Cost in Tickets
Hot Dog	7
Veggie Burger	8
Lemonade	4
Popcorn	3
Peanuts	5
Frozen Yogurt	6

- Tickets cost 40¢ each. They are needed for all purchases.
- Each ride takes about 5 minutes to complete.
- The wait in the snack bar line is about 10 minutes.

Plan your activities.

1. How much does each ride cost?

____

____

2. How much does each food item cost?

____

____

3. Make a schedule that shows which rides you would take and which foods you would buy.

____

____

____

Name ________________________________

Extend Your Thinking
12-6

Critical Thinking

Order each set of statements from certain to impossible.

Use: 1—certain, 2—likely, 3—equally likely as unlikely, 4—unlikely, 5—impossible

1. Basketball

_______ A college basketball game requires 5 players on a team.

_______ You and your friends play basketball inside.

_______ Your class team members are selected to play professional basketball next year.

_______ Each player scores 25 points in a game.

_______ 10 points or more will be scored by at least one team.

2. Baseball

_______ Baseball is played with 4 bases.

_______ The baseball game is played on Monday, Wednesday, or Friday.

_______ A baseball game must be played with 27 players.

_______ There is at least one home run in a professional game.

_______ The pitcher strikes out every player.

3. Choose a different sport or game. Write 5 sentences for a classmate to order from certain to impossible.

_______ ____

_______ ____

_______ ____

_______ ____

_______ ____

Name ______________________________________ **Extend Your Thinking 12-7**

Visual Thinking

Match the shapes in the first design to the second design. Write the correct letter in each section of the drawing.

1.

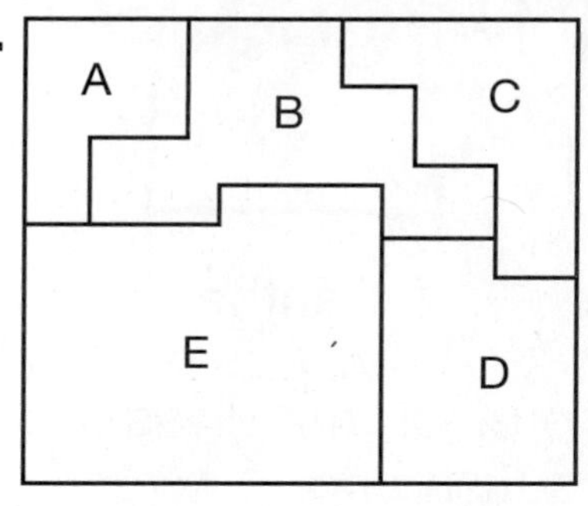

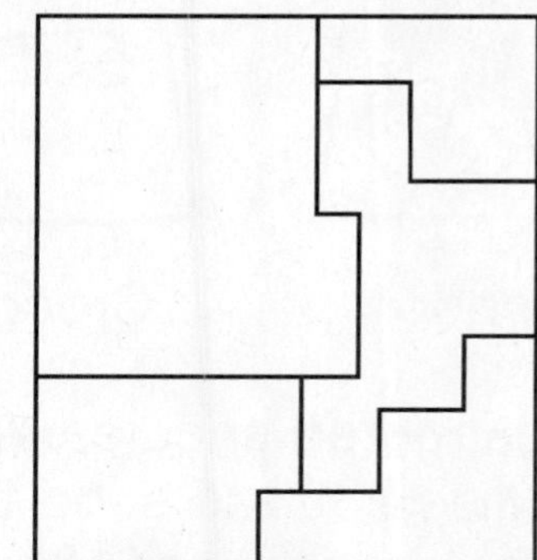

2.

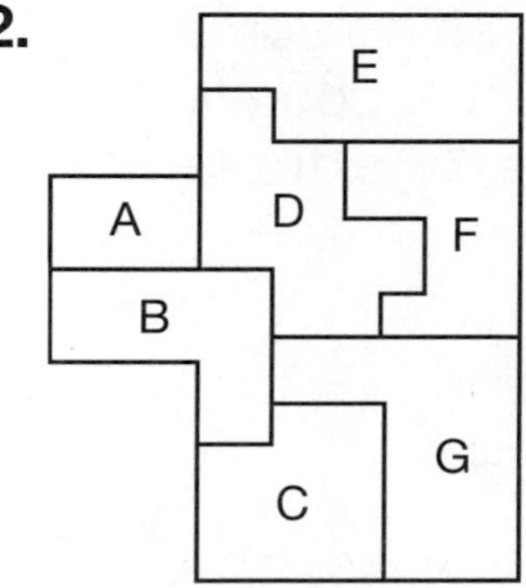

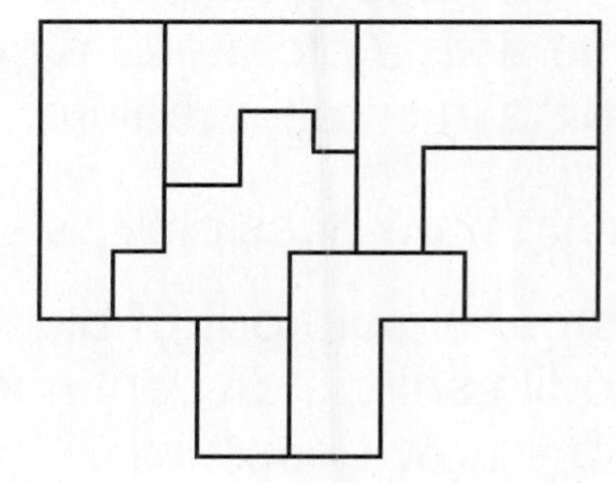

3.

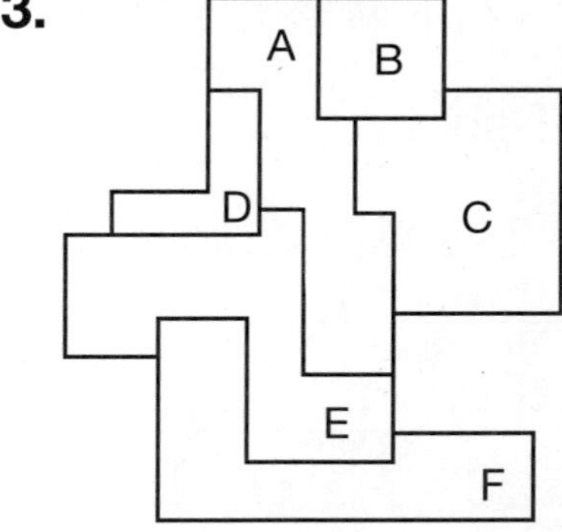

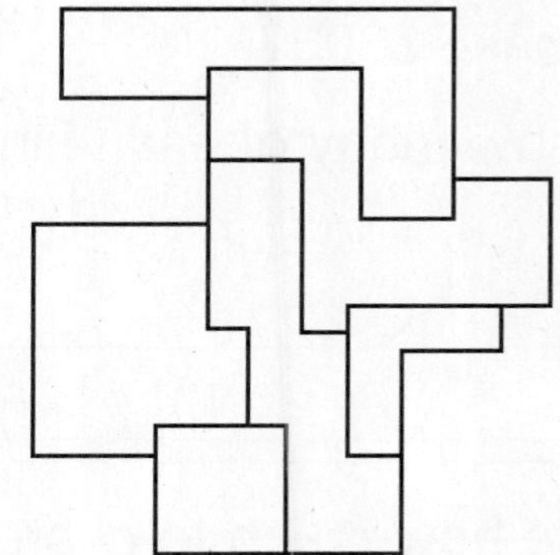

4.

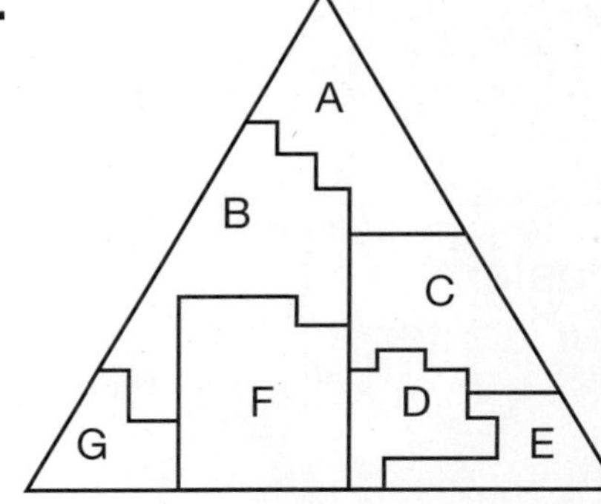

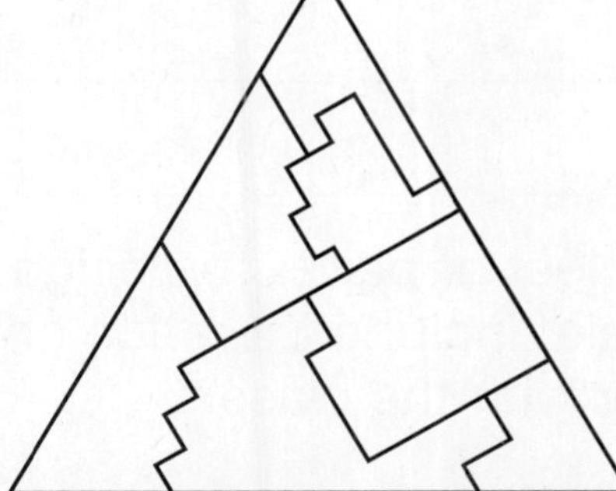

Name ______________________________ **Extend Your Thinking 12-8**

Decision Making

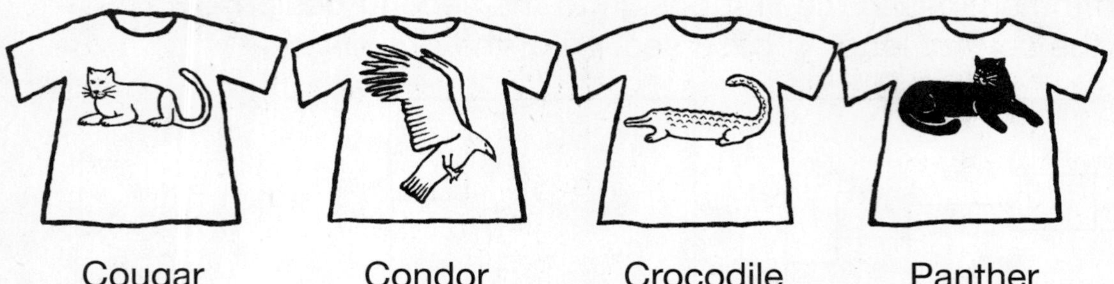

Cougar Condor Crocodile Panther

Your class has studied endangered species. As a project, the class decides to sell T-shirts to raise $300 to send to the Fish and Wildlife Service to help with the recovery of the species.

A T-shirt factory will make T-shirts for $3.50 each. The shirts come in black or white. They come with a picture of a crocodile, cougar, panther, or condor. They come in small, medium, large, or extra-large.

1. How many different T-shirts are possible? ________
2. Suppose the T-shirt factory is sold out of black shirts. Suppose that the crocodile shirt is discontinued. How many different T-shirts are now possible? ________
3. If a T-shirt sells for $5.50, how many T-shirts will the class need to sell to make $300? ________
4. How will you decide how many of each kind of T-shirt to order?

____

____

5. How would you decide how much to charge for each T-shirt? Explain.

____

____

6. Use a separate sheet of paper to design a poster advertising the sale. Include the price on your poster. Share your poster with the class.

Name ____________________

Critical Thinking

1. Use the numbers 2, 3, 4, or 5. A number may be used more than once, or not at all. Label each number cube net pattern so the probability of getting a 4, *P(4)*, on one toss is the given probability.

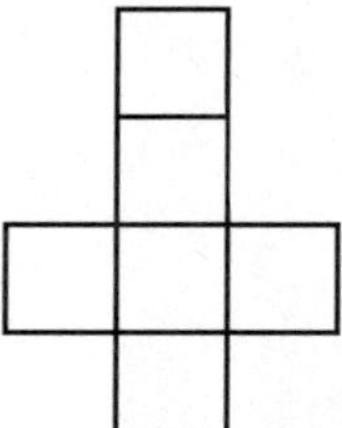
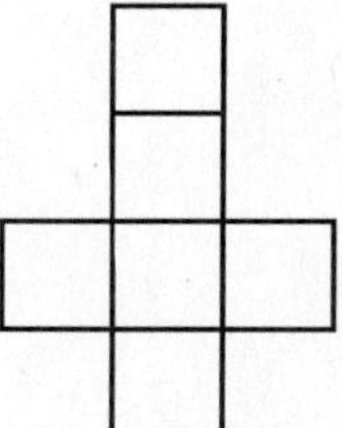
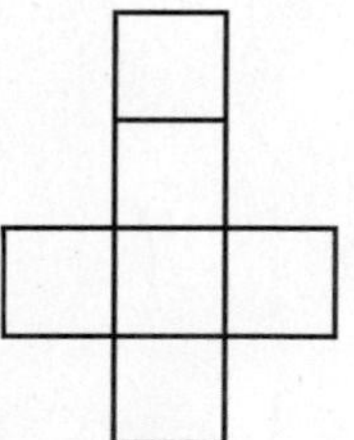
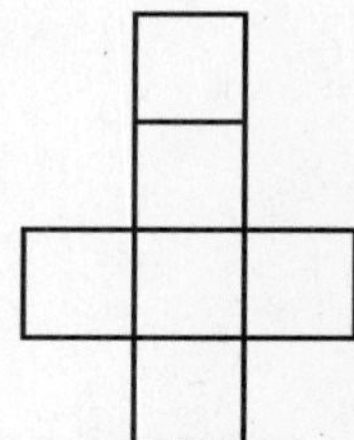

a. P(4) $= \frac{1}{2}$ **b.** P(4) $= \frac{5}{6}$ **c.** P(4) $= \frac{1}{3}$ **d.** P(4) $= \frac{1}{6}$

2. Use R for red, B for blue, G for green, and Y for yellow. Label each spinner to show the given probabilities. It is not necessary to use every color in each spinner.

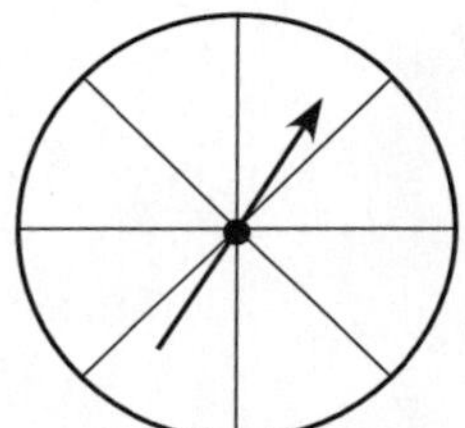
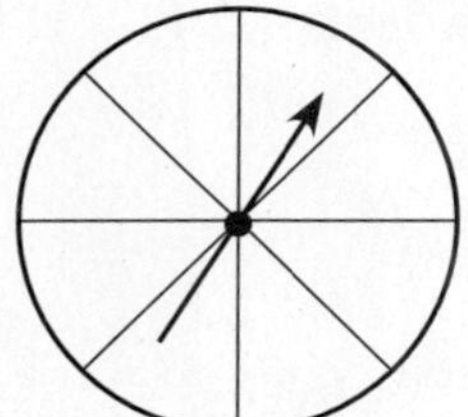

a. P(Y) $= \frac{5}{8}$, P(G) $= \frac{3}{8}$ **b.** P(R) $= \frac{1}{4}$, P(G) $= \frac{3}{8}$

3. Mike and Susie are playing a game using this spinner.

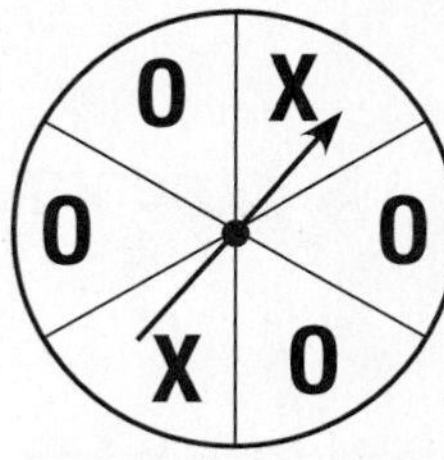

a. What is the probability that Mike will spin X? ______

b. What is the probability that Susie will spin O? ______

c. What is the probability that Mike will spin M? ______

d. What is the probability that Susie will spin either X or O? ______

Name ______________________________

Extend Your Thinking
12-10

Patterns in Data

Draw as many striaght line segments as you can that connect 2 points.

Record the number of segments in the table.

1. 1 point

segments: ________

2. 2 points

segments: ________

3. 3 points

segments: ________

4. 4 points

segments: ________

5. 5 points

segments: ________

6. 6 points

segments: ________

7. Find a pattern. Complete the chart.

Number of Points	1	2	3	4	5	6	7	8	9	10	11
Number of Segments	0										

8. Describe the pattern.

____

____

Name ______________________

Patterns in Geometry

Look at the arrangements of unit squares. Use a different color to shade each larger 2 by 2 square.

1. One row has ________ 2 by 2 squares.

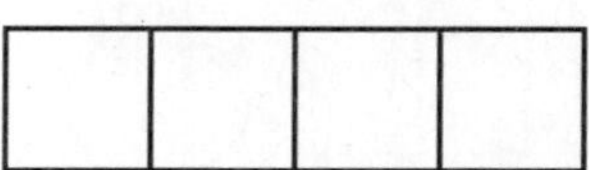

2. Two rows have ________ 2 by 2 squares.

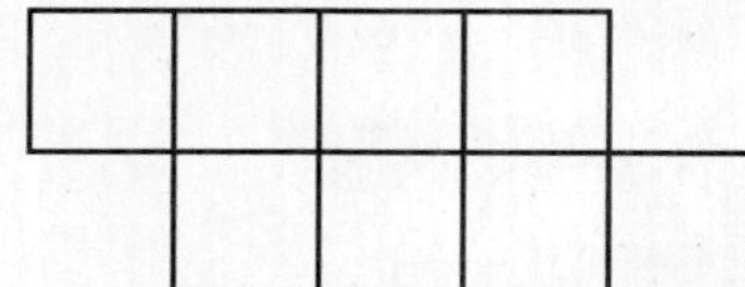

3. Three rows have ________ 2 by 2 squares.

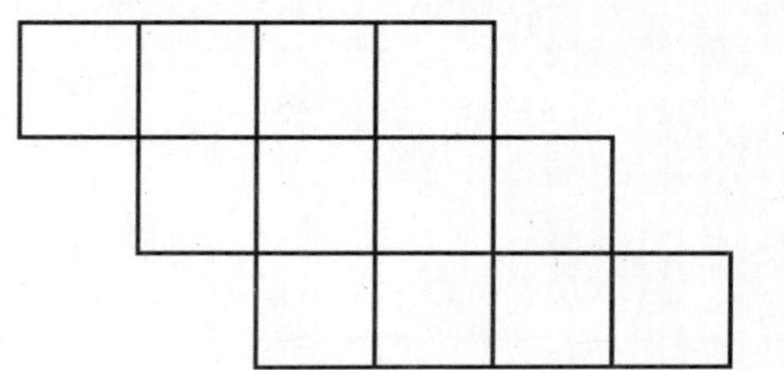

4. Four rows have ________ 2 by 2 squares.

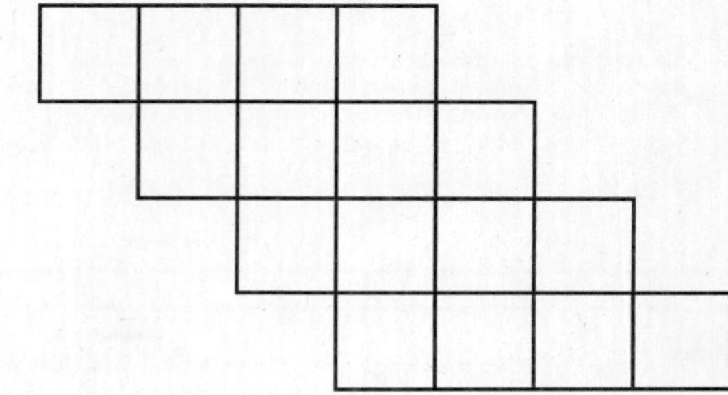

5. Draw a 5-row arrangement. How many 2 by 2 squares are there?

____

6. Continue the pattern and complete the table.

Rows	1	2	3	4	5	6	12
2 by 2 Squares							

7. Describe the pattern.

____

____

Name ______________________ **Extend Your Thinking 1-1**

Decision Making

Ms. McCarthy owns a small grocery store. She needs to hire extra help for the cold weather. Normally, Ms. McCarthy earns about $16,000 per month. The bar graph shows how much Ms. McCarthy earns during these months.

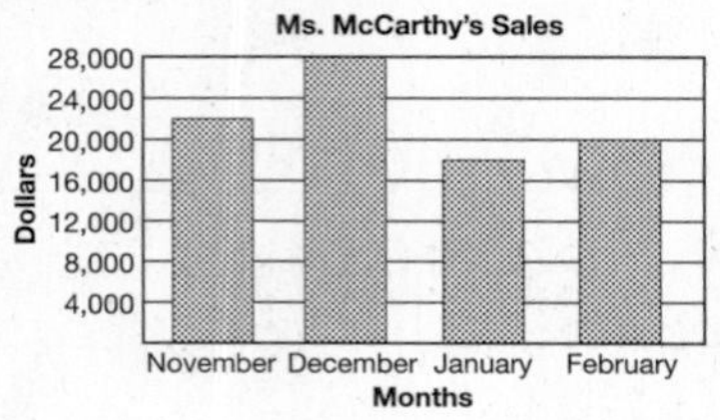

Ms. McCarthy needs to hire 1 worker for every extra $2,000 she earns in a month. How many extra workers does she need:

1. in November? **3 workers**
2. in December? **6 workers**
3. in January? **1 worker**
4. in February? **2 workers**
5. Draw a pictograph for Ms. McCarthy's data. Let one symbol show each extra worker that must be hired.

Number of Extra Workers to be Hired

November	웃 웃 웃
December	웃 웃 웃 웃 웃 웃
January	웃
February	웃 웃

웃 = 1 extra worker

6. Ms. McCarthy doesn't want to hire new workers every month. She decides to hire some in November and more in December. How many workers should Ms. McCarthy hire each time? Explain your reasoning. **Possible answer: Hire 3 workers in Nov. to cover Nov., hire 3 more workers in Dec.**

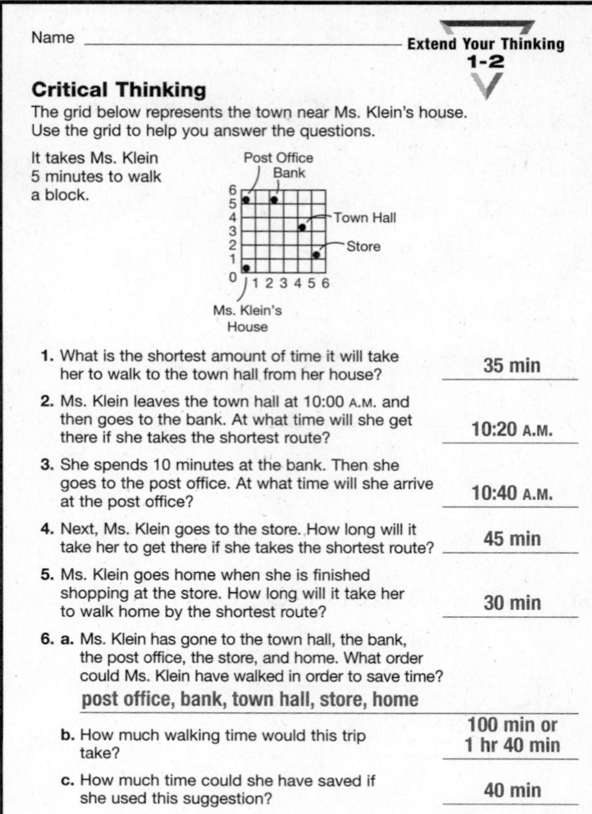

Name ______________________ **Extend Your Thinking 1-2**

Critical Thinking

The grid below represents the town near Ms. Klein's house. Use the grid to help you answer the questions.

It takes Ms. Klein 5 minutes to walk a block.

1. What is the shortest amount of time it will take her to walk to the town hall from her house? **35 min**
2. Ms. Klein leaves the town hall at 10:00 A.M. and then goes to the bank. At what time will she get there if she takes the shortest route? **10:20 A.M.**
3. She spends 10 minutes at the bank. Then she goes to the post office. At what time will she arrive at the post office? **10:40 A.M.**
4. Next, Ms. Klein goes to the store. How long will it take her to get there if she takes the shortest route? **45 min**
5. Ms. Klein goes home when she is finished shopping at the store. How long will it take her to walk home by the shortest route? **30 min**
6. a. Ms. Klein has gone to the town hall, the bank, the post office, the store, and home. What order could Ms. Klein have walked in order to save time? **post office, bank, town hall, store, home**

   b. How much walking time would this trip take? **100 min or 1 hr 40 min**

   c. How much time could she have saved if she used this suggestion? **40 min**

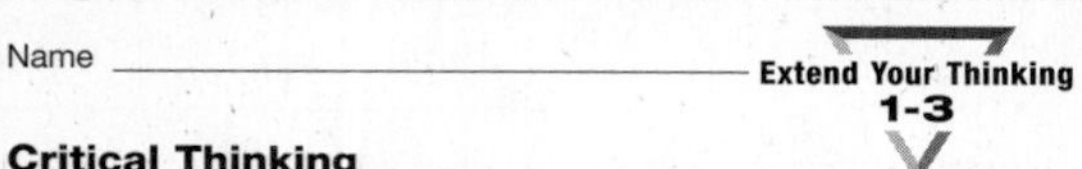

Name ______________________ **Extend Your Thinking 1-3**

Critical Thinking

Rainbow's Ice Cream Parlor displayed these graphs to show that they are much more popular than Sunny's Ice Cream Parlor.

Use the graph to answer **1–3.**

1. a. About how many scoops were sold in June at Rainbow's Ice Cream Parlor? **8,000 scoops**

   b. About how many were sold in June at Sunny's? **8,000 scoops**
2. a. About how many scoops total did Rainbow's sell that summer? **26,000 scoops**

   b. About how many scoops were sold at Sunny's? **26,000 scoops**
3. Do these graphs show that one ice cream parlor sold more than the other? Explain. **Possible answer: No; Both ice cream parlors sold about the same amount. They look different because different scales were used.**

The following year, Sunny's Ice Cream Parlor displayed these graphs to show that they were more popular than Rainbow's Ice Cream Parlor.

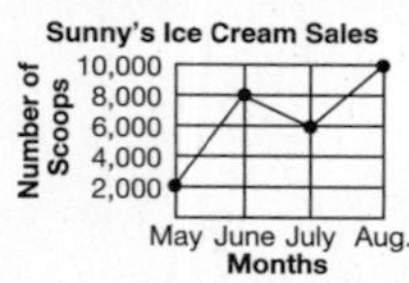

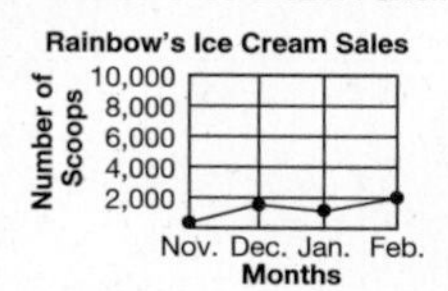

4. Can you tell from these two graphs, which ice cream parlor is more popular? Explain. **Possible answer: No; Different months were used for each graph.**

Name ______________________ **Extend Your Thinking 1-4**

Visual Thinking

These two shapes are the same. One is just turned.

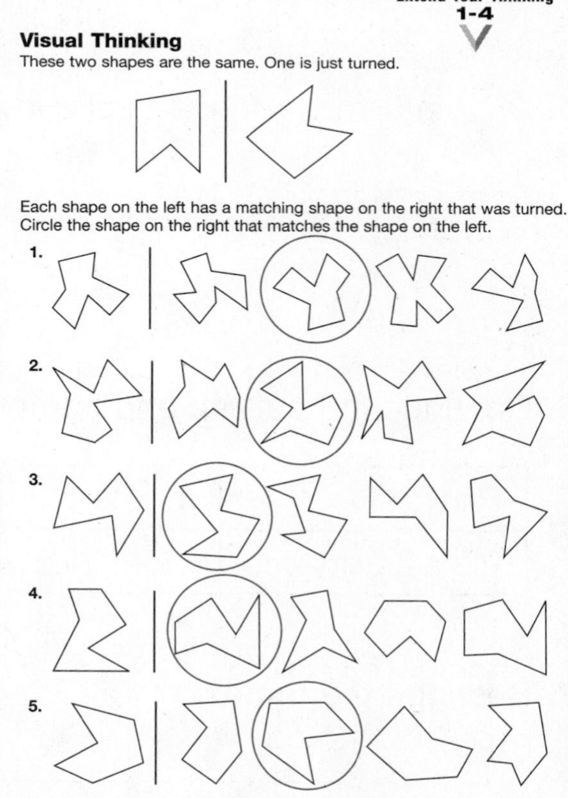

Each shape on the left has a matching shape on the right that was turned. Circle the shape on the right that matches the shape on the left.

1.
2.
3.
4.
5.

Name ______________________ **Extend Your Thinking 1-5**

Visual Thinking

Draw the missing figure.

Example

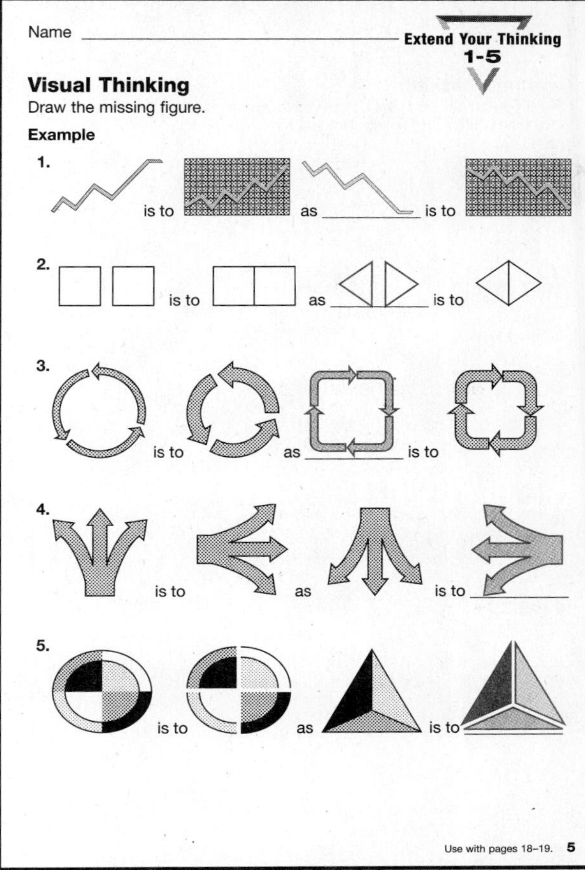

Name ______________________ **Extend Your Thinking 1-6**

Patterns in Data

Automatic Teller Machines (ATMs) are like banks. People can use them to withdraw or deposit money into their accounts. The two graphs below show different information about ATMs and how people use them. Use the graphs to answer the questions.

Monthly ATM Use Per 100 People

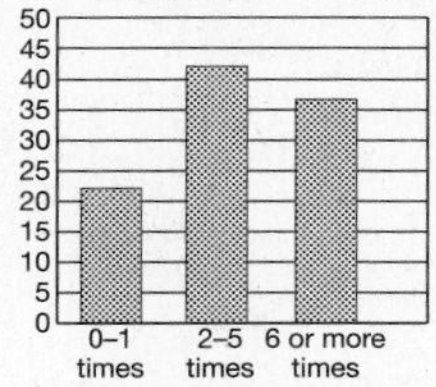

(Bar graph: 0–50 scale; 0–1 times, 2–5 times, 6 or more times)

How ATMs Are Used on Vacation

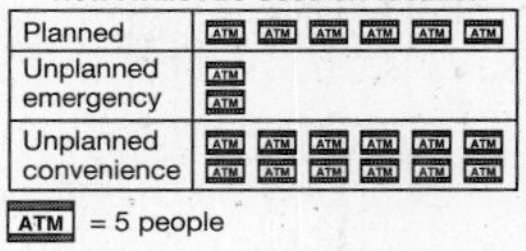

Planned	ATM ATM ATM ATM ATM ATM
Unplanned emergency	ATM ATM
Unplanned convenience	ATM ATM ATM ATM ATM ATM ATM ATM ATM ATM ATM ATM

ATM = 5 people

1. How often do the greatest number of people use ATMs? **2–5 times a month**
2. Why does the largest group of people use ATMs while they are on vacation? **Unplanned convenience**
3. **a.** Which sentences describe the average ATM user? **II.**

   I. "I use ATM's about once a month. On vacation I only use them for emergencies."
   II. "I use ATM's 4 times a month. On vacation I use them for convenience."

   b. Explain your reasoning. **Possible answer: Statement II relates to the greatest number on each graph.**
4. About how many people per hundred use ATMs more than 6 times a month? **36**
5. How does the second largest group of people use ATMs while on vacation? **Planned use**

Name ______________________ **Extend Your Thinking 1-7**

Decision Making

Janice has 6 dogs to feed. Each dog eats 2 pounds of food a week. Which food should she buy?

Dog's Delicacy	Dog Delight	Nature's Best
$4 for 3 pounds	$3 for 2 pounds	$5 for 4 pounds
We add important vitamins your dog needs!	All natural! Your dog will live years longer.	Dogs love our tasty food!!

1. What is the total amount of food the dogs eat per week? **12 pounds**
2. Compare costs.
   a. weekly supply of Dog's Delicacy costs **$16**.
   b. weekly supply of Dog Delight costs **$18**.
   c. weekly supply of Nature's Best costs **$15**.
3. Why might Janice buy Dog's Delicacy? **Possible answer: Medium priced, added vitamins**
4. Why might Janice buy Dog Delight? **Possible answer: All natural**
5. Why might Janice buy Nature's Best? **Possible answer: Lowest priced, tasty**
6. Which dog food should she buy? Explain. **Look for answers that consider both price and the food's benefits.**
7. Which part or parts of each ad is probably opinion? **Possible answers: Vitamins your dog needs; dog will live longer; tasty food dogs love**

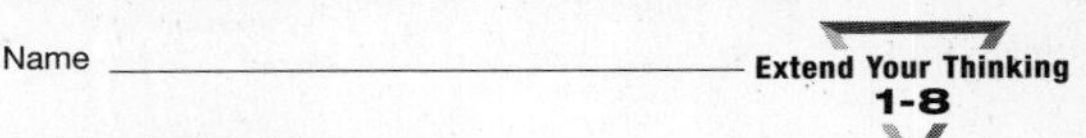

Name ______________________ **Extend Your Thinking 1-8**

Critical Thinking

1. Fill in the number of times each letter appears in these directions. Then use the data to make a bar graph below.

Letter	Number of Times	Letter	Number of Times
f	2	e	15
i	6	u	2
l	4	a	9
n	5	c	2
t	10	p	3

Number of Times Each Letter Appears

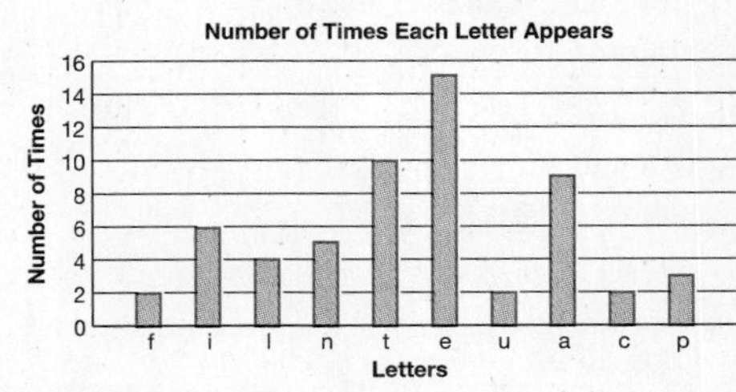

2. Which letters appeared the same number of times? **f, u, and c**
3. Based on the data here, which two letters would you predict are most common in written English? Explain your reasoning. **Possible answers: e and t because they occur 2 and 3 times more often than most letters, or e and a because we use one or more vowels in every word.**

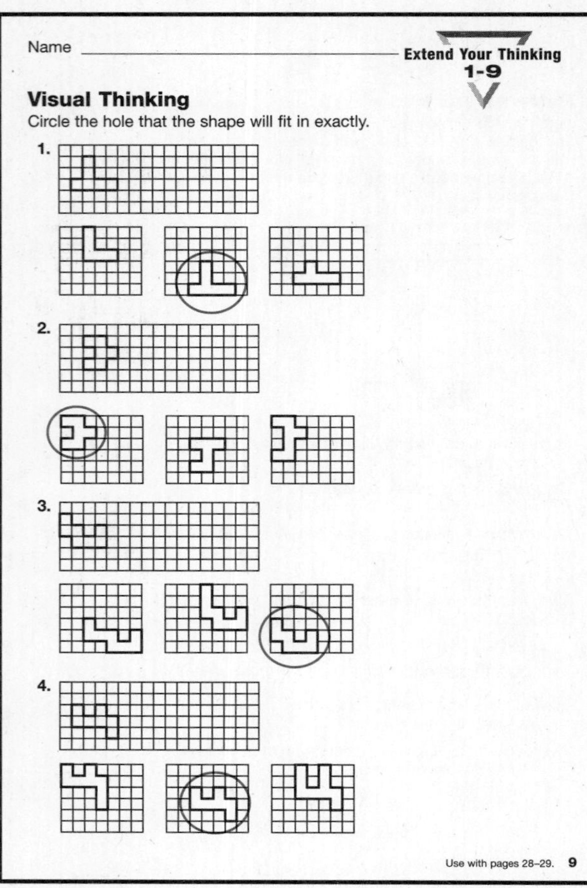
Name ______________________ Extend Your Thinking 1-9

Visual Thinking

Circle the hole that the shape will fit in exactly.

1.
2.
3.
4.

Use with pages 28–29. 9

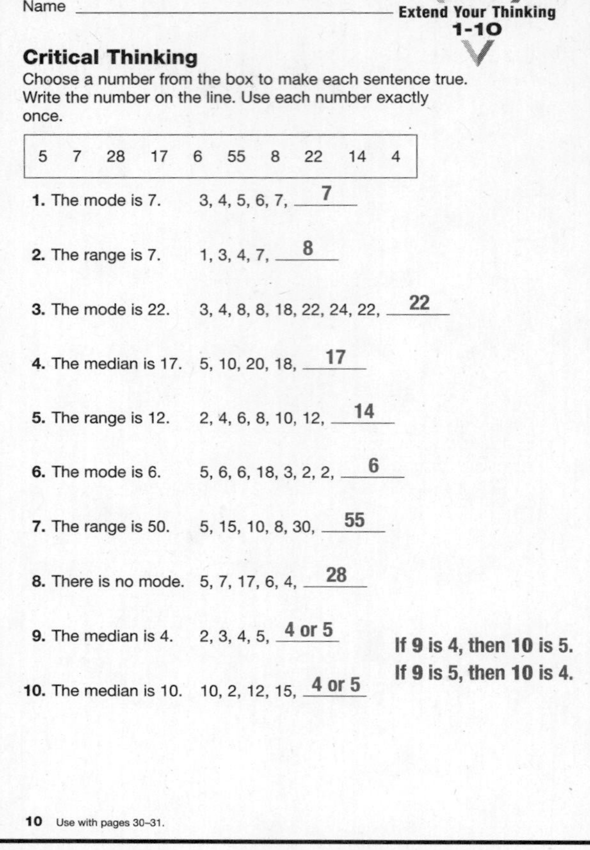
Name ______________________ Extend Your Thinking 1-10

Critical Thinking

Choose a number from the box to make each sentence true. Write the number on the line. Use each number exactly once.

5	7	28	17	6	55	8	22	14	4

1. The mode is 7. 3, 4, 5, 6, 7, 7
2. The range is 7. 1, 3, 4, 7, 8
3. The mode is 22. 3, 4, 8, 8, 18, 22, 24, 22, 22
4. The median is 17. 5, 10, 20, 18, 17
5. The range is 12. 2, 4, 6, 8, 10, 12, 14
6. The mode is 6. 5, 6, 6, 18, 3, 2, 2, 6
7. The range is 50. 5, 15, 10, 8, 30, 55
8. There is no mode. 5, 7, 17, 6, 4, 28
9. The median is 4. 2, 3, 4, 5, 4 or 5
10. The median is 10. 10, 2, 12, 15, 4 or 5

If 9 is 4, then 10 is 5.
If 9 is 5, then 10 is 4.

10 Use with pages 30–31.

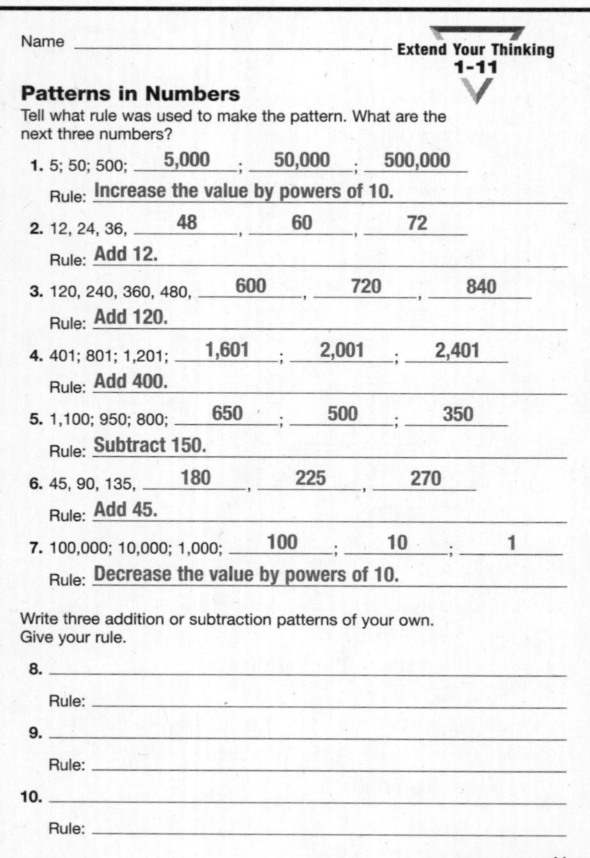
Name ______________________ Extend Your Thinking 1-11

Patterns in Numbers

Tell what rule was used to make the pattern. What are the next three numbers?

1. 5; 50; 500; 5,000; 50,000; 500,000
   Rule: Increase the value by powers of 10.
2. 12, 24, 36, 48, 60, 72
   Rule: Add 12.
3. 120, 240, 360, 480, 600, 720, 840
   Rule: Add 120.
4. 401; 801; 1,201; 1,601; 2,001; 2,401
   Rule: Add 400.
5. 1,100; 950; 800; 650; 500; 350
   Rule: Subtract 150.
6. 45, 90, 135, 180, 225, 270
   Rule: Add 45.
7. 100,000; 10,000; 1,000; 100; 10; 1
   Rule: Decrease the value by powers of 10.

Write three addition or subtraction patterns of your own. Give your rule.

8. ______________________
   Rule: ______________________
9. ______________________
   Rule: ______________________
10. ______________________
   Rule: ______________________

Use with pages 32–33. 11

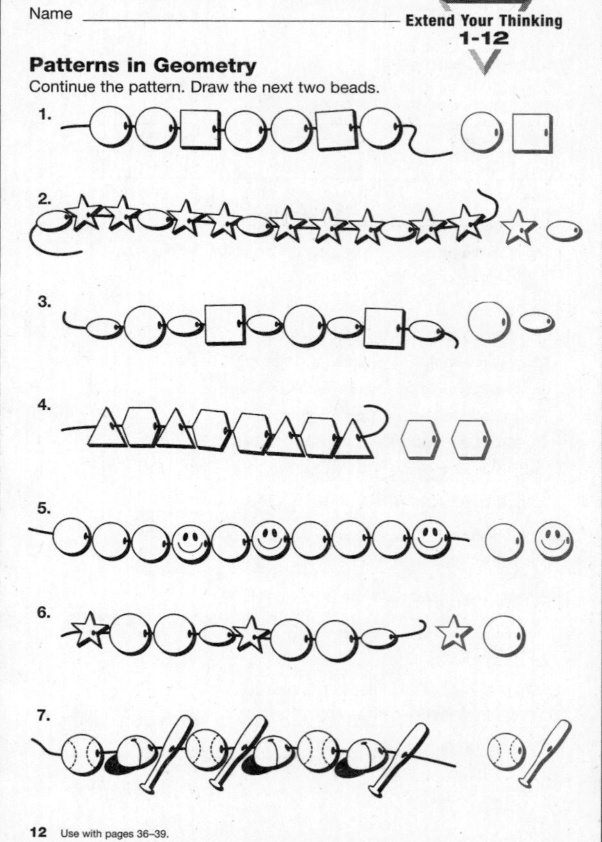
Name ______________________ Extend Your Thinking 1-12

Patterns in Geometry

Continue the pattern. Draw the next two beads.

1.
2.
3.
4.
5.
6.
7.

12 Use with pages 36–39.

Name ______________________ Extend Your Thinking 2-1

Visual Thinking

Accept reasonable estimates.

Estimation About how many shapes are in each drawing?

1. About 120
2. About 30
3. About 1,000
4. About 400
5. About 60
6. About 700

Use with pages 52–53. 13

Name ______________________ Extend Your Thinking 2-2

Critical Thinking

Hundreds

S H O E L A C E S

1 2 3 4 5 6 7 8 9

Tens

P O R C U P I N E

1 2 3 4 5 6 7 8 9

Ones

C O N D U C T O R

1 2 3 4 5 6 7 8 9

Each letter in the words above has been assigned a digit. "Shoelaces" represents the hundreds digits, "porcupine" represents the tens digits, and "conductor" represents the ones digits.

Use the code to write the word for each number.

Example

1 7 7

S I T

1. 5 2 7 — L O T
2. 2 5 7 — H U T
3. 9 7 9 — S I R
4. 7 2 4 — C O D
5. 1 5 3 — S U N
6. 7 2 7 — C O T
7. 5 7 4 — L I D
8. 2 2 7 — H O T
9. 7 5 7 — C U T

14 Use with pages 54–55.

Name ______________________ Extend Your Thinking 2-3

Critical Thinking

Estimation How much is a million? Read each situation. Circle your best guess. Explain what you could do to check your estimate.

1. If one million kids climbed onto each other's shoulders they would be:
   a. as tall as a 110-story building
   (b.) farther up than airplanes can fly
   c. past the moon

   Possible answer: Find out about how tall 100 kids would be, then multiply by 10,000.

2. If you wanted to count from one to one million, it would take you about:
   (a.) 12 days
   b. 2 years
   c. 95 years

   Possible answer: Find out how long it takes you to count to 100 or 1,000, then multiply by 10,000 or 1,000.

3. The world's largest peanut measured 4 in. How far would a million similar peanuts stretch if they were laid end to end?
   a. 1 mile
   (b.) 63 miles
   c. 40 feet

   Possible answer: Find the number of feet, then miles equal to 4 million inches.

Use with pages 56–57. 15

Name ______________________ Extend Your Thinking 2-4

Patterns in Numbers

Tell what rule was used to make the pattern. What are the next two numbers?

1. 30, 40, 50, 60, 70, 80
   Rule: Add 10.
2. 1; 10; 100; 1,000; 10,000; 100,000
   Rule: Multiply by 10.
3. 2, 4, 8, 16, 32, 64
   Rule: Multiply by 2.
4. 26; 260; 2,600; 26,000; 260,000; 2,600,000
   Rule: Multiply by 10.
5. 22,195; 22,190; 22,185; 22,180; 22,175; 22,170
   Rule: Subtract 5.
6. 3; 30; 300; 3,000; 30,000; 300,000
   Rule: Multiply by 10.
7. 360,000; 36,000; 3,600; 360; 36
   Rule: Divide by 10.
8. 520,000; 52,000; 5,200; 520; 52
   Rule: Divide by 10.

Make up your own number patterns. Leave some blank spaces. Give them to a classmate to solve. Answers will vary. Check students' patterns.

9. ______, ______, ______, ______, ______
10. ______, ______, ______, ______, ______

16 Use with pages 58–61.

Name ______________________________ **Extend Your Thinking 2-5**

Decision Making

Have you ever needed to decide which of two choices is a better deal for you? At the Amazing Amusement Park you can buy rides and food in two different ways.

	Ticket A	Ticket B
Rides	Unlimited rides $10/hour (first hour) Unlimited rides $5/hour (after the first hour) Must buy and use tickets in pairs	Each ride $1 apiece No requirements
Food	Free juice and hot dog	Juice costs $0.75. Hot dogs cost $1.50.
Extras	Free camera rental	Camera rental $5 a day

You are going with a friend and plan on staying for 3 hours. You figure you can ride on 8 rides per hour. You have your own camera.

1. Which ticket will cost less for you and your friend?
   Possible answer: Ticket A costs $20 total each. Ticket B costs $24 for rides alone. So Ticket A will cost less.
2. If you only go on 6 rides an hour which ticket will be the better deal?
   Possible answer: Ticket B will cost only $18 each, but no food is included.
3. What if another friend joins you? Which tickets will you buy?
   Possible answer: Ticket B since you must use Ticket A in pairs.
4. Why might you choose Ticket A?
   Possible answer: You plan on taking many rides, you like hot dogs and juice, and you need a camera.

Name ______________________________ **Extend Your Thinking 2-6**

Critical Thinking

Find your way through the mazes following the rule above each.

Striped Shaded

Rule: If you are on a shaded square, you cannot enter a white square.

1. Start Finish

2. Start Finish

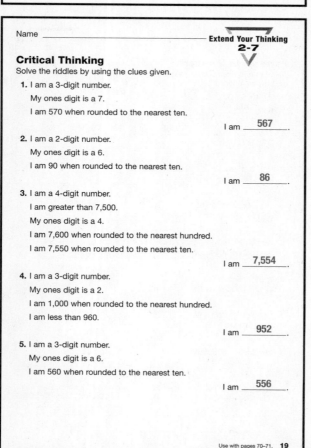

Rule: You can only enter a striped square from a white square.

3. Start Finish

4. Start Finish

5. If start and finish were reversed, would the path through each maze stay the same for each exercise? Explain.
   For Exercises 1 and 2, the path would stay the same, but other paths are possible. For Exercises 3 and 4, you could not start on a striped square.
6. Draw your own maze and write a rule for it. Give it to a classmate to solve.
   Check students' mazes and paths.

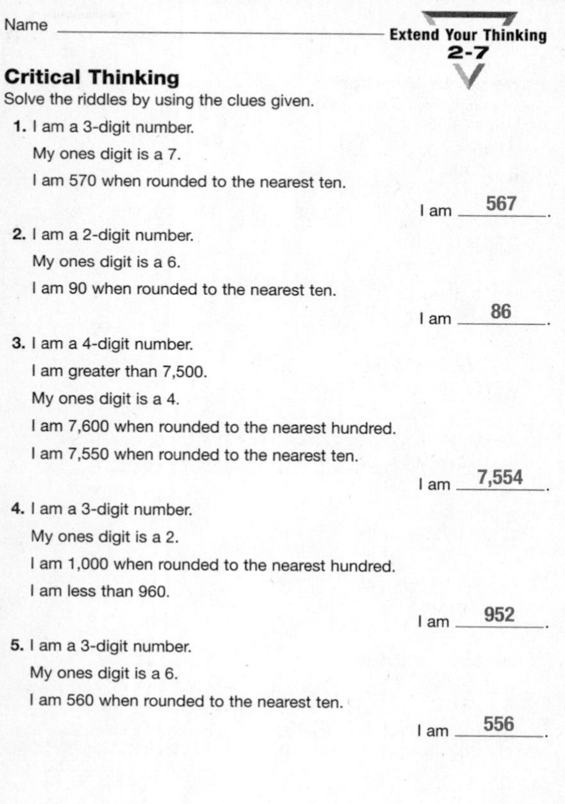

Name ______________________________ **Extend Your Thinking 2-7**

Critical Thinking

Solve the riddles by using the clues given.

1. I am a 3-digit number.
   My ones digit is a 7.
   I am 570 when rounded to the nearest ten.
   I am **567**.
2. I am a 2-digit number.
   My ones digit is a 6.
   I am 90 when rounded to the nearest ten.
   I am **86**.
3. I am a 4-digit number.
   I am greater than 7,500.
   My ones digit is a 4.
   I am 7,600 when rounded to the nearest hundred.
   I am 7,550 when rounded to the nearest ten.
   I am **7,554**.
4. I am a 3-digit number.
   My ones digit is a 2.
   I am 1,000 when rounded to the nearest hundred.
   I am less than 960.
   I am **952**.
5. I am a 3-digit number.
   My ones digit is a 6.
   I am 560 when rounded to the nearest ten.
   I am **556**.

Name ______________________________ **Extend Your Thinking 2-8**

Decision Making

Suppose your class is going on a camping trip. You are assigning the chores for the trip. Each of you has to take 1 of the chores listed. Use the information below to help you decide who should do each chore.

Marilyn "I am good at tending fires, but I can also set up the tents."
Fred "I'll do anything except clean the grounds."
Martha "I don't want to cook or do the dishes."
José "I don't mind doing the dishes, but I don't want to set up the tents."

Write the name of the person who will do each chore. Remember to include yourself. Explain why you assigned the chores as you did. **Answers will vary. Possible answers:**

1. Set up tents.
   Fred; José is the only one who didn't want this chore.
2. Cook.
   Myself; I like to cook.
3. Clean the grounds.
   Martha; She didn't want to cook or do dishes.
4. Do the dishes.
   José; He didn't mind doing dishes.
5. Tend the fire.
   Marilyn; She said she was good with tending fires.

Name ______________________________ **Extend Your Thinking 2-9**

Decision Making

Look at each period of time and choose an activity you think would take that amount of time.

1. less than 1 second **Check students' answers.**
2. between 1 second and 1 minute **Check students' answers.**
3. between 1 minute and 1 hour **Check students' answers.**
4. between 1 hour and 1 day **Check students' answers.**
5. between 1 day and 1 week **Check students' answers.**
6. between 1 week and 1 month **Check students' answers.**
7. between 1 month and 1 year **Check students' answers.**
8. between 1 year and 1 decade **Check students' answers.**
9. between 1 decade and 1 century **Check students' answers.**

Name ______________________________ **Extend Your Thinking 2-10**

Patterns in Data

Find a pattern to answer each question. Then write the rule.

1. Eric takes his medicine at 8:15 A.M., 11:15 A.M., and 2:15 P.M. When will he take his medicine next? **5:15 P.M.**
   Rule: **Every 3 hours**
2. WRKO plays Carla's favorite song at 10:05 A.M., 10:35 A.M. and 11:05 A.M. When will they probably play it next? **11:35 A.M.**
   Rule: **Every 30 minutes**
3. A news program is on the radio at noon, 6:00 P.M., and midnight. When will the news be on again? **6:00 A.M.**
   Rule: **Every 6 hours**
4. Anita's grandmother drinks a glass of water at 8:30 A.M., 10:30 A.M., and 12:30 P.M. When will she have another? **2:30 P.M.**
   Rule: **Every 2 hours**
5. Mayflies hatch in the stream at 5:12 A.M., 5:18 A.M., 5:30 A.M., and 5:54 A.M. When will mayflies hatch again? **6:42 A.M.**
   Rule: **Add 6 minutes then double the number of minutes added each time.**
6. Mr. Kim, the baker, takes bread out of the oven at 4:30 A.M., 5:30 A.M., 7:00 A.M., 8:00 A.M., and 10:30 A.M. When will he take bread out of the oven again? **10:30 A.M.**
   Rule: **Add one hour, then one hour and 30 minutes.**

Name ______________________________ **Extend Your Thinking 2-11**

Critical Thinking

A Chinese one-year calendar has 12 months. It is based on cycles of the moon. It is similar to the calendar you use every day, but only has 29 or 30 days in each month.

Each year is named after one of 12 animals.

Rooster	Dog	Pig	Rat	Ox	Tiger
1981	1982	1983	1984	1985	1986
1993	1994	1995	1996	1997	1998
2005	**2006**	**2007**	**2008**	**2009**	**2010**

Rabbit	Dragon	Snake	Horse	Sheep	Monkey
1987	1988	1989	1990	1991	1992
1999	2000	2001	2002	2003	2004
2011	**2012**	**2013**	**2014**	**2015**	**2016**

1. Look at the years in the calendar. Find a pattern. Then fill in the next year for each animal.
2. Describe the pattern you found.
   Possible answer: The cycle repeats itself every 12 years.
3. What animal is this year named after? **Check students' work.**
4. Name the animal for which the year you were born is named. **Check students' work.**
5. What animal will 2018 be named for? Explain how you found your answer. **Dog; Possible answer: The monkey was the animal for 2016 so I counted over two more.**
6. What animal was 1978 named for? **Horse; Possible answer: 1978 + 12 = 1990; The animal named for 1990 was the animal for 1978.**

Name ______________________________ **Extend Your Thinking 2-12**

Critical Thinking

Here's a pictograph of a videotape schedule.

Video: Downtown School of Kempo Karate

Opening:	(music and scenes)	◴
Part I:	Welcome to the Downtown School	◷◷
Part II:	What is Kempo Karate?	◷◷◷◷◷
Part III:	The Sensei	◷◷◷
Part IV:	Let's Visit some Classes	◷◷◷◷◷◷◷
Part V:	How to Enroll	◷◷◷
Closing:	(music and titles)	◷

◷ = 1 minute

1. Which part of the videotape do you think will have the most information? Why?
   Part IV; Because it has the most clocks
2. How long will it take to explain Kempo Karate? How do you know?
   5 minutes; Each clock symbol represents 1 minute.
3. How long will the whole videotape last? **$21\frac{1}{2}$ minutes**
4. Francine is videotaping Parts I and IV. She has 20 minutes of tape. Can she use all of it? Explain.
   No; She only needs 9 minutes of tape.
5. a. If you started to watch this tape at 3:00 P.M., when would the part about The Sensei start? **About 3:07**
   b. When would you finish watching the tape? **About 3:21 P.M.**
6. Frank started viewing the tape at 10:45. Will he be able to watch the entire tape before 11:00? Explain.
   No; The tape will not finish until 11:06.

Name ______________________ Extend Your Thinking 3-1

Decision Making

Georgia makes beaded bracelets. She needs to make 10 bracelets like the one shown below.

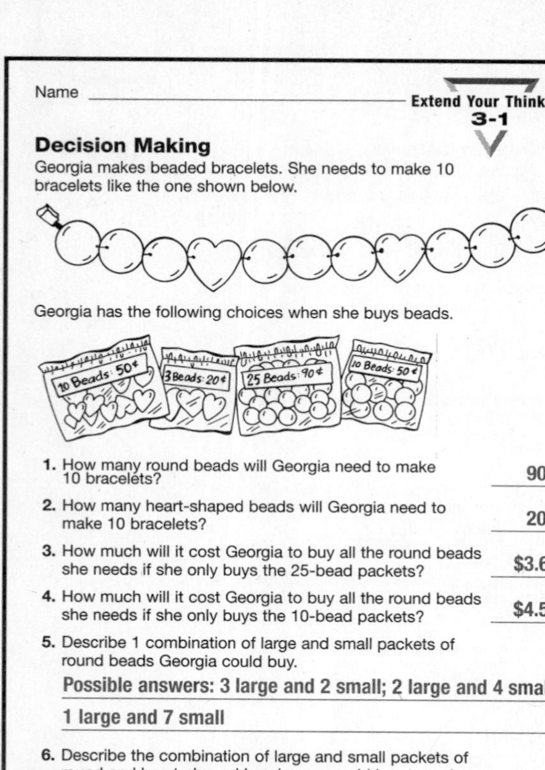

Georgia has the following choices when she buys beads.

1. How many round beads will Georgia need to make 10 bracelets? **90**
2. How many heart-shaped beads will Georgia need to make 10 bracelets? **20**
3. How much will it cost Georgia to buy all the round beads she needs if she only buys the 25-bead packets? **$3.60**
4. How much will it cost Georgia to buy all the round beads she needs if she only buys the 10-bead packets? **$4.50**
5. Describe 1 combination of large and small packets of round beads Georgia could buy.
   Possible answers: 3 large and 2 small; 2 large and 4 small; 1 large and 7 small
6. Describe the combination of large and small packets of round and heart-shaped beads you would buy to make the 10 bracelets. Explain your decision.
   Possible answer: I would buy 4 large packets of round beads and 2 large packets of heart-shaped beads because it costs less.

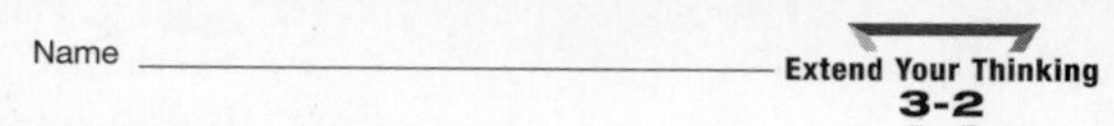

Name ______________________ Extend Your Thinking 3-2

Critical Thinking

Mel's Music World had a sale for five days. On day 1, the store sold 200 of its supply of tapes. On day 2, half of the remaining amount was sold. The same thing happened on days 3, 4 and 5. At the end of the sale, Mel counted the number of tapes left in the store. He discovered there were only 50 tapes left.

1. Mel wanted a record of the sale. He made a chart for the five days of the sale. But, he was so busy waiting on customers that he forgot to fill in the chart! He only recorded the number of tapes left at the end of day 5. How can Mel figure out the number of tapes left at the end of each of the other days?
   Possible answer: Work Backward
2. Use the plan you described above to complete the chart.

Day	Total Number of Tapes Left
1	**800**
2	**400**
3	**200**
4	**100**
5	50

3. Suppose Mel decided to hold the sale for one additional day. If the same pattern of sales continues, how many tapes will be left in the store at the end of day 6? **25**
4. Mel also had a sale on CDs. He sold 120 the first day, twice that number on the second day and twice as many on the third day as on the second. How many CDs did he sell on the third day? **480**

Name ______________________ Extend Your Thinking 3-3

Visual Thinking

A flip moves a figure to create a mirror image with the same size and shape.

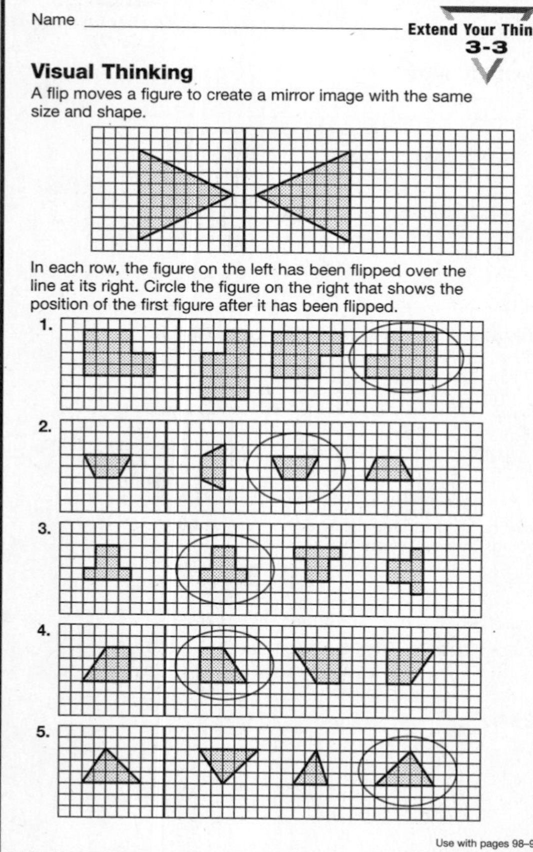

In each row, the figure on the left has been flipped over the line at its right. Circle the figure on the right that shows the position of the first figure after it has been flipped.

1.
2.
3.
4.
5.

Name ______________________ Extend Your Thinking 3-4

Patterns in Data

Mia is reading a 128 page book. She is keeping a record of how many pages she reads each day.

Complete the chart.

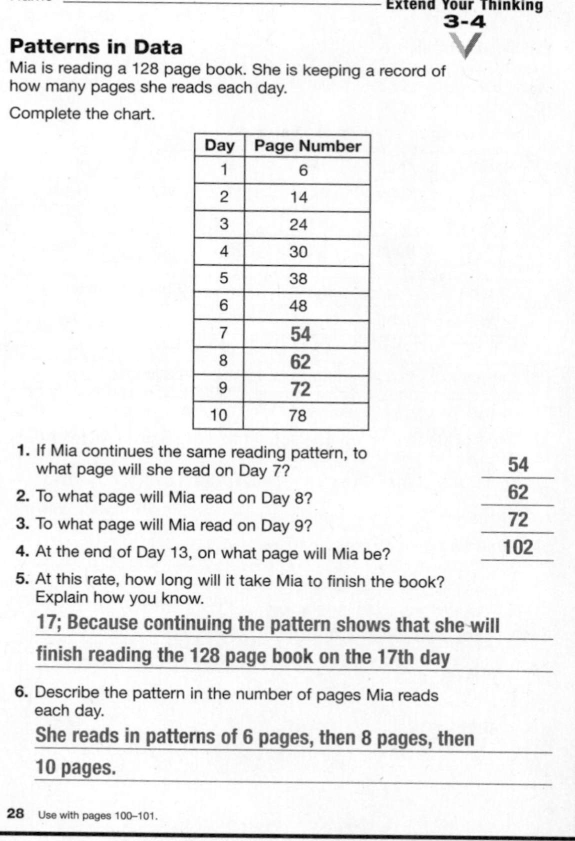

Day	Page Number
1	6
2	14
3	24
4	30
5	38
6	48
7	**54**
8	**62**
9	**72**
10	78

1. If Mia continues the same reading pattern, to what page will she read on Day 7? **54**
2. To what page will Mia read on Day 8? **62**
3. To what page will Mia read on Day 9? **72**
4. At the end of Day 13, on what page will Mia be? **102**
5. At this rate, how long will it take Mia to finish the book? Explain how you know.
   17; Because continuing the pattern shows that she will finish reading the 128 page book on the 17th day
6. Describe the pattern in the number of pages Mia reads each day.
   She reads in patterns of 6 pages, then 8 pages, then 10 pages.

Name ______________________ **Extend Your Thinking 3-5**

Patterns in Geometry

Draw the next three figures in each pattern. Use words to describe each pattern.

1. Pattern: **Square, circle, square, triangle, repeat**

2. Pattern: **Large circle, small circle, medium circle, repeat**

Possible answer shown.

3. Pattern: **Number of diamonds increases by one each time**

4. Pattern: **The number of triangles increases by one each time and is separated by a circle, then a square, and so on.**

5. Pattern: **The pattern continues with the shapes in the same order, only increasing in size.**

Name ______________________ **Extend Your Thinking 3-6**

Patterns in Numbers

Fill in the blanks to complete the pattern. Tell what rule was used to make the pattern.

1. 23, 56, 89, **122**, **155**, **188**
   Rule: **Add 33.**
2. 123, 199, 275, **351**, **427**, **503**
   Rule: **Add 76.**
3. 154, 376, 598, **820**, **1,042**, **1,264**
   Rule: **Add 222.**
4. 12, 24, 48, 96, **192**, **384**, **768**
   Rule: **Add number to itself, or multiply number by 2.**
5. 12, 23, 34, 45, **56**, **67**, **78**
   Rule: **Add 11.**
6. 1, 2, 4, 7, **11**, **16**, **22**
   Rule: **Add 1, 2, 3, 4, and so on.**
7. 25, 22, 32, 29, 39, **36**, **46**, **43**
   Rule: **Subtract 3, add 10.**
8. 10, **23**, **36**, 49, 62, 75, **88**
   Rule: **Add 13.**

Name ______________________ **Extend Your Thinking 3-7**

Critical Thinking

Think about each person's conclusion. Do you think the conclusion is right or wrong? Explain.

1. Barbara counted the chairs in the auditorium. There were 484. Then she counted the programs that were available. There were 225. She concluded that the theater would need 259 more programs.
   The conclusion is not correct. All the tickets may not have been sold.
2. Stan inherited 212 books from his grandfather. He has a special bookcase for them. He has put 124 on the shelves already. He concludes that he still has to find room for 88 books.
   The conclusion is correct. 212 − 124 = 88.
3. The last pair of shoes Kim bought cost $29.99. Kim has $24.86. She concludes that she needs $5.13 before she can get another pair of shoes.
   The conclusion is not correct. Kim's next pair of shoes might be more or less than $29.99.
4. The goal of the library fund drive was $5,000. So far, $3,489 had been donated. Sean concluded that the library fund exceeded their goal by $1,511.
   The conclusion is not correct. The goal has not been met yet.
5. At the school fair, the bake stand sold 296 English muffins. They made 384 and conclude that if they sell another 88 muffins, they will be sold out.
   The conclusion is correct. 384 − 296 = 88.

Name ______________________ **Extend Your Thinking 3-8**

Patterns in Numbers

In each of the tables below, the number in the second column is subtracted from the number in the first column and the result is in the third column.

Fill in the tables. Describe the patterns you found in each.

1,001	123	**878**
2,002	**123**	1,879
3,003	123	2,880
4,004	**123**	3,881
5,005	123	**4,882**
6,006	**123**	5,883

Pattern: **Possible answer: The numbers in the first and last columns increase by 1,001 each time.**

9,052	1,111	7,941
9,052	2,222	**6,830**
9,052	**3,333**	5,719
9,052	4,444	**4,608**
9,052	**5,555**	**3,497**
9,052	**6,666**	2,386

Pattern: **Possible answer: The numbers in the second column increase by 1,111 each time, and the numbers in the third column decrease by 1,111 each time.**

6,284	**5,050**	1,234
7,395	5,050	2,345
8,506	5,050	**3,456**
9,617	**5,050**	4,567
10,728	**5,050**	5,678
11,839	5,050	**6,789**

Pattern: **Possible answer: The numbers in the first and last columns increase by 1,111 each time.**

Name ______________________ **Extend Your Thinking 3-9**

Decision Making

You and your brother have $25 to spend on a birthday gift for your mom. You have a choice of three gifts.

Gift A: a pair of earrings for $14.99 and a box of candy for $8.95

Gift B: a bird feeder for $18.95 and some birdseed for $4.50

Gift C: a potted plant for $11.99, a vase for $8.50, and cut flowers for $4.50

Extra information: You will make your own card and wrapping paper. Sales tax is included.

1. List the gifts from most expensive to least expensive. Include the total cost of each.
   Gift C ($24.99), Gift A ($23.94), Gift B ($23.45)
2. How much money would you have left over if you bought
   a. Gift A? **$1.06**
   b. Gift B? **$1.55**
   c. Gift C? **$0.01**
3. How much would Gift C cost if you didn't buy the vase? **$16.49**
4. Describe the strong and weak points of each gift choice.
   Gift A: **Answers will vary. Look for responses that consider**
   Gift B: **what the recipient would like.**
   Gift C: ______
5. Which gift would you choose? Explain your reasoning.
   Answers will vary.
6. If you had enough money for two gift choices, which two would you choose? Why?
   Answers will vary.

Name ______________________ **Extend Your Thinking 3-10**

Critical Thinking

Some of the tallest dams in the United States were built during the 1900s.

Dam	State	Height	Year Completed
Oroville	California	754 ft	1968
Hoover	Nevada	725 ft	1936
Glen Canyon	Arizona	708 ft	1966
Hungry Horse	Montana	564 ft	1953
Ross	Washington	541 ft	1949

1. What is the difference between the height of the tallest dam on the list and the shortest dam on the list?
   213 feet
2. How could you use mental math to find the difference in height between the Glen Canyon dam and the Hungry Horse dam? Explain.
   Add 36 to both 708 and 564 and subtract.
3. How many years passed between the building of the oldest dam on the list and newest dam on the list?
   32 years
4. Suppose the state of Arizona decided to build a dam which is 1,001 feet tall.
   a. How much taller would the new dam be than the Glen Canyon dam?
   293 feet
   b. If the new dam was completed this year, how many years would have passed from the completion of the Glen Canyon dam to the completion of the new dam?
   Answer should be the current year minus 1966.

Name ______________________ **Extend Your Thinking 3-11**

Critical Thinking

An Idaho farmer is getting ready to plant his spring crop of corn, barley, and oats. He has to decide how much of each grain he will plant. The table shows the number of seeds that he needs for each crop and how much he must spend for each.

Crops	Number of Seeds	Cost
Corn	25,000	$1200
Barley	12,500	$1350
Oats	7200	$ 890

1. In order to make a profit, the farmer must make more money from the sale of his crops than he has spent for seeds. In order to make any profit at all, how much money would the farmer have to make on the sale of the crops? Explain.
   Total cost is $3440. The farmer must sell the crops for at least $3441, to make a profit of $1.
2. Describe how you can use mental math to determine how many more corn seeds the farmer plans to buy than barley seeds.
   Possible answer: 25,000 − 12,000 = 13,000; 13,000 − 500 = 12,500.
3. Which seeds cost more per seed, corn or barley? Explain.
   Barley seeds cost more per seed than corn seeds. Even though the farmer is buying fewer barley seeds than corn seeds, the total cost of barley seeds is higher than the total cost of corn seeds.

Name ______________________ **Extend Your Thinking 3-12**

Critical Thinking

The units of currency known as dollars and cents are used in other countries besides the United States, such as Australia and Canada, for example. But many countries have different currencies. Use the information given to answer each question.

1. In Germany, there are 100 pfennigs to the mark. If you had 2 marks and 70 pfennigs, and someone gave you 3 10-pfennig coins, how much money would you have?
   3 marks
2. In France, there are 100 centimes to the franc. If you had 8 francs and 45 centimes, and someone gave you a 5-franc coin and a 20-centime coin, how much money would you have?
   13 francs and 65 centimes
3. In Japan, the currency is called yen. If you had 490 yen and someone gave you two 500-yen coins and a 10-yen coin, how much money would you have?
   1,500 yen
4. In Greece, the currency is called drachma. If you had 1,000 drachma and someone gave you one 50-drachma bill, two 20-drachma coins and three 5-drachma coins, how much money would you have?
   1,105 drachma
5. In Saudi Arabia, there are 100 halalahs to the riyal. If you had 6 riyals and 34 halalahs and someone gave you a 5-riyal bill, a 50-halalah coin and three 10-halalah coins, how much money would you have?
   12 riyals and 14 halalahs
6. In Zambia, there are 100 ngwee to the kwacha. If you had 54 ngwee and someone gave you one 20-ngwee coin, six 10-ngwee coins, three 2-ngwee coins and one 1-ngwee coin, how much money would you have?
   1 kwacha and 41 ngwee
7. In the United Kingdom, there are 100 pence to the pound. If you had 5 pounds and someone gave you two 1-pound coins, one 20-pence coin, two 5-pence coins, six 2-pence coins and four 1-pence coins, how much money would you have?
   7 pounds and 46 pence

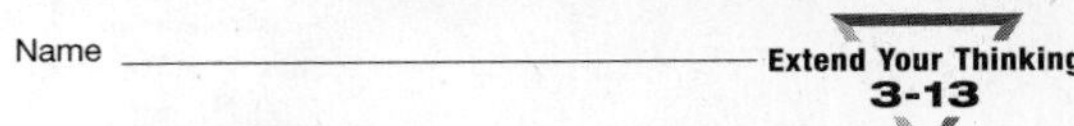

Name ______________________ **Extend Your Thinking 3-13**

Decision Making

Winchester High School is putting on a school play. The expenses of the show have to be covered by ticket sales. You are in charge of the budget.

Item	Cost
Salary for director	\$ 500
Salary for conductor	\$ 300
Lumber	\$ 120
Nails	\$ 16
Paint	\$ 29
Costumes:	
Fabric	\$ 112
Thread, buttons, trim	\$ 13
1 new stage light	\$ 226
Makeup for actors	\$ 57

1. What are the total expenses for the play? **\$1373**
2. Last year, Winchester's school play made \$1000 in profit. If they still have that money to spend this year, what is the extra amount that must be made in order to meet the total expenses? **\$373**
3. The costume maker was able to buy fabric and trim on sale for \$75. By how much did this lower the budget? **\$50**
4. What are some options you have in making sure expenses are covered? List three ways you could make sure all expenses are covered.

   Possible answers: Look for sales on some of the other items needed; increase ticket prices; increase ticket sales.
5. Which way listed in question **4** would you choose to make sure all expenses were paid for?

   Answers will vary.

Use with pages 128–129. 37

Name ______________________ **Extend Your Thinking 3-14**

Critical Thinking

The United Kingdom uses a system of money that is very much like ours. Instead of the dollar bill, the British use a coin called the pound. Their bills are called notes and the symbol they use for a pound looks like this: £. They also have 5-pound, 10-pound, 20-pound and 50-pound notes. A pound is worth about \$1.70 in American money.

1. About how much in American money would the British 5-pound note be worth? **\$8.50**
2. Below is a picture of some British money. How many pounds are shown here? **£17**
3. About how much is this worth in American money? **\$28.90**

4. Imagine that you work in a store that accepts British money, but gives change in American money! A British tourist makes a purchase of \$7.60. She hands you £10.

   a. Will this be enough money to pay for her purchase? Explain.
   Yes. In American money she has given you about \$17.00

   b. How much change will you give her in American money?
   \$9.40 (\$17.00 – \$7.60)

38 Use with pages 130–131.

Name ______________________ **Extend Your Thinking 3-15**

Visual Thinking

Use the pictures to help you determine the value of *n*. Draw a picture to represent *n* in each box. Write the value of *n*.

1. 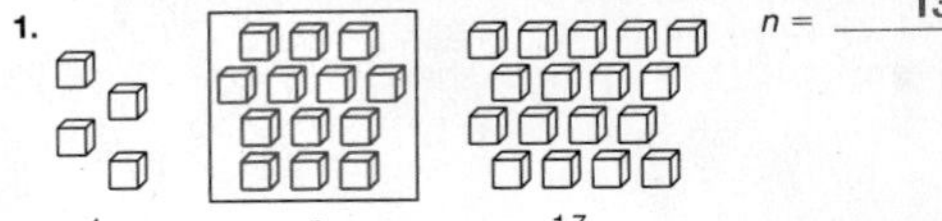

   4 + *n* = 17 $n =$ **13**

2. 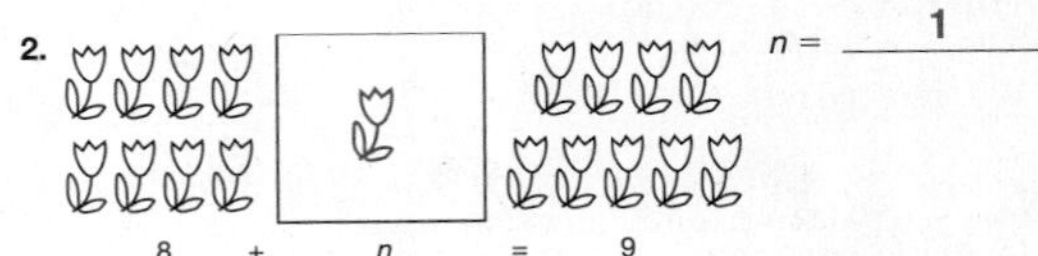

   8 + *n* = 9 $n =$ **1**

3. 

   n + *n* + 3 = 13 $n =$ **5**

4. 

   n + 6 + *n* = 18 $n =$ **6**

5. 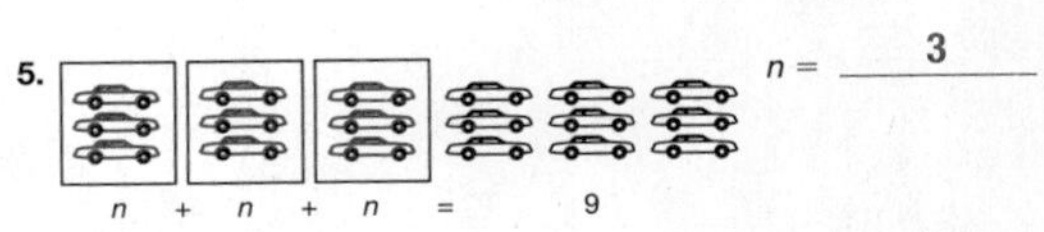

   n + *n* + *n* = 9 $n =$ **3**

Use with pages 134–135. 39

Name ______________________ **Extend Your Thinking 3-16**

Patterns in Data

Henderson Lake in British Columbia, Canada is a very wet place. During one year, rain and snowfall measured 262 inches! Here are rain and snowfall measurements for the first 7 months of that year.

January	22 inches	July	2 inches
February	25 inches	August	**10 inches**
March	32 inches	September	**40 inches**
April	40 inches	October	**32 inches**
May	10 inches	November	**25 inches**
June	2 inches	December	**22 inches**

1. The rain and snowfall measurements for December are the same as those of January. Similarly the measurements for November are the same as those of February. Use the pattern to complete the table.
2. What is the total rain and snowfall for the year shown in the table? **262 inches**
3. Suppose that in the following year, the rainfall in August is twice that of May, while the rainfall in October is half that of March.

   a. What would the August rainfall be? **20 inches**

   b. What would the October rainfall be? **16 inches**
4. If the rainfall for August and October is the only data that changed in the following year, what was the total rain and snowfall for the year? Explain how you found your answer.

   256 inches; Possible answer: 262 – (10 + 32) = 220, 220 + 20 + 16 = 256

40 Use with pages 136–137.

Name ______________________ Extend Your Thinking 4-1

Visual Thinking

Circle the figure with the same pattern as the figure on the left.

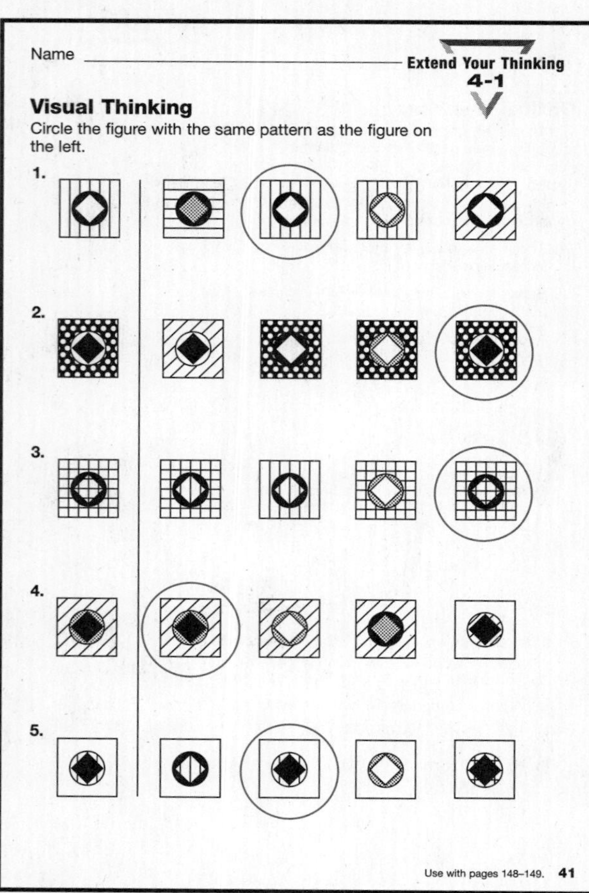

Use with pages 148–149. 41

Name ______________________ Extend Your Thinking 4-2

Visual Thinking

These figures are mirror images of each other because their positions are reversed.

Circle the figure on the right that is the mirror image of the figure on the left.

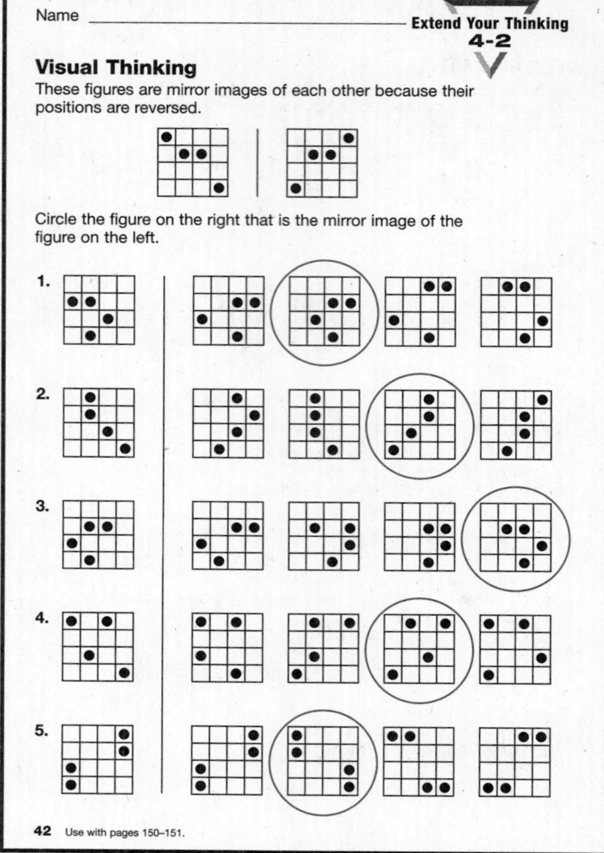

42 Use with pages 150–151.

Name ______________________ Extend Your Thinking 4-3

Decision Making

You are having a party for 24 people. You have $60 to spend on supplies. You can choose between two stores for supplies.

Store A is 3 miles away
- Forks: set of 4 for $1.00
- Plates: set of 6 for $3.00
- Cups: set of 3 for $2.00

Store B is 2 miles away
- Forks: set of 6 for $3.00
- Plates: set of 8 for $5.00
- Cups: set of 6 for $3.00

1. Suppose you buy all your supplies at Store A.
   a. How many sets of each item would you have to buy?
   forks **6 sets** plates **4 sets** cups **8 sets**
   b. How much would each item cost?
   forks **$6.00** plates **$12.00** cups **$16.00**
   c. How much would you pay all together? **$34.00**
2. Suppose you buy all your supplies at Store B.
   a. How many sets of each item would you have to buy?
   forks **4 sets** plates **3 sets** cups **4 sets**
   b. How much would each item cost?
   forks **$12.00** plates **$15.00** cups **$12.00**
   c. How much would you pay all together? **$39.00**
3. Suppose you buy the least expensive items from Store A and Store B.
   a. How much money would each item cost?
   forks **$6.00** plates **$12.00** cups **$12.00**
   b. How much money would you pay all together? **$30.00**
4. Would you choose to buy all your supplies at one store, or go to both stores to get the least expensive supplies? Explain.
   Possible answer: I would just go to Store A because it isn't worth going to two stores to save $4.00.

Use with pages 152–153. 43

Name ______________________ Extend Your Thinking 4-4

Critical Thinking

You can add products to find other products.

1. Draw an array of 5 × 9. Shade the array to show that (3 × 9) + (2 × 9) = 5 × 9. **Student should draw a 5 × 9 array. Look for shading to show 3 × 9 and 2 × 9.**
2. How could you use the product of 9 × 7 and the product of 8 × 7 to find the product of 17 × 7?
   Add the products of 9 × 7 and 8 × 7.
3. Find 12 × 17 by adding two products. **Possible answer:**
   a. 12 × 17 = (12 × **10**) + (12 × **7**)
   b. 12 × 17 = **120** + **84**
   c. 12 × 17 = **204**
   d. What other numbers have a sum of 17? **Possible answer: 12 and 5**
4. Find what number multiplied by 9 equals 135.
   a. 9 × **9** = 81
   b. 9 × **6** = 54
   c. 81 + 54 = **135**
   d. 9 × **15** = 135
5. 7 × 11 = 77 and 25 × 7 = 175. Explain how you could use these products to find 7 × 14. Then find 7 × 14.
   Find 175 − 77; 7 × 14 = 98
6. Find 24 × 4 by adding 3 products.
   a. 24 × 4 = (**10** + **10** + **4**) × 4
   b. 24 × 4 = (**10** × 4) + (**10** × 4) + (**4** × 4)
   c. 24 × 4 = **40** + **40** + **16**
   d. 24 × 4 = **96**

44 Use with pages 154–157.

Name ______________________ **Extend Your Thinking 4-5**

Patterns in Numbers

Complete each pattern. Then write the rule used for each pattern.

1. 8, 16, 24, **32**, **40**, **48**
   Rule: **Add 8.**
2. 4, 8, 12, **16**, **20**, **24**
   Rule: **Add 4.**
3. 5, 10, 15, **20**, **25**, **30**
   Rule: **Add 5.**
4. 0, 24, 48, 72, **96**, **120**, **144**
   Rule: **Add 24.**

Look at **1–4** again. Describe each pattern in terms of multiples.

5. **1** shows multiples of **8**
6. **2** shows multiples of **4**
7. **3** shows multiples of **5**
8. **4** shows multiples of **24**
9. Write your own patterns of multiples. Describe each pattern using multiples and then by an addition rule. **Check students' answers.**
   Pattern: ______
   Multiples of: ______
   Rule: ______
   Pattern: ______
   Multiples of: ______
   Rule: ______

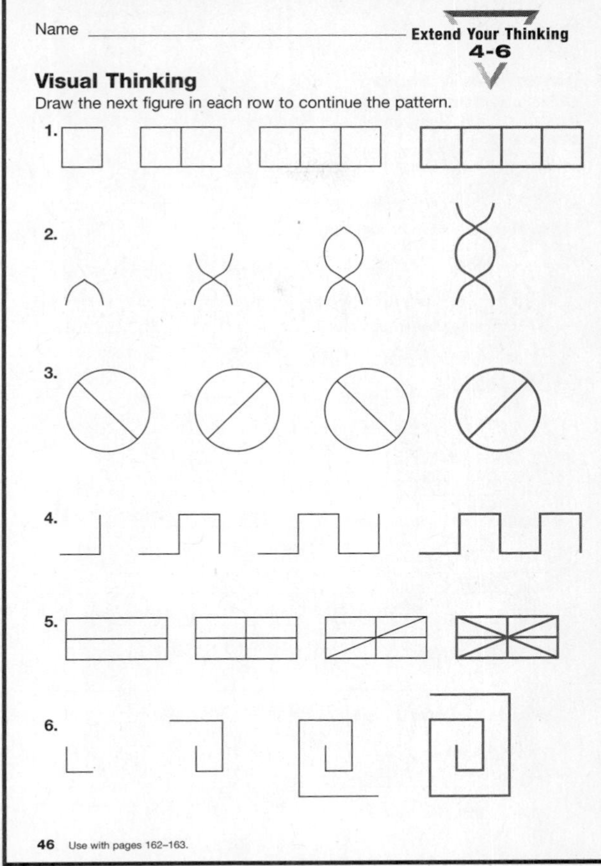

Name ______________________ **Extend Your Thinking 4-6**

Visual Thinking

Draw the next figure in each row to continue the pattern.

1.
2.
3.
4.
5.
6.

Name ______________________ **Extend Your Thinking 4-7**

Critical Thinking

Answer the riddles using the numbers below.

1. I am a 2-digit number. I am divisible by 5 and 2. I am less than 20. What number am I? **10**
2. I am a 1-digit number. I am only divisible by myself. If you multiply a number by me, you get that number. What number am I? **1**
3. I am a 2-digit number. I am divisible by 1, 2, 3, 4, 6, 9, 12, 18, and 36. I am less than 50. What number am I? **36**
4. I am a 1-digit number. I am a factor of 18, 27, 36, and 45. I am not 1. I am less than 5. What number am I? **3**
5. I am a 2-digit number. I am divisible by 6 different numbers that include 3, 4, and 6. I am a factor of 12, 24, 36, and 48. What number am I? **12**
6. I am a 2-digit number. I am a factor of 80, 60, 40, and 20. I am divisible by 6 different numbers that include 4, 5, and 10. What number am I? **20**
7. I am a 1-digit number. I only have 2 factors. I am a factor of 6, 9, and 12. What number am I? **3**
8. I am a 1-digit number. If you multiply any number by me, you always get the same product. What number am I? **0**

Name ______________________ **Extend Your Thinking 4-8**

Visual Thinking

Write the multiplication and division fact families for the following pictures. **Order may vary.**

1. **6 × 7 = 42**
   7 × 6 = 42
   42 ÷ 7 = 6
   42 ÷ 6 = 7
2. **4 × 1 = 4**
   1 × 4 = 4
   4 ÷ 4 = 1
   4 ÷ 1 = 4

Write fact families for each set of numbers.

3. 21, 3, 7 **3 × 7 = 21, 7 × 3 = 21, 21 ÷ 7 = 3, 21 ÷ 3 = 7**
4. 36, 6, 6 **6 × 6 = 36, 36 ÷ 6 = 6**
5. 56, 7, 8 **7 × 8 = 56, 8 × 7 = 56, 56 ÷ 7 = 8, 57 ÷ 8 = 7**
6. Choose one of the fact families from **3–5** and draw a picture for it.
   Check students' drawings.
7. Write a story using your own fact family and picture.
   Check students' stories.

Name ______________ **Extend Your Thinking 4-9**

Patterns in Numbers

Write the next three numbers in each pattern below. Write the rule used for each pattern. Then write what the numbers in the pattern have in common.

1. 2, 4, 6, 8, 10, 12, 14
   Rule: Add 2.
   What do they have in common? Multiples of 2; divisible by 2
2. 45, 40, 35, 30, 25, 20, 15
   Rule: Subtract 5.
   What do they have in common? Multiples of 5; divisible by 5
3. 12, 15, 18, 21, 24, 27, 30
   Rule: Add 3.
   What do they have in common? Multiples of 3; divisible by 3
4. 72, 63, 54, 45, 36, 27, 18
   Rule: Subtract 9.
   What do they have in common? Multiples of 9; divisible by 9
5. 42, 36, 30, 24, 18, 12, 6
   Rule: Subtract 6.
   What do they have in common? Multiples of 6; divisible by 6
6. 21, 28, 35, 42, 49, 56, 63
   Rule: Add 7.
   What do they have in common? Multiples of 7; divisible by 7
7. 64, 56, 48, 40, 32, 24, 16
   Rule: Subtract 8.
   What do they have in common? Multiples of 8; divisible by 8

Name ______________ **Extend Your Thinking 4-10**

Patterns in Numbers

Write the rule. Then find the next number to continue the pattern.

1. 3, 6, 9, 12, 15, 18
   Rule: Multiply by 3.
2. 16, 8, 4, 2, 1
   Rule: Divide the number by 2.
3. 14, 17, 20, 23, 26, 29, 32, 35
   Rule: Add 3.
4. 14, 24, 34, 44, 54, 64, 74
   Rule: Add 10.
5. 114, 116, 119, 121, 124, 126, 129
   Rule: Add 2, add 3.
6. 59,049; 6,561; 729; 81; 9
   Rule: Divide by 9.
7. 81, 83, 86, 90, 95
   Rule: Add 2, add 3, add 4, and so on.
8. 65; 130; 260; 520; 1,040
   Rule: Multiply by 2.
9. 1, 1, 2, 3, 5, 8, 13
   Rule: Add the 2 previous numbers.
10. 779, 776, 773, 770, 767
    Rule: Subtract 3.
11. 1, 1, 2, 6, 6, 12, 36, 36
    Rule: Multiply by 1, then 2, then 3, and repeat.

Name ______________ **Extend Your Thinking 4-11**

Decision Making

Andrew, Belinda, and Carl went to a fruit stand. They each had the following amounts of money.

Andrew: 30¢
Belinda: 20¢
Carl: 40¢

Price List	
Apples	5¢ each, bags of 6 for 15¢
Oranges	10¢ each, bags of 6 for 30¢
Bananas	2¢ each, bags of 6 for 5¢

1. If they each only buy one type of fruit, how many individual pieces (not in bags) of fruit can each person buy with the money they have?

	Apples	Oranges	Bananas
Andrew:	6	3	15
Belinda:	4	2	10
Carl:	8	4	20

2. If they each only buy one type of fruit, how many bags of six can each person buy with the money they have?

	Apples	Oranges	Bananas
Andrew:	2	1	6
Belinda:	1	0	4
Carl:	2	1	8

3. If they put their money together, can they buy more fruit? Explain your answer.
   Possible answer: Yes; because the more money they can pool, the more bags of fruit they can get, which is cheaper than getting individual pieces of fruit.
4. How do you think Andrew, Belinda, and Carl should spend their money for fruit? Explain your reasoning. Possible answer: They should pool their money and buy 1 bag of oranges, 2 bags of apples, and 6 bags of bananas. This way, they get a lot of fruit, but they also get some of each type of fruit.

Name ______________ **Extend Your Thinking 4-12**

Critical Thinking

Your teacher has given you this challenge.

"Here are 150 squares of paper. Create 3 pyramid shapes on the bulletin board. Each pyramid must be one row higher than the last. The top row of every pyramid will be one block long and every row must be two squares longer than the row above it. The team that uses the most squares wins."

Your team won! You used 149 squares to make 3 pyramids on the board.

1. a. How many rows did your first pyramid have? 6
   b. How many total blocks? 36
2. a. How many rows did your second pyramid have? 7
   b. How many total blocks? 49
3. a. How many rows did your third pyramid have? 8
   b. How many total blocks? 64
4. Describe patterns you see in the number of blocks for each pyramid.
   Possible answer: To calculate the number of total blocks for each pyramid, multiply the number of rows by itself.
5. Draw a pyramid with 25 blocks using the pattern above.

Pyramid Challenge

Name ______________________ Extend Your Thinking 4-13

Patterns in Numbers

Write what comes next in each pattern. Then write the rule used for each pattern.

1. 11, 13, 15, 17, 19, 21, 23
   Rule: Add 2.
2. 48, 41, 34, 27, 20, 13, 6
   Rule: Subtract 7.
3. 3, 7, 12, 18, 25, 33, 42
   Rule: Add 4, 5, 6, and so on.
4. 3, 9, 27, 81, 243, 729
   Rule: Multiply by 3.
5. 12, 13, 15, 16, 17, 19, 20, 21, 23, 24
   Rule: Add 1, add 2, add 1, and repeat.
6. 1, 2, 6, 24, 120, 720, 5,040
   Rule: Multiply by 2, 3, 4, and so on.
7. 1; 10; 101; 1,010; 10,101; 101,010; 1,010,101
   Rule: Alternate placing 1 or 0 to the right of the previous number.
8. Write your own number pattern. Write its rule.
   Pattern: Check students' answers.
   Rule: ______

Name ______________________ Extend Your Thinking 4-14

Critical Thinking

Suppose you are an ancient Egyptian stone worker. The Queen has hired you to make a pyramid sculpture for her garden.

"I will give you 140 blocks of stone," she said. "Do not waste them."

The Queen showed you a model using 14 blocks. The model is 3 blocks high. The top layer has 1 block, the 2nd layer has 4 blocks, and the 3rd layer has 9 blocks.

A mathematician whispered to you, "You will be able to use all the blocks if you follow the Queen's model. Just look for the pattern."

After a while, the pattern becomes clear. You build the pyramid, using all the blocks, and are richly rewarded by the Queen.

1. How many layers did your finished pyramid have? 7
2. How many blocks did you use for each layer?
   (In order:) 1, 4, 9, 16, 25, 36, and 49
3. Describe the pattern the mathematician was talking about.
   The number of blocks per layer is determined by the next largest square number. (Or, layer 1 has 1×1 blocks, layer 2 has 2×2 or 4 blocks, layer 3 has 3×3 or 9 blocks, and so on.)
4. Could you make another pyramid with 200 blocks following the same pattern? Explain.
   No, to continue the pattern, the next layer should have 64 blocks. $140 + 64 = 204$
5. How many blocks of stone would you need to follow the same pattern and make a pyramid:
   a. 8 blocks high? 204
   b. 9 blocks high? 285
   c. 10 blocks high? 385

Name ______________________ Extend Your Thinking 4-15

Decision Making

The Math Club has raised $450 for this year's trip. They've decided to go to New York City. Today, all 8 members will vote on what to do when they get there. They must choose from among the following choices:

A. Go to a Broadway play.
   - Each matinee ticket costs $28.
   - A play lasts for 2 or 3 hours.
   - There is 1 matinee a day, usually at 2:00 P.M.

B. See a show at Radio City Music Hall.
   - Each ticket costs $12.
   - A show lasts about 90 minutes.
   - There are 5 shows a day, starting at 9:00 A.M.

C. Go to the Museum of Natural History.
   - Each ticket costs $5.
   - The museum is free to the public on Wednesdays.
   - The museum is across the street from Central Park.

D. Go to the Statue of Liberty.
   - Each ticket costs $11.
   - The statue is in New York Harbor.
   - The ferry ride to the statue takes about 20 minutes.

The train ride to New York takes 1 hour and costs $12 each way. Lunch costs about $10 per person, unless you bring your own.

If you were in the Math Club, how would you vote to spend the day? Explain.

Accept any answer, as long as student accommodates the $56.25 allotted per club member. Student may choose to augment this with pocket money from each member. Possible answer: Go on a Wednesday. Go to Radio City in the morning, then to the Museum, have lunch in a restaurant, then visit the Statue of Liberty in the afternoon. Cost: (train) $24, (Radio City) $12, (Museum) free, (lunch) $10 (Statue) $11, for a total of $57. Everyone has to bring at least one dollar of their own.

Name ______________________ Extend Your Thinking 4-16

Decision Making

The astronomy club is putting on a school dance to raise money for a field trip. They surveyed 50 students and found out that 25 read the school bulletin board, 29 read the newspaper, and 41 listen to announcements.

1. Make a bar graph in the space below to show the data above.
   Check students' graphs.
2. The astronomy club wants to advertise their dance to get as many students to attend as possible. How should they do this?
   Possible answers: They should advertise on the announcements, on the board, and in the newspaper to get the most students to go to the dance.
3. Suppose there are the following limits:
   - The dance can only be talked about on the announcements one time during a week.
   - A poster advertising the dance can only be posted on the school bulletin board for one week.
   - An advertisement in the newspaper costs $10 for each day that it runs.

   How would these limits affect your answers to **2**? Explain.
   Possible answers: The club should advertise in the newspaper only a couple of times because of the cost, and should put up a poster on the board only during the week right before the dance, and read an announcement on Friday before the dance.

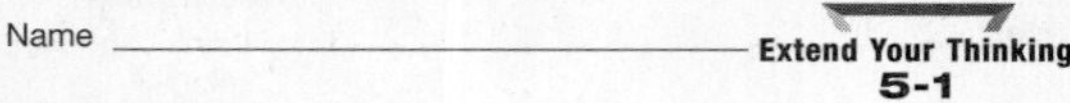

Name ______________________ **Extend Your Thinking 5-1**

Critical Thinking

Mr. Jones had 10 chickens on his farm. Each chicken lays an average of 1 egg a day.

1. Finish the table recording the number of eggs laid in a week on Mr. Jones' farm.

Days	1	2	3	4	5	6	7
Eggs	10	20	30	40	50	60	70

Answer the questions using your data.

2. How many eggs did Mr. Jones collect after 4 days? **40 eggs**
3. Estimate the number of eggs Mr. Jones will collect in two weeks. Explain your reasoning.
   140 eggs; He collected 10 eggs a day. 14 tens is 140.
4. If he sells half the eggs each day, how many eggs would he have left on the third day? Explain.
   15 eggs; Half of 30 is 15. 5 eggs × 3 days = 15 eggs
5. Suppose Mr. Jones adds 10 more chickens to his flock.
   a. How many eggs will he collect in a week? Explain.
   140 eggs. 20 eggs × 7 days = 140 eggs
   b. Why is the number of eggs collected in one week the same as the answer to **3**?
   Possible answer: 10 chickens lay the same number of eggs in 14 days as 20 chickens lay in 7 days.
   10 × 14 = 140; 20 × 7 = 140

Name ______________________ **Extend Your Thinking 5-2**

Visual Thinking

In each row, circle the figure on the right that will complete the analogy.

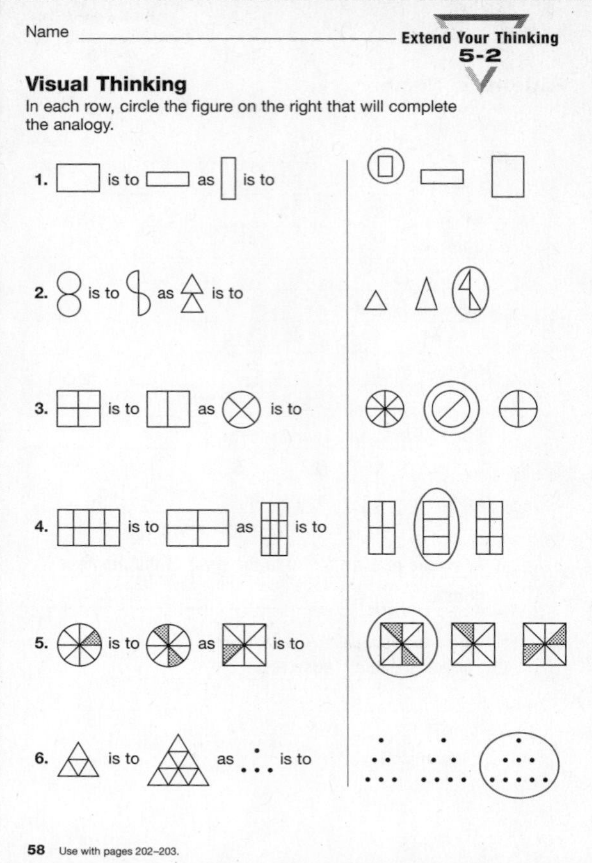

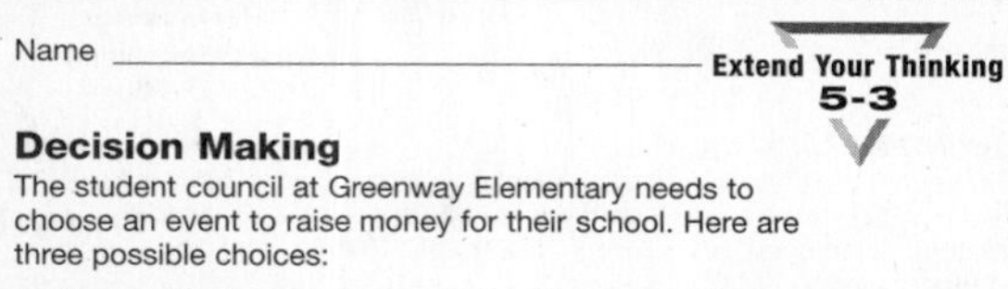

Name ______________________ **Extend Your Thinking 5-3**

Decision Making

The student council at Greenway Elementary needs to choose an event to raise money for their school. Here are three possible choices:

A. Rent-a-Student. Costs involved in the Rent-a-Student program total $100. The Council estimates that 27 students are available for 8 hours each. The cost to rent a student is $1 an hour.

B. Ticket Raffle. The students raffle two tickets to a professional basketball game. Each ticket to the game costs $74. Each raffle ticket will sell for $2. The students should be able to sell 378 tickets in a week.

C. Juice Sale. The students sell juice at the school carnival. They think they can sell 6 cases of juice at $18 a case. The booth is open for 6 hours. The juice costs $12 for 1 case.

1. Estimate the cost of each choice.
   Choice A **$100** Choice B **$140** Choice C **$60**
2. About how much money will each choice earn?
   Choice A **$240** Choice B **$800** Choice C **$120**
3. About how much profit does the school earn from each choice?
   Choice A **$140** Choice B **$660** Choice C **$60**
4. Besides profit, what other factors should the student council consider before making their decision?
   Possible answers: Number of volunteers each event requires; The amount of time and hard work needed to set up and complete each event
5. Which event would be the best choice? Explain.
   Possible answer: B is the easiest to arrange and earns the greatest profit.

Name ______________________ **Extend Your Thinking 5-4**

Visual Thinking

Which musical instruments match the ones on the left? Write the correct answer on the blank.

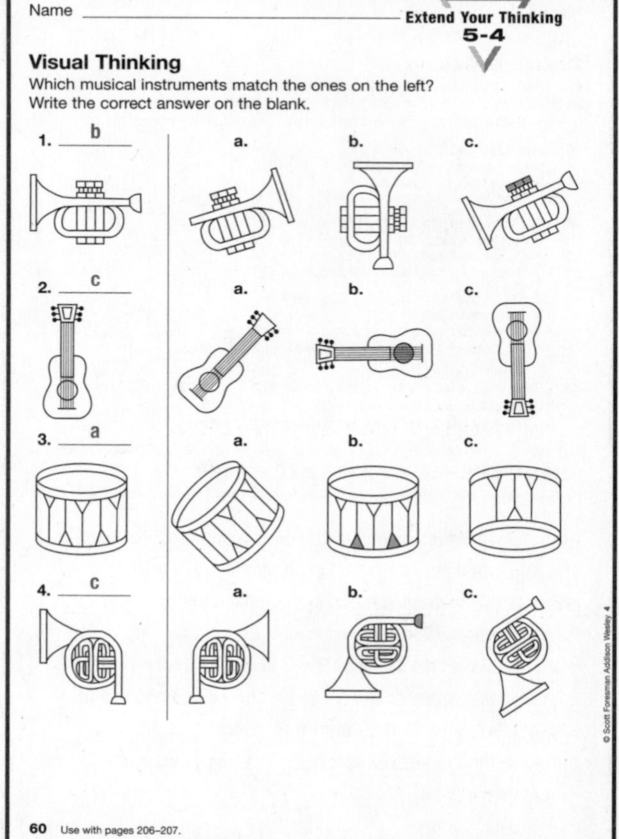

Name ______________________ Extend Your Thinking 5-5

Critical Thinking

Complete each multiplication exercise.

1. 16 × 7 = 112
2. 31 × 4 = 124
3. 48 × 5 = 240
4. 56 × 4 = 224
5. 36 × 5 = 180
6. 41 × 4 = 164
7. 61 × 2 = 122
8. 77 × 8 = 616
9. 62 × 7 = 434
10. 18 × 6 = 108
11. 62 × 2 = 124
12. 38 × 7 = 266
13. 62 × 6 = 372
14. 34 × 5 = 170
15. 44 × 6 = 264
16. 75 × 9 = 675

17. Describe how you found a missing digit in the product.
Possible answer: Multiplied as usual, filling in the missing digit

18. Describe how you found a missing digit in one of the factors.
Possible answer: Used basic facts and missing factors to find a number that would give the product

Name ______________________ Extend Your Thinking 5-6

Critical Thinking

Use a calculator to find the missing numbers.

1. $143 × 7 = $1,001
2. $206 × 8 = $1,648
3. $333 × 4 = $1,332
4. $807 × 9 = $7,263
5. $987 × 3 = $2,961
6. $456 × 8 = $3,648
7. $923 × 5 = $4,615
8. $499 × 6 = $2,994
9. $586 × 7 = $4,102
10. $192 × 6 = $1,152
11. $465 × 3 = $1,395
12. $787 × 7 = $5,509

Name ______________________ Extend Your Thinking 5-7

Decision Making

Approximately 220 dinosaur egg sites have been found around the world in Asia, North America, Europe, South America, and Africa.

Professor Jenkins and her assistant are planning a scientific research trip to visit a dinosaur egg site. These 3 trips are available. Which destination should they choose?

Destination	Number of Days	Cost per Person	Other Information
Asia	8	$1,750	Asia has the greatest number of dinosaur egg sites.
North America	10	$979	There is only one dinosaur egg site in North America.
Europe	7	$ 1,549 (meals not included)	Europe has two dinosaur egg sites.

1. Which trip could Professor Jenkins and her assistant take for less than $3,000? Explain.
North America; 2 × $979 is less than $3,000.

2. If meals in Europe cost an additional $175 per person, how much would a trip to Europe for 2 cost? **$3,448**

3. On which trip(s) will Professor Jenkins and her assistant be able to see at least 2 dinosaur egg sites?
Europe and Asia

4. What additional information could you use to help Professor Jenkins and her assistant make their decision?
Possible answers: What are the additional expenses? How many days would they like to travel? How close to each other are the dinosaur egg sites in Asia?

5. Which trip should they choose? Explain how you made your decision.
Check students' reasoning.

Name ______________________ Extend Your Thinking 5-8

Critical Thinking

Joe Smith is an all-star running back for his football team. This card shows his record for five years.

Year	Total Yards	Touchdowns	Carries
1990	1,220	9	210
1991	1,340	7	264
1992	1,220	6	190
1993	1,640	9	283
1994	1,084	8	186

1. a. Estimate the total number of yards Joe ran from 1990 to 1994. Should you use a calculator? Explain.
About 6,000; You can round the numbers and add mentally to estimate.

b. Explain how you used multiplication to estimate the total number of yards.
The total number of yards for 4 years rounds to 1,000, so you can find the estimate by multiplying 4 by 1,000 and adding the final 2,000.

2. Estimate the total number of carries Joe made. Can you use multiplication? Explain.
About 1,200; you could use multiplication with grouping. (200 × 3) + (300 × 2)

3. Would you estimate to find the total number of touchdowns Joe made? How many did he make?
No; 39

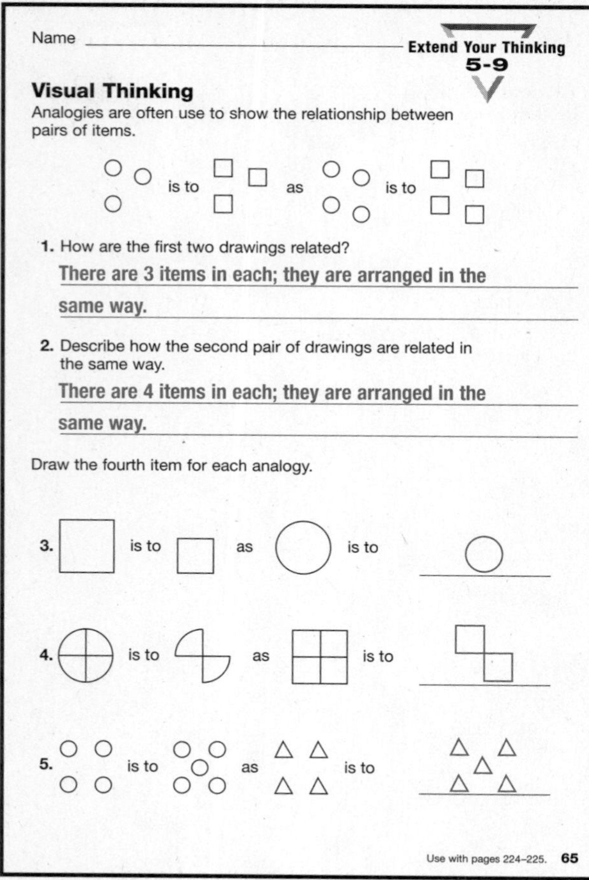

Name ______________________

Extend Your Thinking 5-9

Visual Thinking

Analogies are often use to show the relationship between pairs of items.

is to as is to

1. How are the first two drawings related?
   There are 3 items in each; they are arranged in the same way.

2. Describe how the second pair of drawings are related in the same way.
   There are 4 items in each; they are arranged in the same way.

Draw the fourth item for each analogy.

3. is to as is to

4. is to as is to

5. is to as is to

Use with pages 224–225. 65

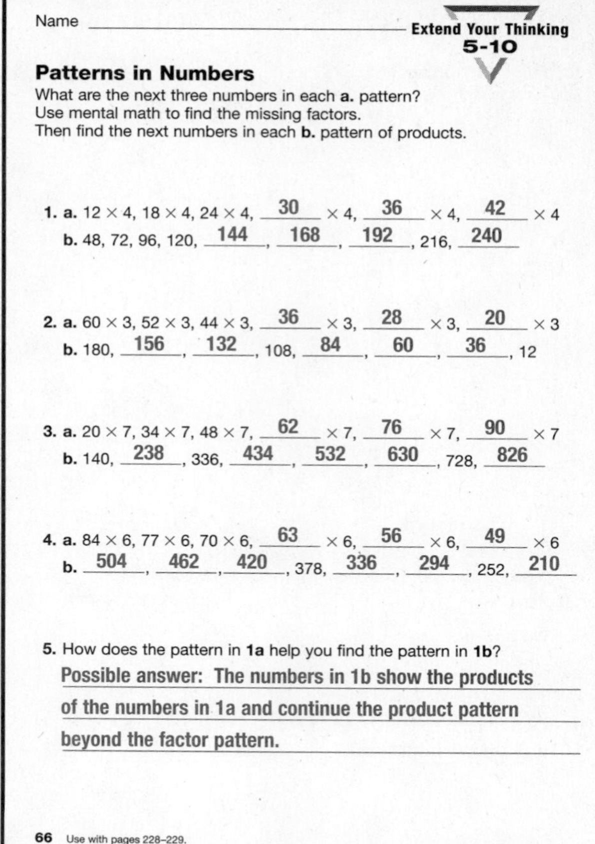

Name ______________________

Extend Your Thinking 5-10

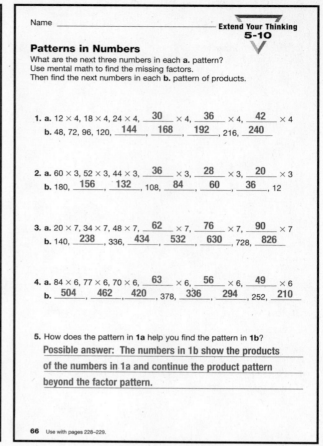

Patterns in Numbers

What are the next three numbers in each **a.** pattern?
Use mental math to find the missing factors.
Then find the next numbers in each **b.** pattern of products.

1. **a.** 12 × 4, 18 × 4, 24 × 4, 30 × 4, 36 × 4, 42 × 4
   b. 48, 72, 96, 120, 144, 168, 192, 216, 240

2. **a.** 60 × 3, 52 × 3, 44 × 3, 36 × 3, 28 × 3, 20 × 3
   b. 180, 156, 132, 108, 84, 60, 36, 12

3. **a.** 20 × 7, 34 × 7, 48 × 7, 62 × 7, 76 × 7, 90 × 7
   b. 140, 238, 336, 434, 532, 630, 728, 826

4. **a.** 84 × 6, 77 × 6, 70 × 6, 63 × 6, 56 × 6, 49 × 6
   b. 504, 462, 420, 378, 336, 294, 252, 210

5. How does the pattern in **1a** help you find the pattern in **1b**?
   Possible answer: The numbers in 1b show the products of the numbers in 1a and continue the product pattern beyond the factor pattern.

66 Use with pages 228–229.

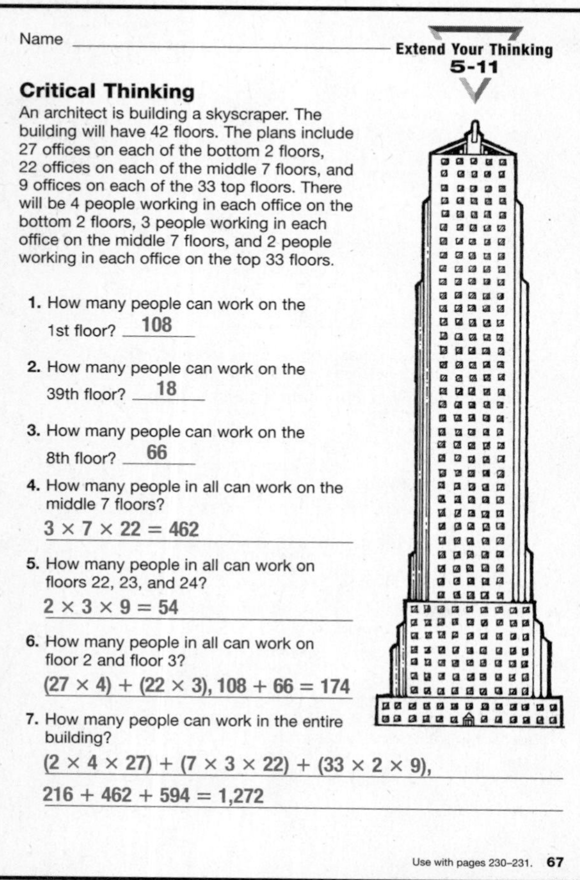

Name ______________________

Extend Your Thinking 5-11

Critical Thinking

An architect is building a skyscraper. The building will have 42 floors. The plans include 27 offices on each of the bottom 2 floors, 22 offices on each of the middle 7 floors, and 9 offices on each of the 33 top floors. There will be 4 people working in each office on the bottom 2 floors, 3 people working in each office on the middle 7 floors, and 2 people working in each office on the top 33 floors.

1. How many people can work on the 1st floor? 108

2. How many people can work on the 39th floor? 18

3. How many people can work on the 8th floor? 66

4. How many people in all can work on the middle 7 floors?
   3 × 7 × 22 = 462

5. How many people in all can work on floors 22, 23, and 24?
   2 × 3 × 9 = 54

6. How many people in all can work on floor 2 and floor 3?
   (27 × 4) + (22 × 3), 108 + 66 = 174

7. How many people can work in the entire building?
   (2 × 4 × 27) + (7 × 3 × 22) + (33 × 2 × 9),
   216 + 462 + 594 = 1,272

Use with pages 230–231. 67

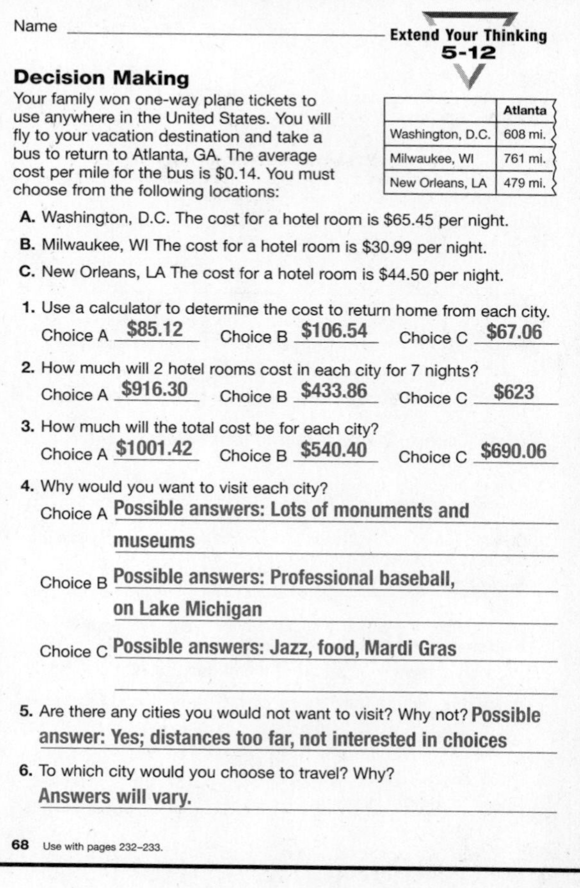

Name ______________________

Extend Your Thinking 5-12

Decision Making

Your family won one-way plane tickets to use anywhere in the United States. You will fly to your vacation destination and take a bus to return to Atlanta, GA. The average cost per mile for the bus is $0.14. You must choose from the following locations:

	Atlanta
Washington, D.C.	608 mi.
Milwaukee, WI	761 mi.
New Orleans, LA	479 mi.

A. Washington, D.C. The cost for a hotel room is $65.45 per night.
B. Milwaukee, WI The cost for a hotel room is $30.99 per night.
C. New Orleans, LA The cost for a hotel room is $44.50 per night.

1. Use a calculator to determine the cost to return home from each city.
   Choice A $85.12 Choice B $106.54 Choice C $67.06

2. How much will 2 hotel rooms cost in each city for 7 nights?
   Choice A $916.30 Choice B $433.86 Choice C $623

3. How much will the total cost be for each city?
   Choice A $1001.42 Choice B $540.40 Choice C $690.06

4. Why would you want to visit each city?
   Choice A Possible answers: Lots of monuments and museums
   Choice B Possible answers: Professional baseball, on Lake Michigan
   Choice C Possible answers: Jazz, food, Mardi Gras

5. Are there any cities you would not want to visit? Why not? Possible answer: Yes; distances too far, not interested in choices

6. To which city would you choose to travel? Why?
   Answers will vary.

68 Use with pages 232–233.

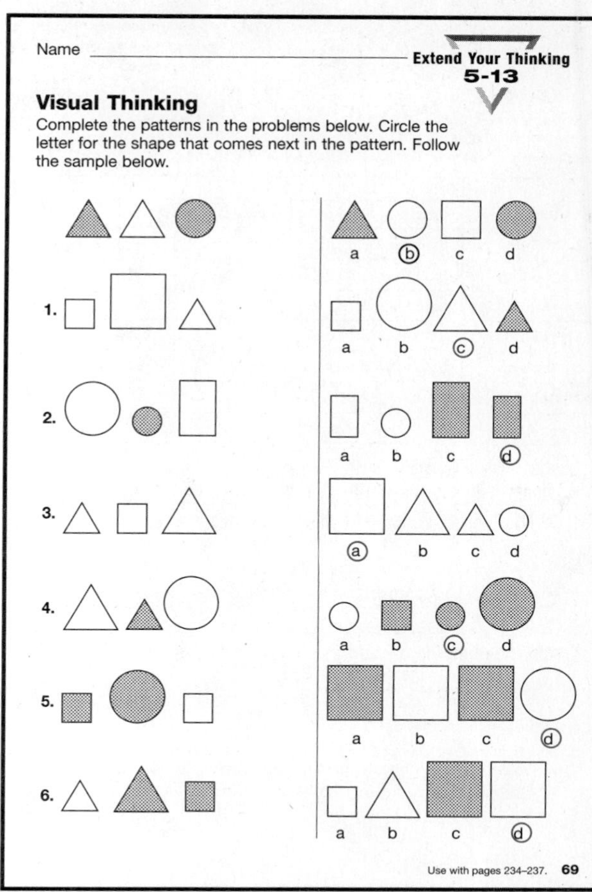

Name ______________________ **Extend Your Thinking 5-13**

Visual Thinking

Complete the patterns in the problems below. Circle the letter for the shape that comes next in the pattern. Follow the sample below.

a (b) c d

1. a b (c) d

2. a b c (d)

3. (a) b c d

4. a b (c) d

5. a b c (d)

6. a b c (d)

Use with pages 234–237. 69

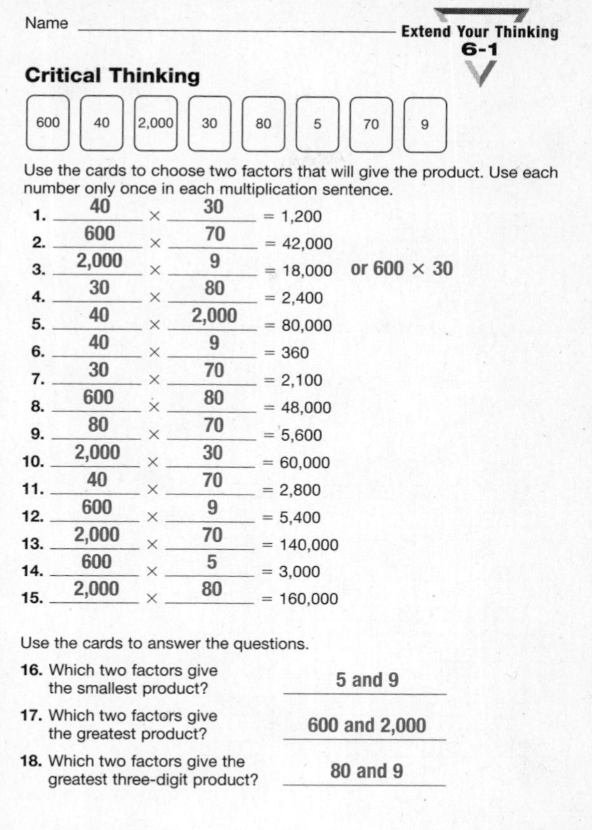

Name ______________________ **Extend Your Thinking 6-1**

Critical Thinking

600 | 40 | 2,000 | 30 | 80 | 5 | 70 | 9

Use the cards to choose two factors that will give the product. Use each number only once in each multiplication sentence.

1. 40 × 30 = 1,200
2. 600 × 70 = 42,000
3. 2,000 × 9 = 18,000 or 600 × 30
4. 30 × 80 = 2,400
5. 40 × 2,000 = 80,000
6. 40 × 9 = 360
7. 30 × 70 = 2,100
8. 600 × 80 = 48,000
9. 80 × 70 = 5,600
10. 2,000 × 30 = 60,000
11. 40 × 70 = 2,800
12. 600 × 9 = 5,400
13. 2,000 × 70 = 140,000
14. 600 × 5 = 3,000
15. 2,000 × 80 = 160,000

Use the cards to answer the questions.

16. Which two factors give the smallest product? 5 and 9
17. Which two factors give the greatest product? 600 and 2,000
18. Which two factors give the greatest three-digit product? 80 and 9

70 Use with pages 250–251.

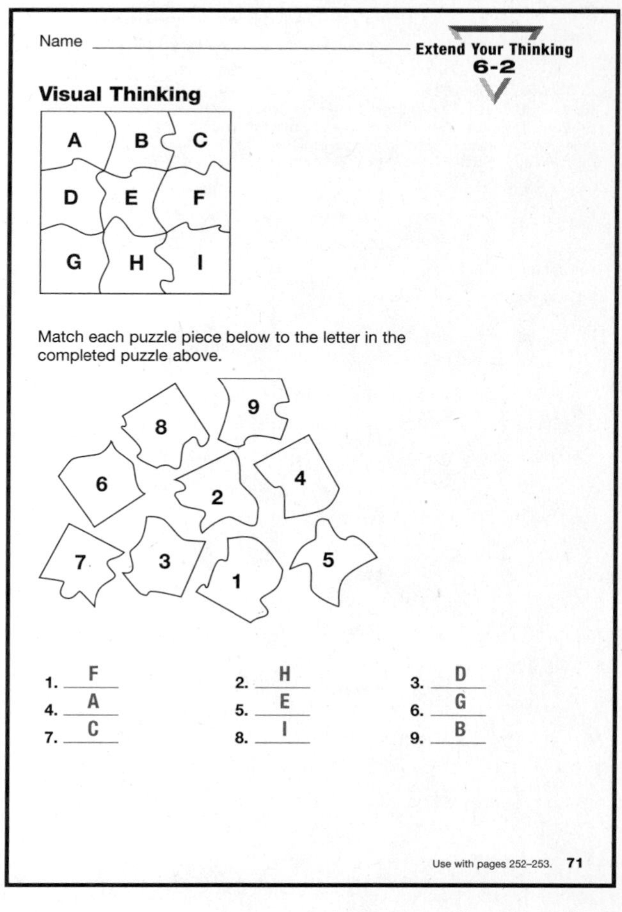

Name ______________________ **Extend Your Thinking 6-2**

Visual Thinking

Match each puzzle piece below to the letter in the completed puzzle above.

1. F 2. H 3. D
4. A 5. E 6. G
7. C 8. I 9. B

Use with pages 252–253. 71

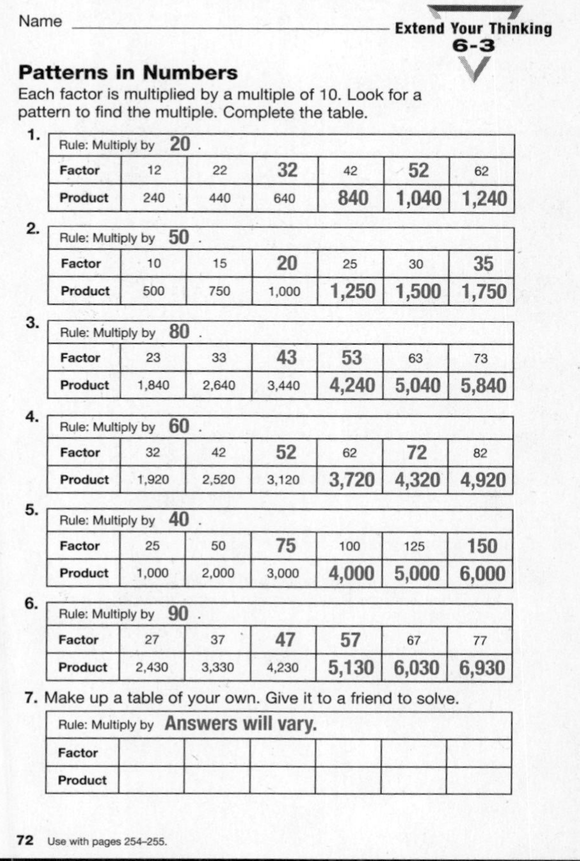

Name ______________________ **Extend Your Thinking 6-3**

Patterns in Numbers

Each factor is multiplied by a multiple of 10. Look for a pattern to find the multiple. Complete the table.

1. Rule: Multiply by 20.

Factor	12	22	32	42	52	62
Product	240	440	640	840	1,040	1,240

2. Rule: Multiply by 50.

Factor	10	15	20	25	30	35
Product	500	750	1,000	1,250	1,500	1,750

3. Rule: Multiply by 80.

Factor	23	33	43	53	63	73
Product	1,840	2,640	3,440	4,240	5,040	5,840

4. Rule: Multiply by 60.

Factor	32	42	52	62	72	82
Product	1,920	2,520	3,120	3,720	4,320	4,920

5. Rule: Multiply by 40.

Factor	25	50	75	100	125	150
Product	1,000	2,000	3,000	4,000	5,000	6,000

6. Rule: Multiply by 90.

Factor	27	37	47	57	67	77
Product	2,430	3,330	4,230	5,130	6,030	6,930

7. Make up a table of your own. Give it to a friend to solve.

Rule: Multiply by Answers will vary.

Factor						
Product						

72 Use with pages 254–255.

Name ________________ **Extend Your Thinking 6-4**

Visual Thinking

Shapes' Kitten Picture

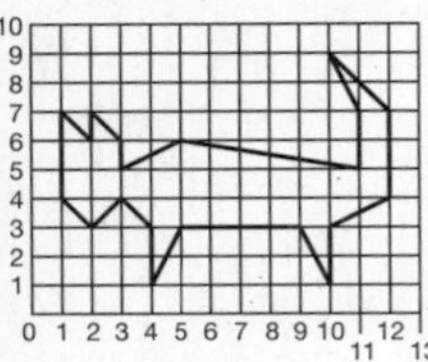

Shapes, the cat, has grown. Make a picture on the large grid to see just how big he has become. Find each point on Shapes' kitten picture. Then find the equivalent point on the larger grid. Use a ruler to join the points to show a picture of Shapes as an adult cat.

Shapes the Cat

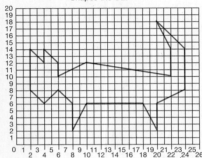

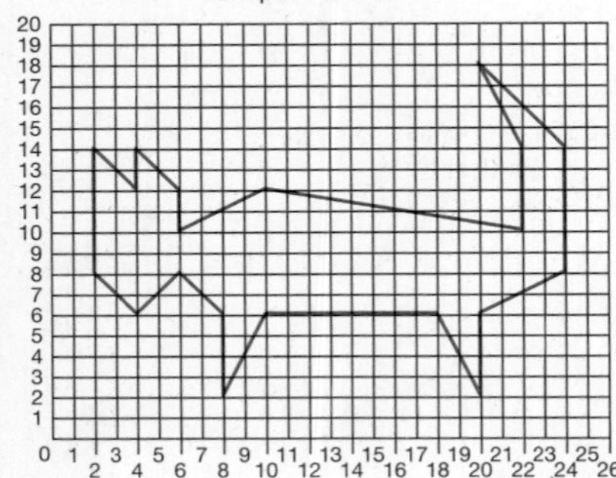

Name ________________ **Extend Your Thinking 6-5**

Critical Thinking

Mel has a part-time job at a sandwich shop. He earns $6 per hour. He made a spreadsheet so he could keep track of his earnings. Refer to the spreadsheet to answer the questions.

	A	B	C	D	E
1	Day	Time in	Time out	Hours worked	Amount earned
2	Monday	3:15 P.M.	5:30 P.M.	$2\frac{1}{4}$	$13.50
3	Tuesday	3:30 P.M.	6:30 P.M.	3	$18.00
4	Wednesday	3:00 P.M.	6:15 P.M.	$3\frac{1}{4}$	$19.50
5	Thursday	4:00 P.M.	6:45 P.M.	$2\frac{3}{4}$	$16.50
6	Friday	3:45 P.M.	5:00 P.M.	$1\frac{1}{4}$	$7.50
7	Saturday	10:00 A.M.	2:00 A.M.	4	$24.00
8			Total:	$16\frac{1}{2}$	$99.00

1. How can you figure out what to put in cell **D4**?
   Possible answer: Count from 3:00 P.M. to 6:00 P.M. and add on 15 minutes, which is $3\frac{1}{4}$ hours in total.
2. How can you figure out what to put in cell **E7**?
   Multiply 4 (hours worked) by 6 (amount per hour).
3. How can you figure out what to put in cells **D8** and **E8**?
   Add the numbers on cells D2–D7, then the numbers in cells E2–E7.
4. Complete the spreadsheet.
5. Suppose Mel gets a raise to $6.25 and keeps the same schedule. What would you put in cell **E8**? Explain. **$103.13; Possible answer: Multiply the amount in cell D8 by 6.25.**

Name ________________ **Extend Your Thinking 6-6**

Decision Making

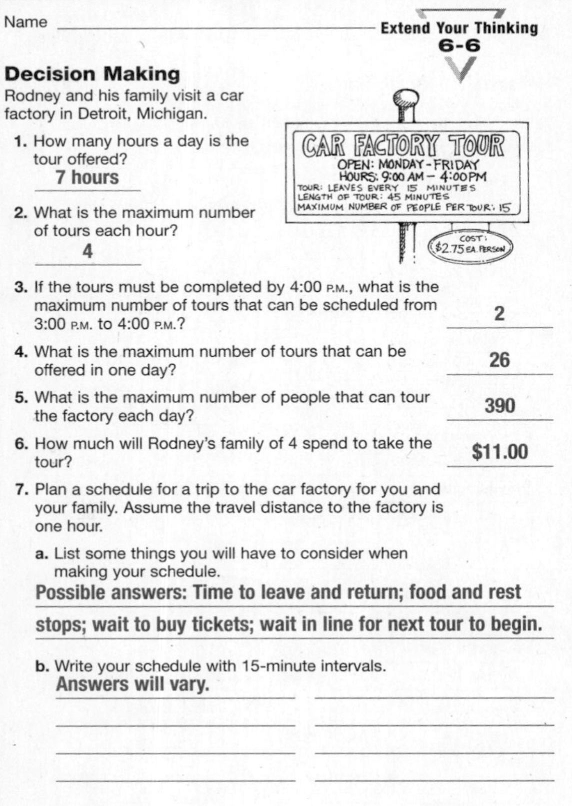

CAR FACTORY TOUR
OPEN: MONDAY - FRIDAY
HOURS: 9:00 AM – 4:00 PM
TOUR: LEAVES EVERY 15 MINUTES
LENGTH OF TOUR: 45 MINUTES
MAXIMUM NUMBER OF PEOPLE PER TOUR: 15
COST: $2.75 EA. PERSON

Rodney and his family visit a car factory in Detroit, Michigan.

1. How many hours a day is the tour offered? **7 hours**
2. What is the maximum number of tours each hour? **4**
3. If the tours must be completed by 4:00 P.M., what is the maximum number of tours that can be scheduled from 3:00 P.M. to 4:00 P.M.? **2**
4. What is the maximum number of tours that can be offered in one day? **26**
5. What is the maximum number of people that can tour the factory each day? **390**
6. How much will Rodney's family of 4 spend to take the tour? **$11.00**
7. Plan a schedule for a trip to the car factory for you and your family. Assume the travel distance to the factory is one hour.
   a. List some things you will have to consider when making your schedule.
   Possible answers: Time to leave and return; food and rest stops; wait to buy tickets; wait in line for next tour to begin.
   b. Write your schedule with 15-minute intervals.
   Answers will vary.

Name ________________ **Extend Your Thinking 6-7**

Critical Thinking

Guess and check. Guess how many digits are in each product. Then calculate the product to check the number of digits. Write the product and your calculation method. **Guesses and calculation methods will vary. Check students' answers.**

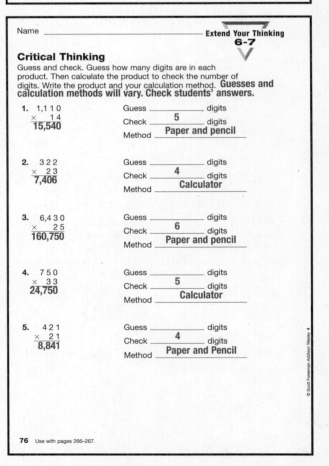

1. 1,110 × 14 = **15,540** — Guess ____ digits; Check **5** digits; Method **Paper and pencil**
2. 322 × 23 = **7,406** — Guess ____ digits; Check **4** digits; Method **Calculator**
3. 6,430 × 25 = **160,750** — Guess ____ digits; Check **6** digits; Method **Paper and pencil**
4. 750 × 33 = **24,750** — Guess ____ digits; Check **5** digits; Method **Calculator**
5. 421 × 21 = **8,841** — Guess ____ digits; Check **4** digits; Method **Paper and Pencil**

Name ______________________ **Extend Your Thinking 6-8**

Patterns in Data

The table below gives information about 2 rides at the fair. Read the information. Figure out the cost per minute for each ride. Then answer the questions.

	Giant Ferris Wheel $3.00 for 15 minutes		Flying Falcon $4.50 for 15 minutes	
	Minutes	**Cost**	**Minutes**	**Cost**
1.	1	**$0.20**	1	**$0.30**
2.	2	**$0.40**	2	**$0.60**
3.	3	**$0.60**	3	**$0.90**
4.	4	**$0.80**	4	**$1.20**
5.	5	**$1.00**	5	**$1.50**
6.	6	**$1.20**	6	**$1.80**

7. Which ride is the best buy per minute?
Giant Ferris Wheel

8. How many minutes would you get on the Giant Ferris Wheel for the cost of 4 minutes on the Flying Falcon? **6 minutes**

9. How many minutes would you get on the Flying Falcon for the cost of 3 minutes on the Giant Ferris Wheel? **2 minutes**

10. The Wind Tunnel costs $5.00 for 20 minutes. Is this better value per minute than the Giant Ferris Wheel? the Flying Falcon? Explain.
Better value than Flying Falcon but not the Giant Ferris Wheel.
$0.20 < $0.25 < $0.30

Name ______________________ **Extend Your Thinking 6-9**

Decision Making

The table below shows how consumers rated each of 5 brands of mouthwash. Read over the table to decide which is the best buy.

(excellent face) = excellent (good face) = good (fair face) = fair (poor face) = poor

Brand	Cost	Taste	Freshness	Time it Lasted	Overall
Bright Smile	$2.75	fair	fair	poor	fair
Shine	$3.25	good	good	excellent	excellent
Fresh Breath	$2.00	excellent	good	good	good
Winter Mint	$3.30	good	excellent	good	good
Mint Wave	$2.10	fair	poor	poor	poor

1. Which mouthwash costs the least? **Fresh Breath**
How much less is
a. Fresh Breath than Bright Smile? **$0.75**
b. Fresh Breath than Shine? **$1.25**
c. Mint Wave than Winter Mint? **$1.20**
d. Mint Wave than Shine? **$1.15**

2. Which mouthwash received the highest score for
a. taste? **Fresh Breath**
b. freshness? **Winter Mint**
c. time it lasted? **Shine**

3. Which mouthwash has a combination of low cost and high ratings? **Fresh Breath**

4. Which mouthwash would you choose? Why?
Possible answer: Fresh Breath. It costs less, tastes best, and is reasonably fresh and long-lasting.

Name ______________________ **Extend Your Thinking 6-10**

Decision Making

Dana and Austin are having a car wash to raise money for the local museum. They each made a sign. Which one should they use?

Sign 1	Sign 2
Support the Winston Museum Car Wash $2.50	Support the Winston Museum Car Wash $3.50

1. Dana estimates that they can wash 3 cars per hour. They expect to work for 7 hours. Should they overestimate or underestimate the number of cars they can wash? Explain.
They should underestimate; they may not be able to wash 3 cars every hour.

2. How might they adjust the numbers to estimate many cars they could wash in one day?
They could lower the number of hours from 7 to 6 or the number of cars per hour from 3 to 2.

3. Estimate the number of cars they can wash in a day. **14–18**

4. Based on your estimate, how much could they earn in one day with Sign 1? With Sign 2?
$35.00 – $45.00; $49.00 – $63.00

5. Which sign might bring in more cars? Explain.
Sign 1. The price is lower.

6. Which sign would you use? Explain your reasoning.
Possible answer: Sign 1: It is more likely to bring in 3 cars an hour.

Name ______________________ **Extend Your Thinking 6-11**

Visual Thinking

Write a word problem to go with each picture. Give it to a friend to solve.

1.

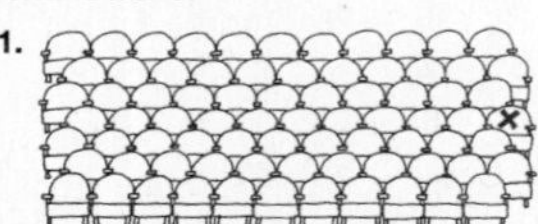

Possible answer: Ana sits in row 4 at the movies. There are 7 rows in all and each row has 11 seats. How many people are seated in front of Ana?

2.

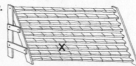

Possible answer: Terry is in row 3, seventh seat from the right, at a baseball game. There are 9 rows in all and each row has 10 seats. How many people are to his left?

3.

Possible answer: Sasha wants the pumpkin in row 6 of the 17-row patch. There are 8 pumpkins to its left and 8 pumpkins to its right. How many pumpkins are behind the pumpkin Sasha wants?

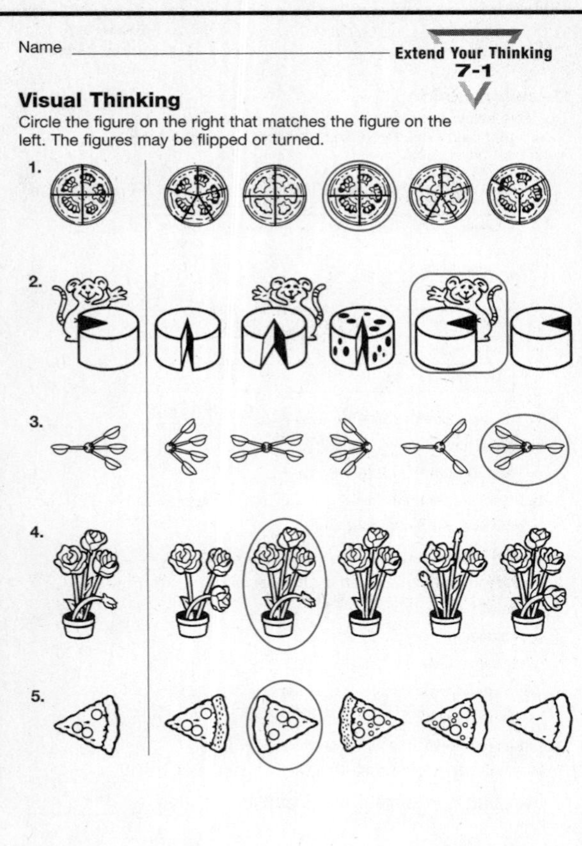

Name ______________________ **Extend Your Thinking 7-1**

Visual Thinking

Circle the figure on the right that matches the figure on the left. The figures may be flipped or turned.

1.

2.

3.

4.

5.

Use with pages 292–293. **81**

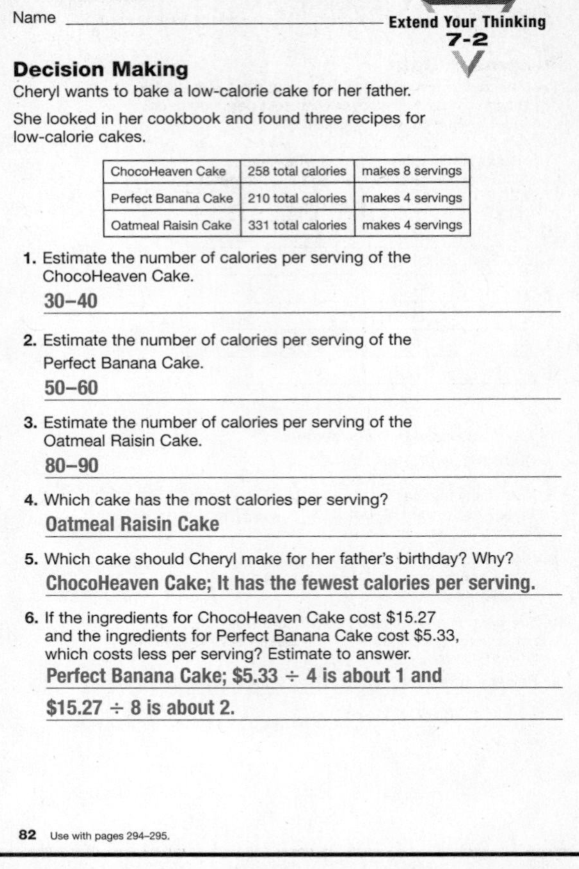

Name ______________________ **Extend Your Thinking 7-2**

Decision Making

Cheryl wants to bake a low-calorie cake for her father.

She looked in her cookbook and found three recipes for low-calorie cakes.

ChocoHeaven Cake	258 total calories	makes 8 servings
Perfect Banana Cake	210 total calories	makes 4 servings
Oatmeal Raisin Cake	331 total calories	makes 4 servings

1. Estimate the number of calories per serving of the ChocoHeaven Cake.
   30–40
2. Estimate the number of calories per serving of the Perfect Banana Cake.
   50–60
3. Estimate the number of calories per serving of the Oatmeal Raisin Cake.
   80–90
4. Which cake has the most calories per serving?
   Oatmeal Raisin Cake
5. Which cake should Cheryl make for her father's birthday? Why?
   ChocoHeaven Cake; It has the fewest calories per serving.
6. If the ingredients for ChocoHeaven Cake cost $15.27 and the ingredients for Perfect Banana Cake cost $5.33, which costs less per serving? Estimate to answer.
   Perfect Banana Cake; $5.33 ÷ 4 is about 1 and $15.27 ÷ 8 is about 2.

82 Use with pages 294–295.

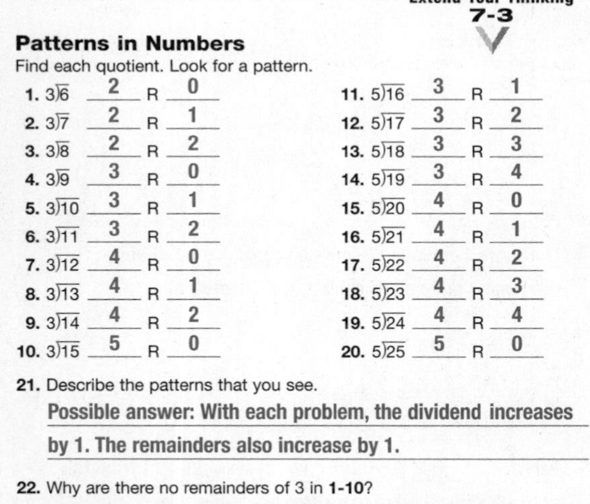

Name ______________________ **Extend Your Thinking 7-3**

Patterns in Numbers

Find each quotient. Look for a pattern.

1. 3)6	**2** R **0**	**11.** 5)16	**3** R **1**
2. 3)7	**2** R **1**	**12.** 5)17	**3** R **2**
3. 3)8	**2** R **2**	**13.** 5)18	**3** R **3**
4. 3)9	**3** R **0**	**14.** 5)19	**3** R **4**
5. 3)10	**3** R **1**	**15.** 5)20	**4** R **0**
6. 3)11	**3** R **2**	**16.** 5)21	**4** R **1**
7. 3)12	**4** R **0**	**17.** 5)22	**4** R **2**
8. 3)13	**4** R **1**	**18.** 5)23	**4** R **3**
9. 3)14	**4** R **2**	**19.** 5)24	**4** R **4**
10. 3)15	**5** R **0**	**20.** 5)25	**5** R **0**

21. Describe the patterns that you see.
    Possible answer: With each problem, the dividend increases by 1. The remainders also increase by 1.
22. Why are there no remainders of 3 in **1-10**?
    Possible answer: There are no remainders of 3 because that would mean another whole group of 3, which would be included in the quotient.
23. How would the patterns change if the divisor in each problem were 4?
    Possible answer: The pattern in the remainders would be 0, 1, 2, 3, 0, 1, 2, 3.
24. If 79 ÷ 6 = 13 R1, use the pattern to find 80 ÷ 6. **13 R2**

Use with pages 296–297. **83**

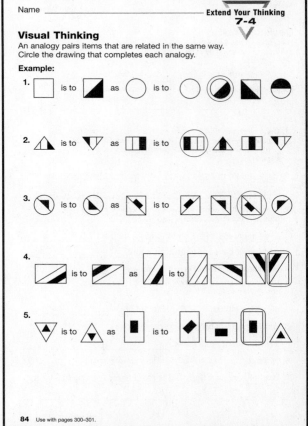

Name ______________________ **Extend Your Thinking 7-4**

Visual Thinking

An analogy pairs items that are related in the same way.
Circle the drawing that completes each analogy.

Example:

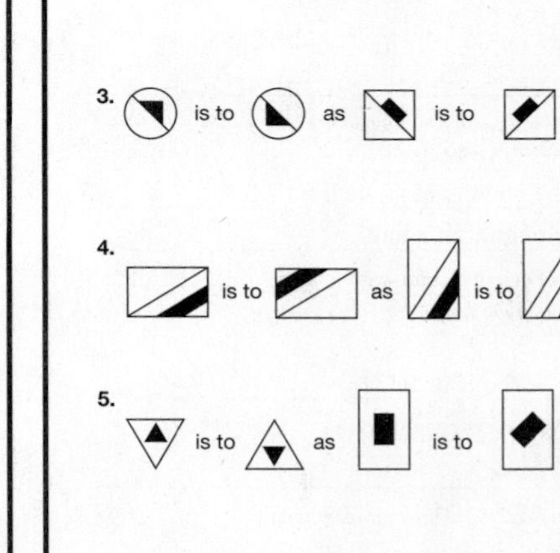

1. is to as is to
2. is to as is to
3. is to as is to
4. is to as is to
5. is to as is to

84 Use with pages 300–301.

Name ______________________ **Extend Your Thinking 7-5**

Patterns in Numbers

What happens when you divide the same 2-digit number by divisors that keep increasing by 1? Is there a pattern?

Solve the following problems to find out.

1. 2)67 **33 R1**
2. 3)67 **22 R1**
3. 4)67 **16 R3**
4. 5)67 **13 R2**
5. 6)67 **11 R1**
6. 2)83 **41 R1**
7. 3)83 **27 R2**
8. 4)83 **20 R3**
9. 5)83 **16 R3**
10. 6)83 **13 R5**
11. 7)83 **11 R6**
12. Describe the patterns you see.
    Possible answers: As the divisors increase, the quotient decreases. The decrease between the quotients gets smaller at each step.
13. If you divide 83 by 8, do you think the quotient would be greater or less than 11? Use **11** above to explain.
    Less; because 8 is greater than 7
14. How can you use the fact that 91 ÷ 6 = 15 R1 and 91 ÷ 9 = 10 R1 to estimate the quotient of 91 ÷ 8?
    The quotient of 91 ÷ 8 is less than 15 but greater than 10.

Name ______________________ **Extend Your Thinking 7-6**

Decision Making

Harleyville Soccer League is planning its annual Awards Banquet. A total of 400 people will attend the banquet. You have been asked to help decide how many tables should be set up for the evening. This is the information you have been given:

a. Three rectangular head tables will be set up. Sixteen league officials will sit at the main head table.

b. Twelve coaches will sit at a second head table.

c. The third head table will be for the assistant coaches. Twelve people will be at this table.

All other people at the banquet will sit at round tables. The round tables come in 2 sizes that seat 8 or 12 people. There is room for 35 to 45 round tables.

1. What is the total number of people who will sit at the three head tables? **40**
2. How many people will sit at the round tables? **360**
3. Suppose you wanted to use the fewest number of tables possible. How many of each type would you use?
   30 tables for 12 and 0 tables for 8
4. Suppose you wanted to use the greatest number of tables possible. How many of each type would you use?
   0 tables for 12 and 45 tables for 8
5. What is another way you could set up the tables?
   Possible answer: 26 tables for 12 and 6 tables for 8.
6. How would you set up the room? Explain.
   Answers will vary.

Name ______________________ **Extend Your Thinking 7-7**

Visual Thinking

A figure has line symmetry if it can be folded along a line so that both sides match. Look at the figures in each row. Circle the figure that has line symmetry.

1.–2.

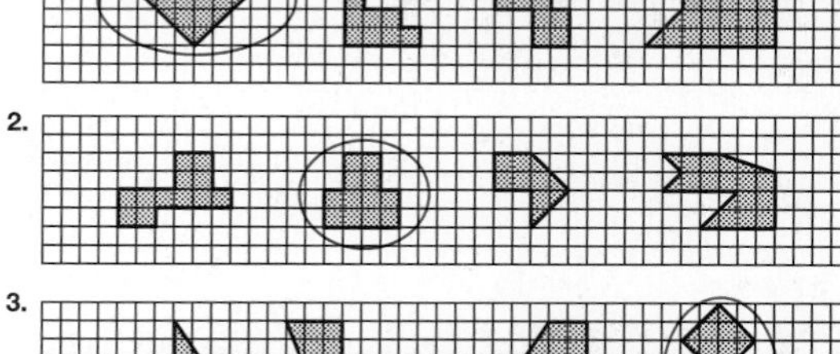

3.–5.

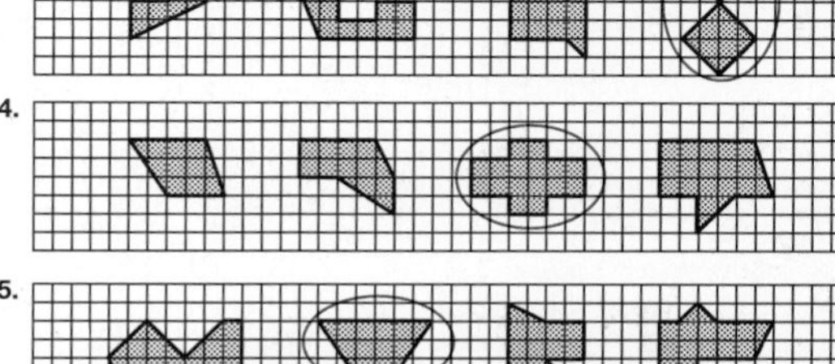

6.

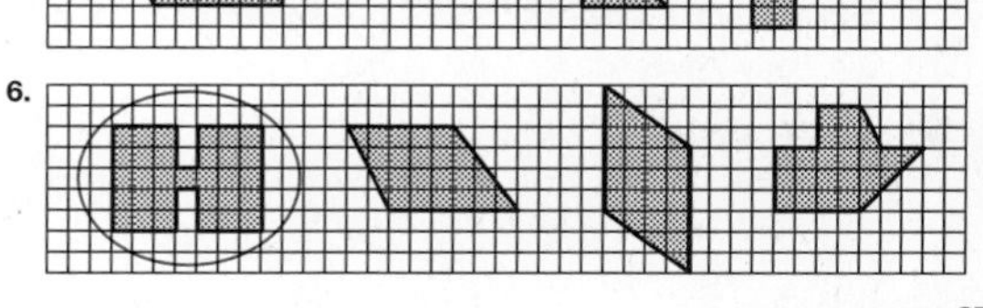

Name ______________________ **Extend Your Thinking 7-8**

Number Patterns

What are the next three numbers in each pattern? Tell what rule was used to make the pattern.

1. 26; 52; 104; 208; **416**, **832**, **1,664**
   Rule: **Multiply by 2.**
2. 46,875; 9,375; 1,875; 375; **75**, **15**, **3**
   Rule: **Divide by 5.**
3. 8,192; 2,048; 512; 128; **32**, **8**, **2**
   Rule: **Divide by 4.**
4. 218,700; 72,900; 24,300; 8,100; **2,700**; **900**; **300**
   Rule: **Divide by 3.**
5. 34; 68; 136; 272; **544**; **1,088**; **2,176**
   Rule: **Multiply by 2.**
6. 11; 22; 66; 264; **1,320**; **7,920**; **55,440**
   Rule: **Multiply by 2, then 3, then 4, and so on.**
7. 21; 84; 336; 1,344; **5,376**; **21,504**; **86,016**
   Rule: **Multiply by 4.**
8. 89,600; 44,800; 22,400; 11,200; **5,600**; **2,800**; **1,400**
   Rule: **Divide by 2.**
9. 606,528; 101,088; 16,848; 2,808; **468**, **78**, **13**
   Rule: **Divide by 6.**

Name ____________________ **Extend Your Thinking 7-9**

Critical Thinking

Who do you think is the greatest baseball hitter of all time? Many people would mention one of these five players. They were some of the best home run hitters of all time!

	Player	Home Runs	At Bats	
1	Hank Aaron	755	12,364	1
5	Harmon Killebrew	573	8,147	5
3	Willie Mays	660	10,881	2
4	Frank Robinson	586	10,006	3
2	Babe Ruth	714	8,399	4

1. Which hitter had the greatest number of home runs?
Hank Aaron
2. What does the number of times each player came to bat tell you about the players?
Answers will vary. Possible answer: The more at bats, the more chances a player has to hit a home run.
3. Which player had the greatest number of at bats? **Hank Aaron**
4. On the left side of the table, rank the players from the player who hit the greatest number of home runs to the player who hit the least. On the right side of the table, rank the players from the one who had the greatest number of at bats to the player who had the least.
5. Analyze your table. Who do you think was the best hitter? Explain.
Answers will vary, but should indicate that the player who hit the greatest number of home runs with the least number of at bats is the greatest hitter. Babe Ruth has the greatest home run average.

Name ____________________ **Extend Your Thinking 7-10**

Visual Thinking

Some shapes can be used to make a larger pattern of the same shape. For example, you can draw 3 more squares of the same size to make a larger square.

Make a large pattern of each shape using 4 of the smaller shapes. **Possible answers:**

1.

2.

3.

Name ____________________ **Extend Your Thinking 7-11**

Decision Making

A group of students from your class is taking a field trip to a museum. There are 3 restaurants in the area of the museum where your class can eat lunch. Each restaurant offers a different price for group lunches. There are 12 students going on the field trip.

A. **Darlene's Diner.** Each student will be served a turkey sandwich, pretzels, and juice. The cost of lunch for 4 students is $9.88.

B. **Rich's Restaurant.** Each student will be served a tuna salad sandwich, soup, and juice. The cost of lunch for 3 students is $6.12.

C. **Pat's Pit-Stop.** Each student will be served a peanut butter and jelly sandwich, salad, and milk. The cost of lunch for 2 students is $4.52.

1. How much will lunch cost for each student at each restaurant? Write the number sentence and find the amount for each restaurant.
Restaurant A: **$9.88 ÷ 4 = $2.47; $2.47 for each student.**
Restaurant B: **$6.12 ÷ 3 = $2.04; $2.04 for each student.**
Restaurant C: **$4.52 ÷ 2 = $2.26; $2.26 for each student.**
2. a. If all of the students on the field trip eat lunch, what will the total cost be for the class to eat at each of the restaurants?
A: **$29.64** B: **$24.48** C: **$27.12**
b. How did you find the total cost for each restaurant?
Possible answer: I multiplied the cost for each student by 12 students to find the total cost.
3. Which restaurant would you choose for the class to go for lunch? Why?
Possible answer: I would choose Pat's Pit-Stop (Choice C), because it serves peanut butter and is not the most expensive choice.

Name ____________________ **Extend Your Thinking 7-12**

Critical Thinking

A group of fourth- and fifth-grade classes took the same test. Here are the average scores for each class.

Fourth Grade Classes	Average Scores	Fifth Grade Classes	Average Scores
Mr. Andrew	82	Ms. Brown	88
Ms. Lim	85	Mr. Shapiro	85
Ms. Somers	86	Ms. King	81
Ms. Bouvet	79	Mr. Cohn	86

1. Find the overall average score for the fourth grade. **83**
2. Find the overall average score for the fifth grade. **85**
3. Which grade has the higher mean test score, fourth grade or fifth grade? Explain.
Fifth grade; because 85 > 83
4. What is the mean score for fourth and fifth grade combined? **84**
5. There are only 8 students in Mr. Andrew's class. The average score for his class is 82. Seven of his student's got the following scores: 81, 82, 89, 91, 72, 73, and 77. Find the eighth student's score. **91**
6. A group of 4 sixth-grade classes took the test. If the mean score for the sixth grade is 90, what is the average score for fourth, fifth, and sixth grade combined? **86**
7. Find the overall average for the top 2 average scores in fourth grade and the top 2 average scores in fifth grade.
About 86

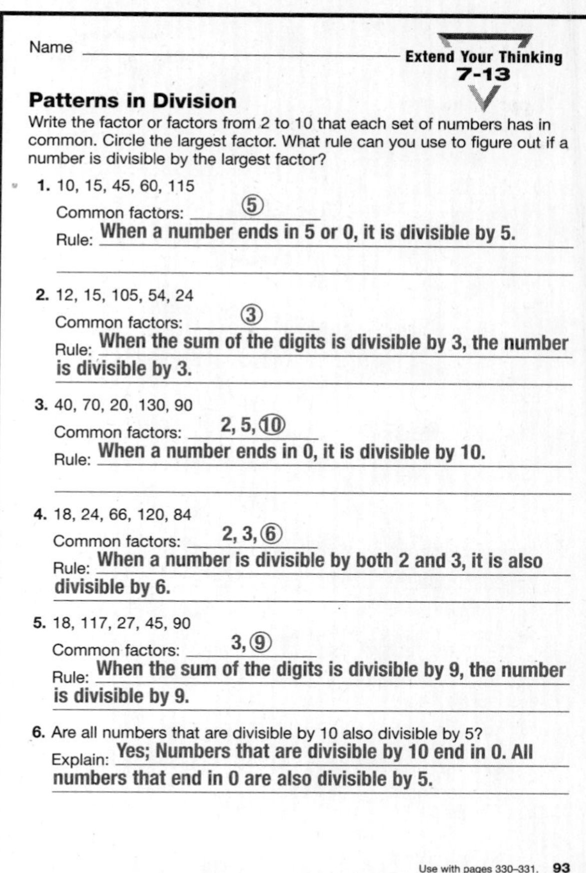

Name ______________________

Extend Your Thinking 7-13

Patterns in Division

Write the factor or factors from 2 to 10 that each set of numbers has in common. Circle the largest factor. What rule can you use to figure out if a number is divisible by the largest factor?

1. 10, 15, 45, 60, 115

   Common factors: (5)

   Rule: **When a number ends in 5 or 0, it is divisible by 5.**

2. 12, 15, 105, 54, 24

   Common factors: (3)

   Rule: **When the sum of the digits is divisible by 3, the number is divisible by 3.**

3. 40, 70, 20, 130, 90

   Common factors: **2, 5, (10)**

   Rule: **When a number ends in 0, it is divisible by 10.**

4. 18, 24, 66, 120, 84

   Common factors: **2, 3, (6)**

   Rule: **When a number is divisible by both 2 and 3, it is also divisible by 6.**

5. 18, 117, 27, 45, 90

   Common factors: **3, (9)**

   Rule: **When the sum of the digits is divisible by 9, the number is divisible by 9.**

6. Are all numbers that are divisible by 10 also divisible by 5?

   Explain: **Yes; Numbers that are divisible by 10 end in 0. All numbers that end in 0 are also divisible by 5.**

Use with pages 330–331. 93

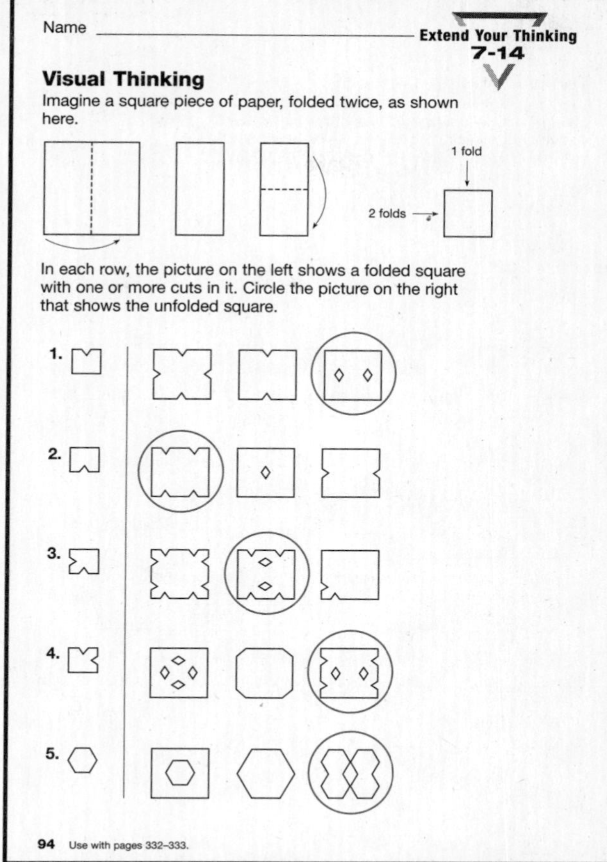

Name ______________________

Extend Your Thinking 7-14

Visual Thinking

Imagine a square piece of paper, folded twice, as shown here.

In each row, the picture on the left shows a folded square with one or more cuts in it. Circle the picture on the right that shows the unfolded square.

1.

2.

3.

4.

5.

94 Use with pages 332–333.

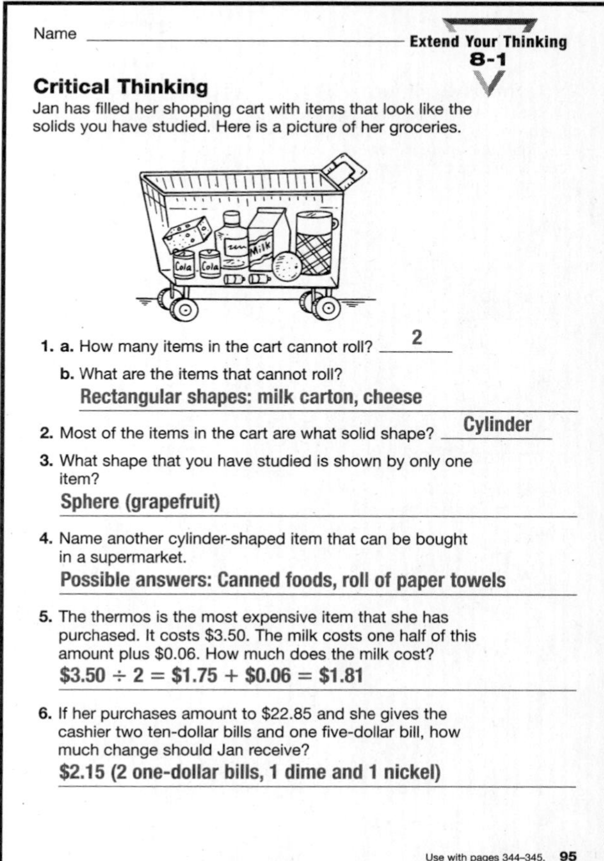

Name ______________________

Extend Your Thinking 8-1

Critical Thinking

Jan has filled her shopping cart with items that look like the solids you have studied. Here is a picture of her groceries.

1. a. How many items in the cart cannot roll? **2**

   b. What are the items that cannot roll?

   Rectangular shapes: milk carton, cheese

2. Most of the items in the cart are what solid shape? **Cylinder**
3. What shape that you have studied is shown by only one item?

   Sphere (grapefruit)

4. Name another cylinder-shaped item that can be bought in a supermarket.

   Possible answers: Canned foods, roll of paper towels

5. The thermos is the most expensive item that she has purchased. It costs $3.50. The milk costs one half of this amount plus $0.06. How much does the milk cost?

   $\$3.50 \div 2 = \$1.75 + \$0.06 = \$1.81$

6. If her purchases amount to $22.85 and she gives the cashier two ten-dollar bills and one five-dollar bill, how much change should Jan receive?

   $2.15 (2 one-dollar bills, 1 dime and 1 nickel)

Use with pages 344–345. 95

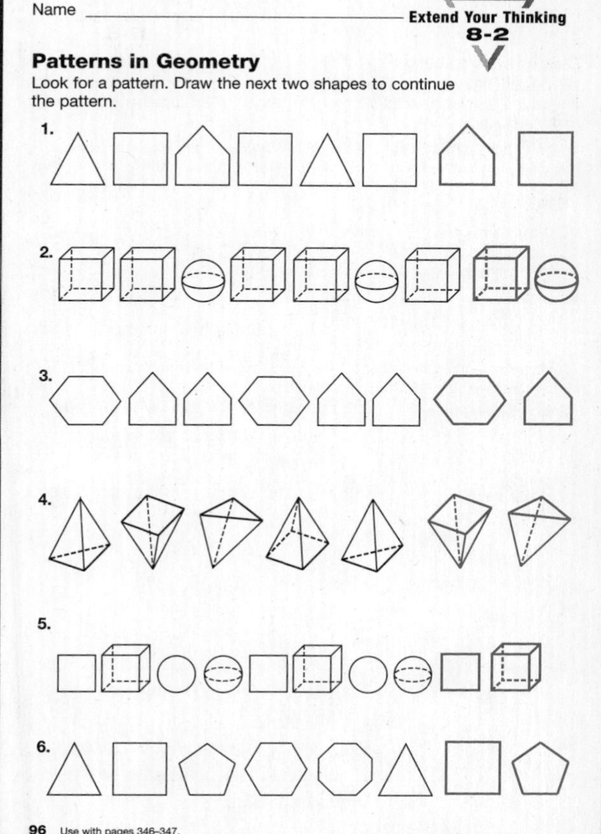

Name ______________________

Extend Your Thinking 8-2

Patterns in Geometry

Look for a pattern. Draw the next two shapes to continue the pattern.

1.

2.

3.

4.

5.

6.

96 Use with pages 346–347.

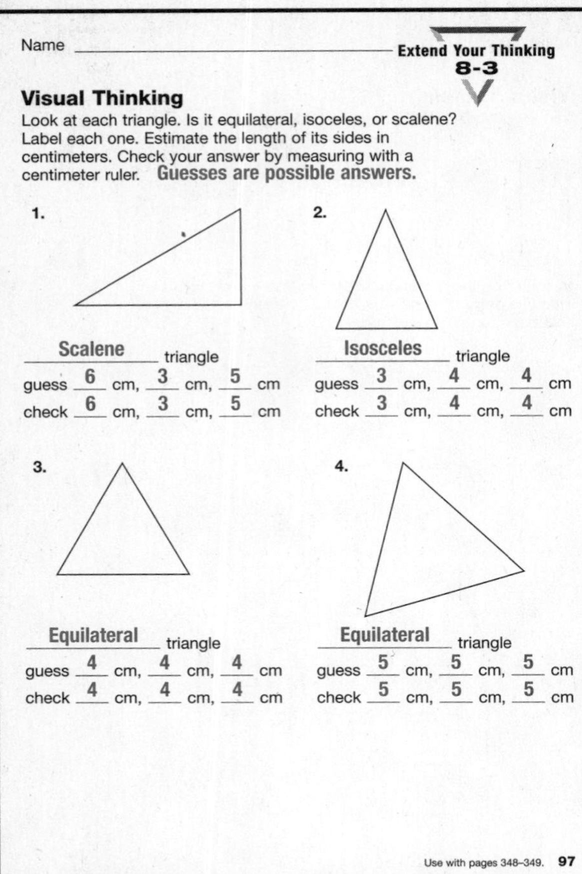

Name ______________________ **Extend Your Thinking 8-3**

Visual Thinking

Look at each triangle. Is it equilateral, isoceles, or scalene? Label each one. Estimate the length of its sides in centimeters. Check your answer by measuring with a centimeter ruler. **Guesses are possible answers.**

1. **Scalene** triangle
guess **6** cm, **3** cm, **5** cm
check **6** cm, **3** cm, **5** cm

2. **Isosceles** triangle
guess **3** cm, **4** cm, **4** cm
check **3** cm, **4** cm, **4** cm

3. **Equilateral** triangle
guess **4** cm, **4** cm, **4** cm
check **4** cm, **4** cm, **4** cm

4. **Equilateral** triangle
guess **5** cm, **5** cm, **5** cm
check **5** cm, **5** cm, **5** cm

Use with pages 348–349. 97

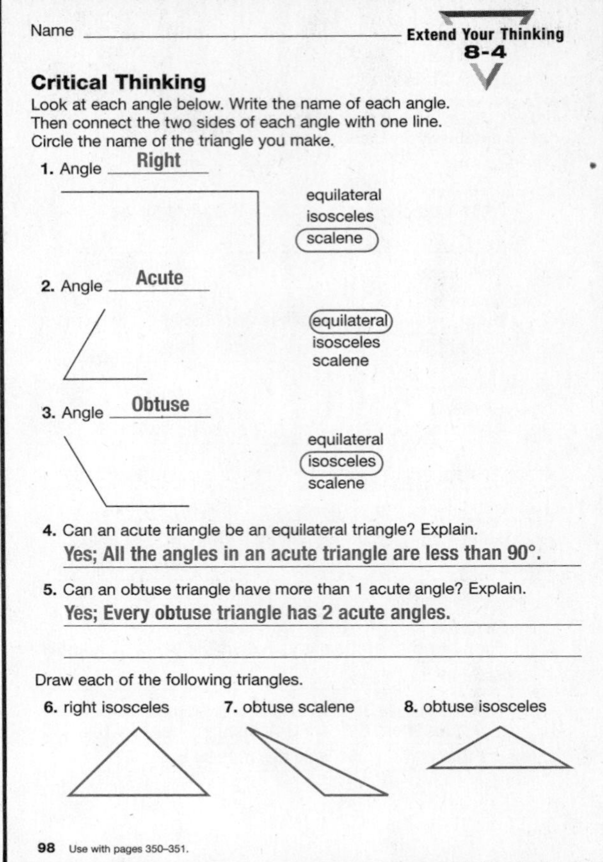

Name ______________________ **Extend Your Thinking 8-4**

Critical Thinking

Look at each angle below. Write the name of each angle. Then connect the two sides of each angle with one line. Circle the name of the triangle you make.

1. Angle **Right** — equilateral / isosceles / (scalene)
2. Angle **Acute** — (equilateral) / isosceles / scalene
3. Angle **Obtuse** — equilateral / (isosceles) / scalene
4. Can an acute triangle be an equilateral triangle? Explain.
Yes; All the angles in an acute triangle are less than 90°.
5. Can an obtuse triangle have more than 1 acute angle? Explain.
Yes; Every obtuse triangle has 2 acute angles.

Draw each of the following triangles.

6. right isosceles
7. obtuse scalene
8. obtuse isosceles

98 Use with pages 350–351.

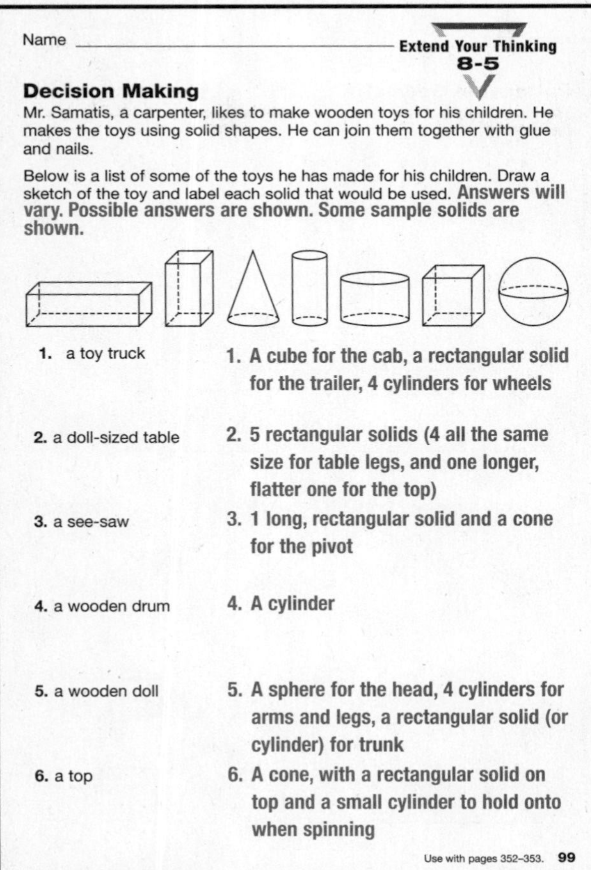

Name ______________________ **Extend Your Thinking 8-5**

Decision Making

Mr. Samatis, a carpenter, likes to make wooden toys for his children. He makes the toys using solid shapes. He can join them together with glue and nails.

Below is a list of some of the toys he has made for his children. Draw a sketch of the toy and label each solid that would be used. **Answers will vary. Possible answers are shown. Some sample solids are shown.**

1. a toy truck — **1. A cube for the cab, a rectangular solid for the trailer, 4 cylinders for wheels**
2. a doll-sized table — **2. 5 rectangular solids (4 all the same size for table legs, and one longer, flatter one for the top)**
3. a see-saw — **3. 1 long, rectangular solid and a cone for the pivot**
4. a wooden drum — **4. A cylinder**
5. a wooden doll — **5. A sphere for the head, 4 cylinders for arms and legs, a rectangular solid (or cylinder) for trunk**
6. a top — **6. A cone, with a rectangular solid on top and a small cylinder to hold onto when spinning**

Use with pages 352–353. 99

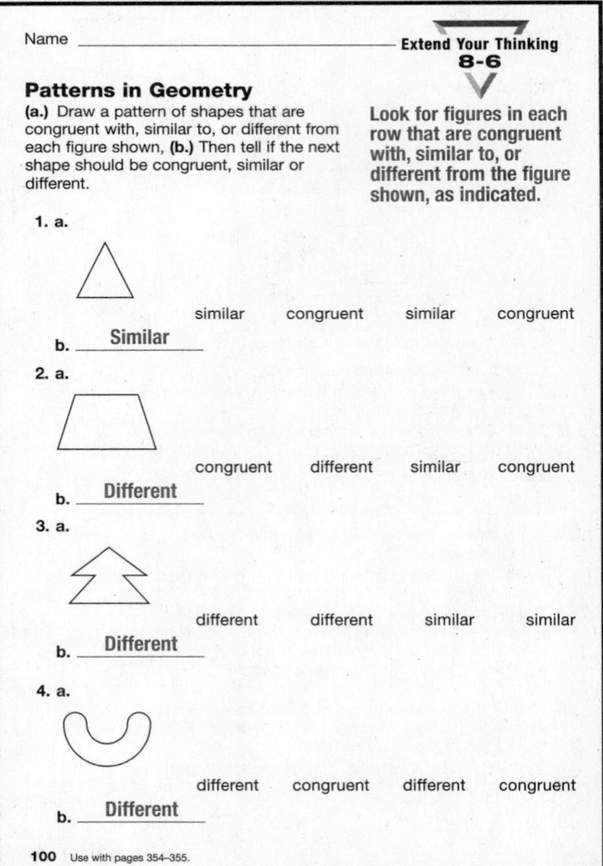

Name ______________________ **Extend Your Thinking 8-6**

Patterns in Geometry

(a.) Draw a pattern of shapes that are congruent with, similar to, or different from each figure shown, **(b.)** Then tell if the next shape should be congruent, similar or different.

Look for figures in each row that are congruent with, similar to, or different from the figure shown, as indicated.

1. a. similar congruent similar congruent
b. **Similar**
2. a. congruent different similar congruent
b. **Different**
3. a. different different similar similar
b. **Different**
4. a. different congruent different congruent
b. **Different**

100 Use with pages 354–355.

Name ______________________

Extend Your Thinking 8-7

Decision Making

There are 102 students in the science club. The club is trying to raise money for an overnight trip to Toronto, Canada, where they will visit a science center. They need to raise $500 for the trip. They have narrowed down their choices for ways to raise money.

Choice A: Hold a dance at school and charge $2.00 per ticket.

Choice B: Sell mail-order fruit baskets. Charge $5.00 per basket.

Choice C: Hold a raffle at school for a free trip to Toronto. Charge $1.00 per raffle ticket.

1. For Choice A, how many tickets to the dance will the club have to sell to meet their goal of raising $500? 250 tickets
2. For Choice B, how many baskets will the club need to sell to meet their goal? 100 baskets
3. For Choice C, how many raffle tickets will the club need to sell to raise $500? 500 raffle tickets
4. Write the advantages and disadvantages for each fundraising choice. Possible answers:

   Choice A: Advantage—a dance would be fun; disadvantage—they would need to advertise to get students to attend.

   Choice B: Advantage—they would only need to sell 100 baskets; disadvantage—baskets may be harder to sell.

   Choice C: Advantage—they could sell the raffle tickets at school; disadvantage—they need to sell 500 tickets.
5. What do you think is the best fundraising choice for the science club? Explain.

   Possible answer: The science club should choose Choice B because they need the least number of people to make purchases. They only need 100 people to buy something, as opposed to 250 people or 500 people.

Name ______________________

Extend Your Thinking 8-8

Visual Thinking

Circle the figure on the right that shows half of the figure on the left.

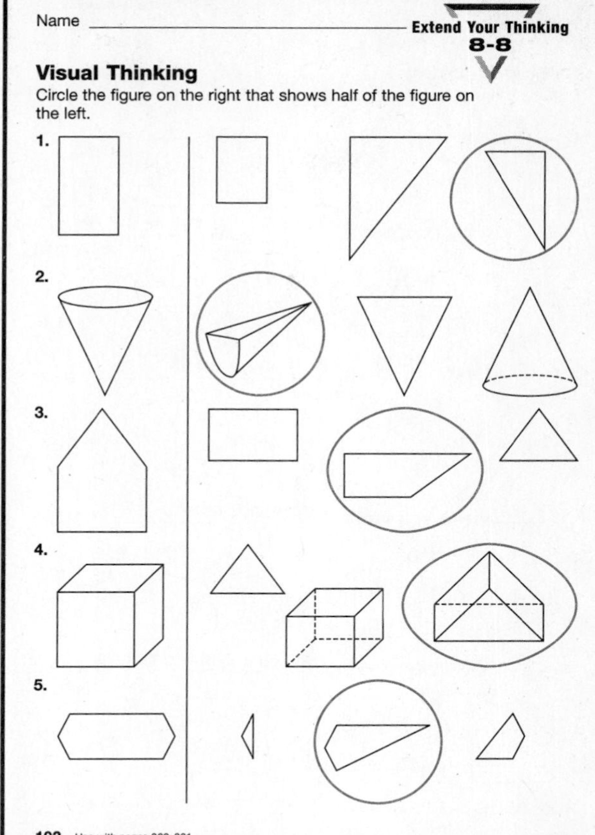

Name ______________________

Extend Your Thinking 8-9

Patterns in Algebra

Each shape represents a number. Write the number that each shape represents inside the shape.

1. (△ 3 × 3) + 7 = 16
2. (⬠ 5 × 5) + 11 = 36
3. (decagon 10 × 6) + 4 = 64
4. (octagon 8 × 7) + 3 = 59
5. (nonagon 9 × 4) + 18 = 54
6. (hexagon 6 × 8) + 9 = 57
7. Describe how you solved **1–6**.

   Possible answer: Guessed and checked the first few and then saw a pattern.
8. What do you notice about the number each shape represents?

   Each shape represents the number of its sides.

Solve by using the pattern you found in **8**.

9. (△ × 6) + 11 = 29
10. (□ × 6) + 11 = 35
11. (⬠ × 6) + 11 = 41
12. (hexagon × 6) + 11 = 47
13. (heptagon × 6) + 11 = 53
14. (octagon × 6) + 11 = 59

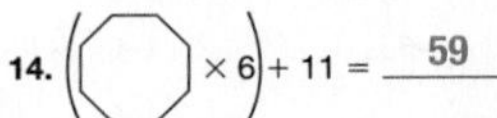

15. Describe the pattern you see in the answers for **9–14**.

    Each answer is 6 more than the previous answer.

Name ______________________

Extend Your Thinking 8-10

Decision Making

Nicky can have a pet rabbit if she pays for its food and takes care of it. Each week, she earns $3 mowing lawns and earns $5 baby sitting. She spends $4 each week on things for school.

Here is what the rabbit eats each week.

Apple Slices	Carrots	Pellets	Hay
2 days per week	4 days per week	every day	every day
50¢ per week	50¢ per week	75¢ per week	75¢ per week

1. How much does the rabbit's food cost per week? $2.50
2. Can Nicky afford the cost of the rabbit food? Explain.

   Yes; She earns $8 per week and has $4 left.
3. Every day Nicky must feed the rabbit, give it fresh water, and let it run outside. Every two days, she must change its litter. Nicky also does homework and chores, and takes gymnastics. She and her friends like to spend time together. Does she have enough money and time to care for the rabbit? Explain your reasoning.

   Possible answer: Caring for the rabbit can be done in about an hour a day. Nicky could do this at night and/or before she goes to school in the morning.
4. Do you think that Nicky should get the rabbit? Explain.

   Possible answer: Nicky can afford the rabbit. She should get it only if she is committed to taking the time to care for it.
5. If Nicky stopped mowing lawns to allow more time for school work, could she afford to have a rabbit? Explain.

   No; $5.00 − $4.00 = $1.00

Name ______________________ **Extend Your Thinking 8-11**

Critical Thinking

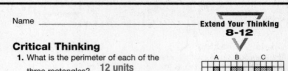

Find the shape that doesn't belong in the group.

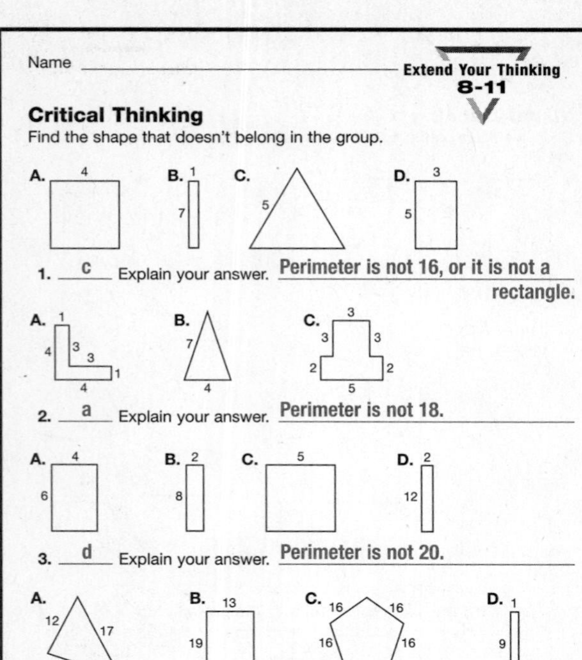

1. c Explain your answer. Perimeter is not 16, or it is not a rectangle.

2. a Explain your answer. Perimeter is not 18.

3. d Explain your answer. Perimeter is not 20.

4. a Explain your answer. Perimeter is an odd number.

5. c Explain your answer. Perimeter is not a multiple of 10.

Name ______________________ **Extend Your Thinking 8-12**

Critical Thinking

1. What is the perimeter of each of the three rectangles? 12 units
2. What are the areas of each rectangle? 5, 8, and 9 square units
3. a. Draw on grid paper all possible rectangles with a perimeter of 16 units. Give the dimensions of each.
   Possible answers: 1, 7; 2, 6; 3, 5; 4, 4
   b. Which of these rectangles has the smallest area? 1, 7
   c. Which has the greatest area? 4, 4
4. What conclusion can you make about the relationship between perimeter and area? Possible answer:
   The closer a shape is to a square, the greater the area.
5. a. A rectangle has a length of 13 cm and a width of 7 cm.
   b. Increase its width by 5 cm.
   c. Increase the length of rectangle **b** by 5 cm.
   d. Record your results and complete the table.

	Length	Width	Perimeter	Area	Change in Perimeter	Change in Area
a.	13 cm	7 cm	40 cm	91 cm²		
b.	13 cm	12 cm	50 cm	156 cm²	10 cm	65 cm²
c.	18 cm	12 cm	60 cm	216 cm²	10 cm	60 cm²

   e. What is the overall change in perimeter and area?
   Perimeter = 20 cm; area = 125 square cm²
   f. Why is the change in area so much greater than the change in perimeter?
   Possible answer: Numbers increase more quickly when they are multiplied than when they are added.

Name ______________________ **Extend Your Thinking 8-13**

Visual Thinking

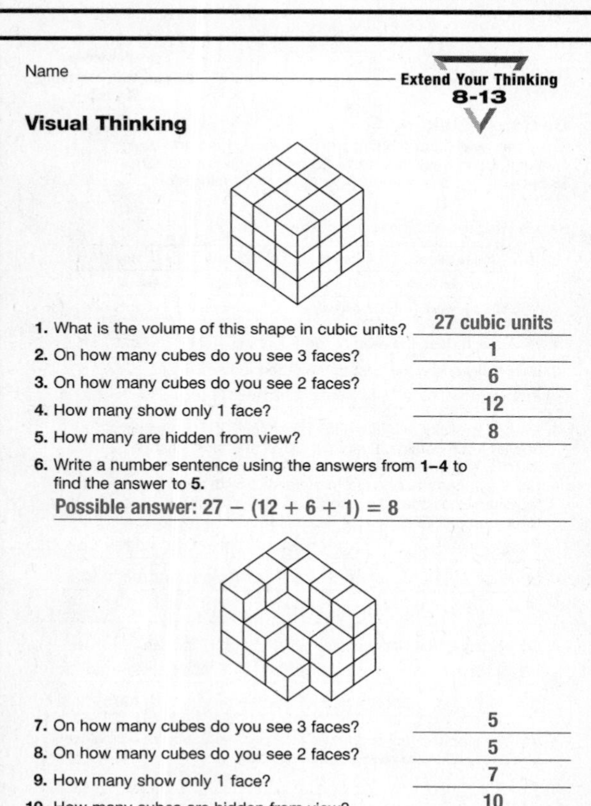

1. What is the volume of this shape in cubic units? 27 cubic units
2. On how many cubes do you see 3 faces? 1
3. On how many cubes do you see 2 faces? 6
4. How many show only 1 face? 12
5. How many are hidden from view? 8
6. Write a number sentence using the answers from **1–4** to find the answer to **5.**
   Possible answer: 27 − (12 + 6 + 1) = 8
7. On how many cubes do you see 3 faces? 5
8. On how many cubes do you see 2 faces? 5
9. How many show only 1 face? 7
10. How many cubes are hidden from view? 10
11. What is the volume of this shape in cubic units? 27 cubic units

Name ______________________ **Extend Your Thinking 8-14**

Decision Making

Suppose you are building a fence for a garden in your yard. Your yard is 50 ft wide and has an area of 500 square ft.

Your father has 88 ft of garden fencing, so your garden has to have a perimeter of 88 feet. How big an area would you set aside for your garden?

1. Suppose you made your garden 5 feet wide.
   a. What would its length be? 39 ft
   b. What would its area be? 195 square ft
   c. What would be the area of the leftover space in the yard? 305 square ft
2. Suppose you made your garden 10 feet wide.
   a. What would its length be? 34 ft
   b. What would its area be? 340 square ft
   c. What would be the area of the leftover space in the yard? 160 square ft
3. Suppose you made your garden 15 feet wide.
   a. What would its length be? 29 ft
   b. What would its area be? 435 square ft
   c. What would be the area of the leftover space in the yard? 65 square ft
4. Suppose you made your garden 22 feet wide.
   a. What would its length be? 22 ft
   b. What would its area be? 484 square ft
   c. What would be the area of the leftover space in the yard? 16 square ft
5. About how wide would you make your garden? Explain your reasoning.
   Possible answer: I would make my garden 5 feet by 39 feet so that I could have more room in my yard.

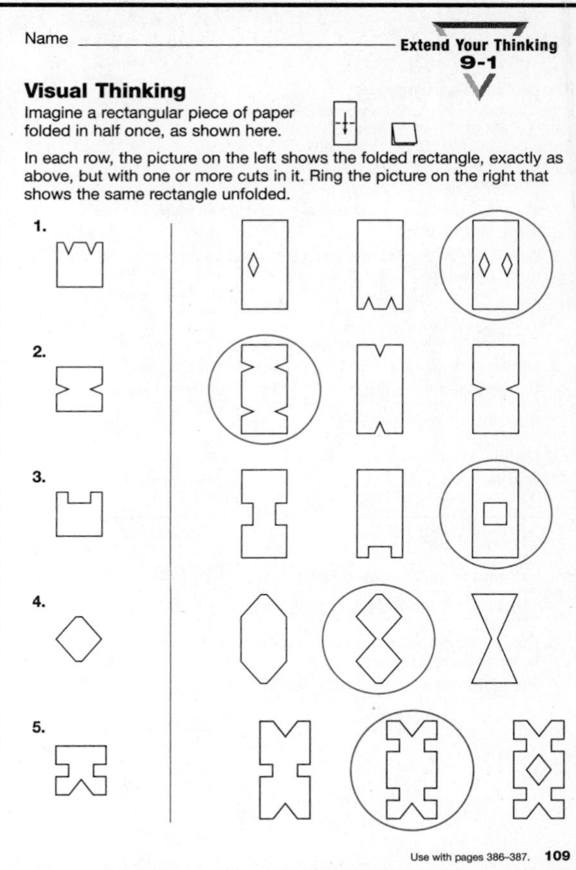

Name ______________________

Extend Your Thinking 9-1

Visual Thinking

Imagine a rectangular piece of paper folded in half once, as shown here.

In each row, the picture on the left shows the folded rectangle, exactly as above, but with one or more cuts in it. Ring the picture on the right that shows the same rectangle unfolded.

1.

2.

3.

4.

5.

Use with pages 386–387. 109

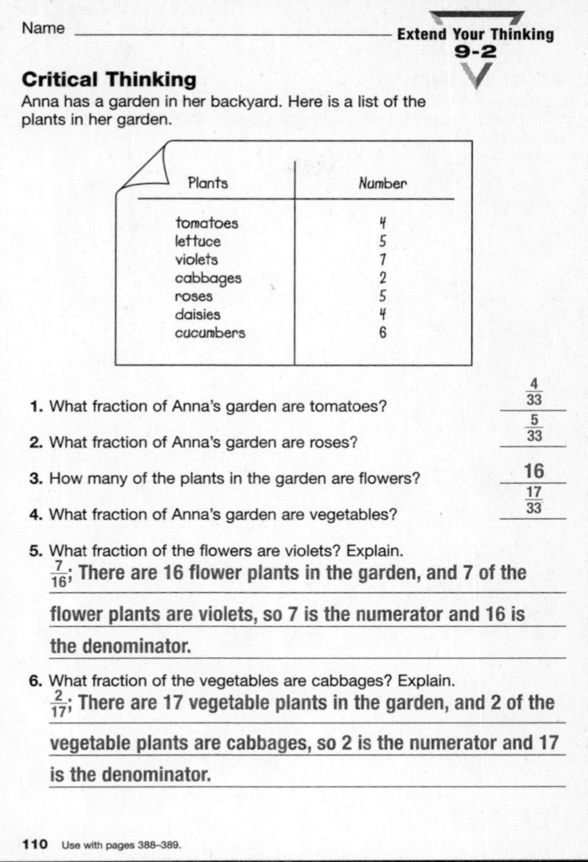

Name ______________________

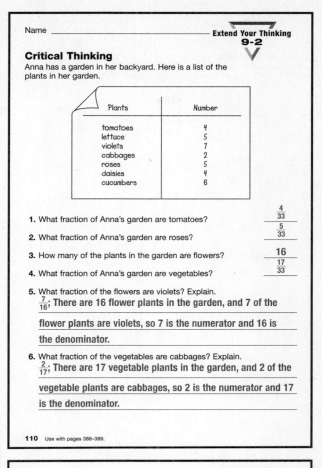

Extend Your Thinking 9-2

Critical Thinking

Anna has a garden in her backyard. Here is a list of the plants in her garden.

Plants	Number
tomatoes	4
lettuce	5
violets	7
cabbages	2
roses	5
daisies	4
cucumbers	6

1. What fraction of Anna's garden are tomatoes? $\frac{4}{33}$
2. What fraction of Anna's garden are roses? $\frac{5}{33}$
3. How many of the plants in the garden are flowers? 16
4. What fraction of Anna's garden are vegetables? $\frac{17}{33}$
5. What fraction of the flowers are violets? Explain.
   $\frac{7}{16}$; There are 16 flower plants in the garden, and 7 of the flower plants are violets, so 7 is the numerator and 16 is the denominator.
6. What fraction of the vegetables are cabbages? Explain.
   $\frac{2}{17}$; There are 17 vegetable plants in the garden, and 2 of the vegetable plants are cabbages, so 2 is the numerator and 17 is the denominator.

110 Use with pages 388–389.

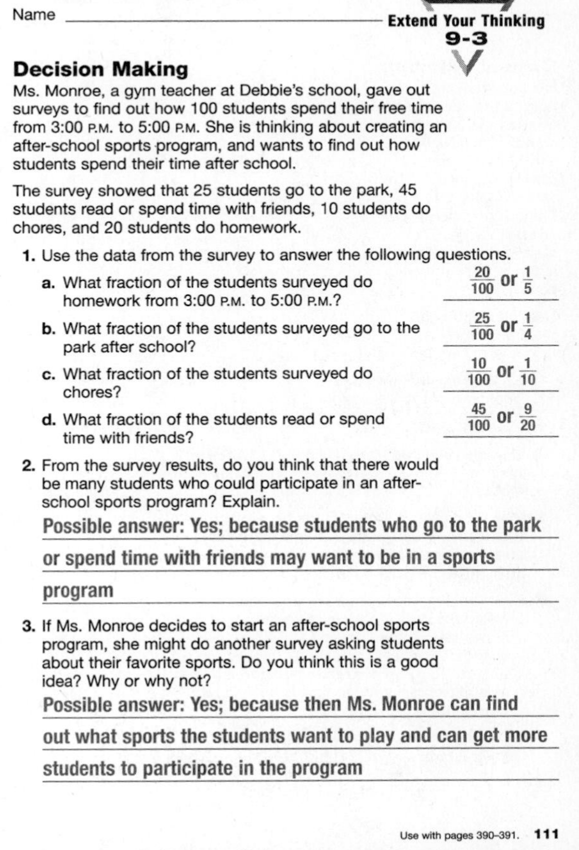

Name ______________________

Extend Your Thinking 9-3

Decision Making

Ms. Monroe, a gym teacher at Debbie's school, gave out surveys to find out how 100 students spend their free time from 3:00 P.M. to 5:00 P.M. She is thinking about creating an after-school sports program, and wants to find out how students spend their time after school.

The survey showed that 25 students go to the park, 45 students read or spend time with friends, 10 students do chores, and 20 students do homework.

1. Use the data from the survey to answer the following questions.
   a. What fraction of the students surveyed do homework from 3:00 P.M. to 5:00 P.M.? $\frac{20}{100}$ or $\frac{1}{5}$
   b. What fraction of the students surveyed go to the park after school? $\frac{25}{100}$ or $\frac{1}{4}$
   c. What fraction of the students surveyed do chores? $\frac{10}{100}$ or $\frac{1}{10}$
   d. What fraction of the students read or spend time with friends? $\frac{45}{100}$ or $\frac{9}{20}$
2. From the survey results, do you think that there would be many students who could participate in an after-school sports program? Explain.
   Possible answer: Yes; because students who go to the park or spend time with friends may want to be in a sports program
3. If Ms. Monroe decides to start an after-school sports program, she might do another survey asking students about their favorite sports. Do you think this is a good idea? Why or why not?
   Possible answer: Yes; because then Ms. Monroe can find out what sports the students want to play and can get more students to participate in the program

Use with pages 390–391. 111

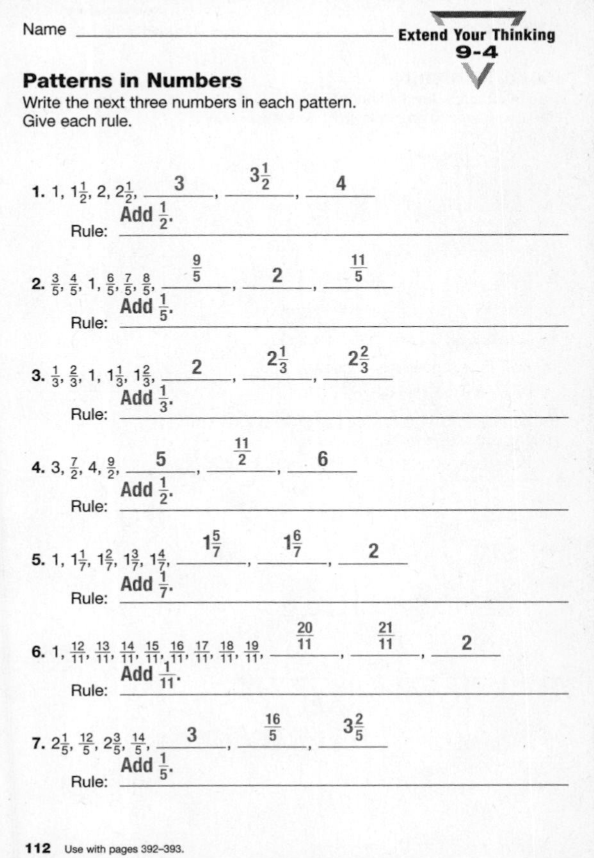

Name ______________________

Extend Your Thinking 9-4

Patterns in Numbers

Write the next three numbers in each pattern. Give each rule.

1. $1, 1\frac{1}{2}, 2, 2\frac{1}{2}$, 3, $3\frac{1}{2}$, 4
   Rule: Add $\frac{1}{2}$.
2. $\frac{3}{5}, \frac{4}{5}, 1, \frac{6}{5}, \frac{7}{5}, \frac{8}{5}$, $\frac{9}{5}$, 2, $\frac{11}{5}$
   Rule: Add $\frac{1}{5}$.
3. $\frac{1}{3}, \frac{2}{3}, 1, 1\frac{1}{3}, 1\frac{2}{3}$, 2, $2\frac{1}{3}$, $2\frac{2}{3}$
   Rule: Add $\frac{1}{3}$.
4. $3, \frac{7}{2}, 4, \frac{9}{2}$, 5, $\frac{11}{2}$, 6
   Rule: Add $\frac{1}{2}$.
5. $1, 1\frac{1}{7}, 1\frac{2}{7}, 1\frac{3}{7}, 1\frac{4}{7}$, $1\frac{5}{7}$, $1\frac{6}{7}$, 2
   Rule: Add $\frac{1}{7}$.
6. $1, \frac{12}{11}, \frac{13}{11}, \frac{14}{11}, \frac{15}{11}, \frac{16}{11}, \frac{17}{11}, \frac{18}{11}, \frac{19}{11}$, $\frac{20}{11}$, $\frac{21}{11}$, 2
   Rule: Add $\frac{1}{11}$.
7. $2\frac{1}{5}, \frac{12}{5}, 2\frac{3}{5}, \frac{14}{5}$, 3, $\frac{16}{5}$, $3\frac{2}{5}$
   Rule: Add $\frac{1}{5}$.

112 Use with pages 392–393.

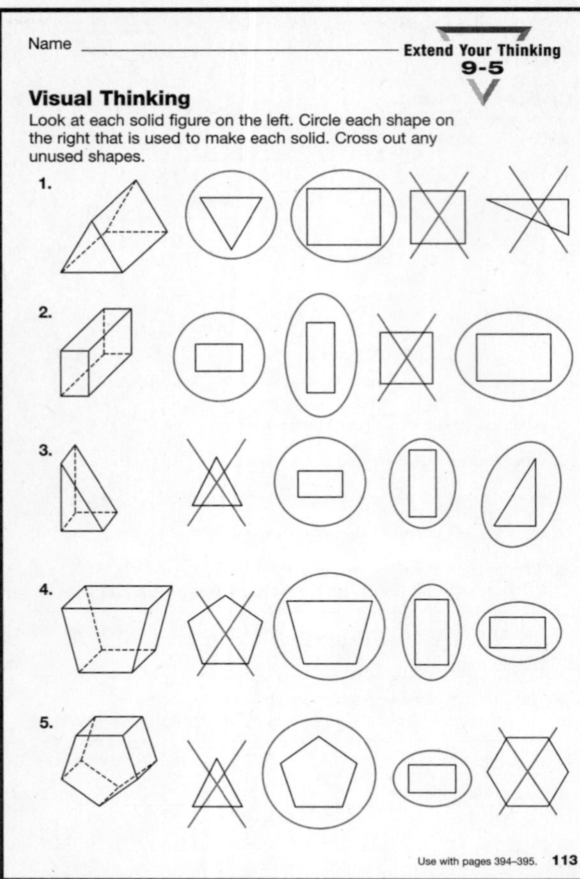
Name ______________________ **Extend Your Thinking 9-5**

Visual Thinking

Look at each solid figure on the left. Circle each shape on the right that is used to make each solid. Cross out any unused shapes.

1.

2.

3.

4.

5.

Use with pages 394–395. **113**

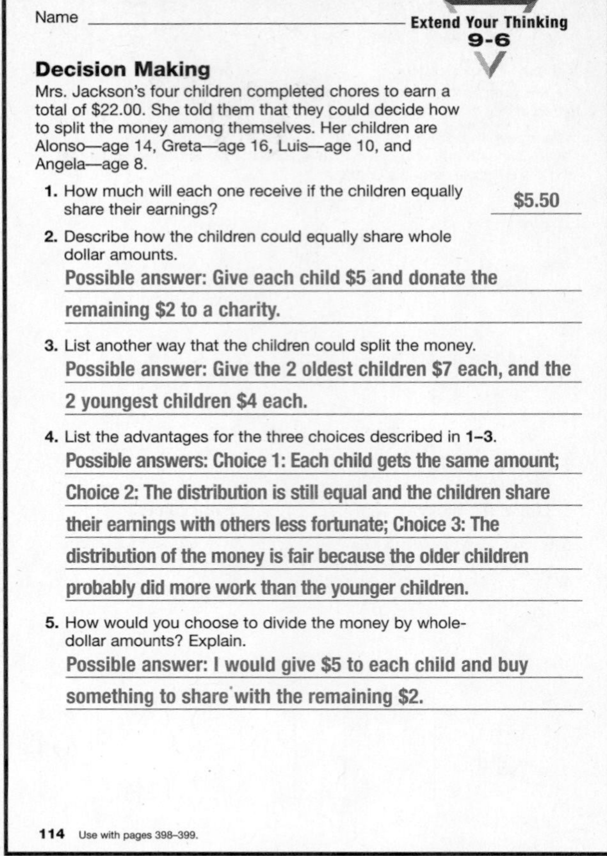
Name ______________________ **Extend Your Thinking 9-6**

Decision Making

Mrs. Jackson's four children completed chores to earn a total of $22.00. She told them that they could decide how to split the money among themselves. Her children are Alonso—age 14, Greta—age 16, Luis—age 10, and Angela—age 8.

1. How much will each one receive if the children equally share their earnings? **$5.50**
2. Describe how the children could equally share whole dollar amounts.
   Possible answer: Give each child $5 and donate the remaining $2 to a charity.
3. List another way that the children could split the money.
   Possible answer: Give the 2 oldest children $7 each, and the 2 youngest children $4 each.
4. List the advantages for the three choices described in **1–3**.
   Possible answers: Choice 1: Each child gets the same amount; Choice 2: The distribution is still equal and the children share their earnings with others less fortunate; Choice 3: The distribution of the money is fair because the older children probably did more work than the younger children.
5. How would you choose to divide the money by whole-dollar amounts? Explain.
   Possible answer: I would give $5 to each child and buy something to share with the remaining $2.

114 Use with pages 398–399.

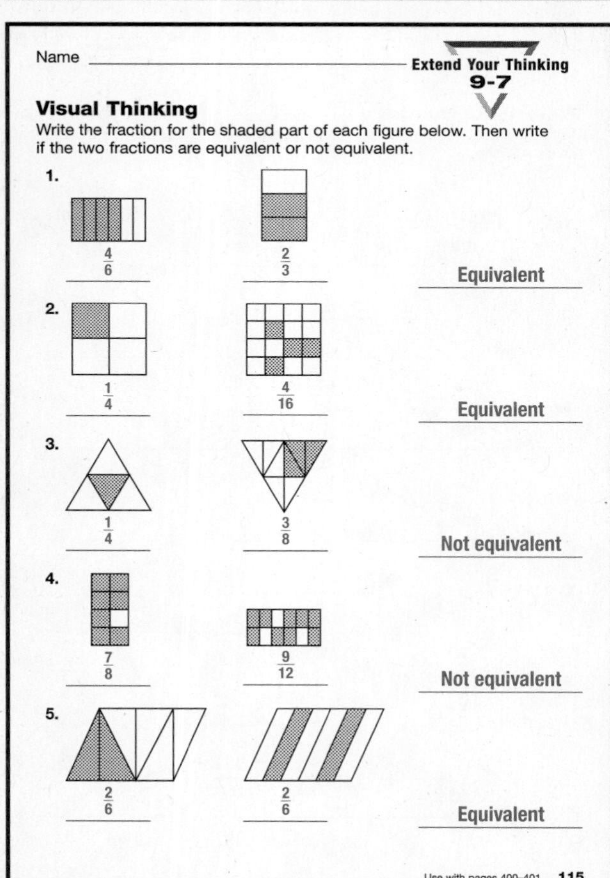
Name ______________________ **Extend Your Thinking 9-7**

Visual Thinking

Write the fraction for the shaded part of each figure below. Then write if the two fractions are equivalent or not equivalent.

	First figure	Second figure	
1.	$\frac{4}{6}$	$\frac{2}{3}$	**Equivalent**
2.	$\frac{1}{4}$	$\frac{4}{16}$	**Equivalent**
3.	$\frac{1}{4}$	$\frac{3}{8}$	**Not equivalent**
4.	$\frac{7}{8}$	$\frac{9}{12}$	**Not equivalent**
5.	$\frac{2}{6}$	$\frac{2}{6}$	**Equivalent**

Use with pages 400–401. **115**

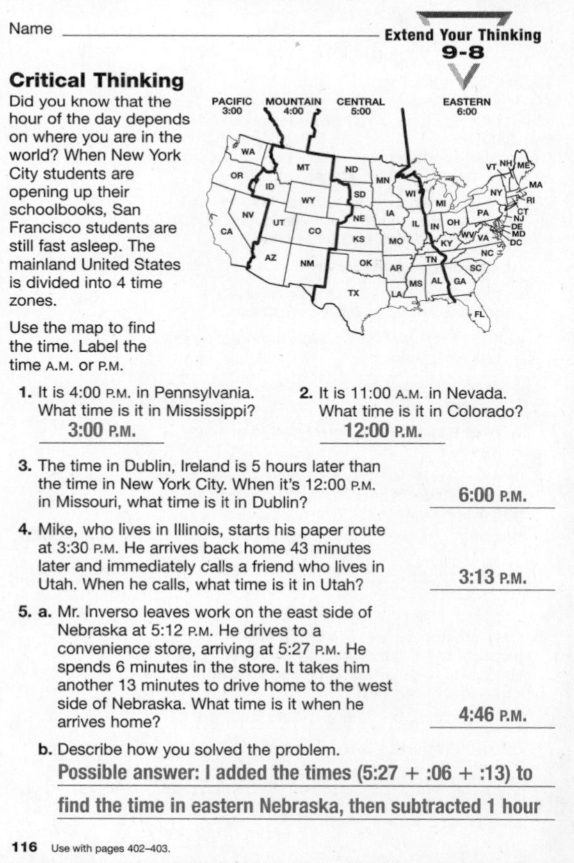
Name ______________________ **Extend Your Thinking 9-8**

Critical Thinking

Did you know that the hour of the day depends on where you are in the world? When New York City students are opening up their schoolbooks, San Francisco students are still fast asleep. The mainland United States is divided into 4 time zones.

Use the map to find the time. Label the time A.M. or P.M.

1. It is 4:00 P.M. in Pennsylvania. What time is it in Mississippi? **3:00 P.M.**
2. It is 11:00 A.M. in Nevada. What time is it in Colorado? **12:00 P.M.**
3. The time in Dublin, Ireland is 5 hours later than the time in New York City. When it's 12:00 P.M. in Missouri, what time is it in Dublin? **6:00 P.M.**
4. Mike, who lives in Illinois, starts his paper route at 3:30 P.M. He arrives back home 43 minutes later and immediately calls a friend who lives in Utah. When he calls, what time is it in Utah? **3:13 P.M.**
5. a. Mr. Inverso leaves work on the east side of Nebraska at 5:12 P.M. He drives to a convenience store, arriving at 5:27 P.M. He spends 6 minutes in the store. It takes him another 13 minutes to drive home to the west side of Nebraska. What time is it when he arrives home? **4:46 P.M.**
   b. Describe how you solved the problem.
   Possible answer: I added the times (5:27 + :06 + :13) to find the time in eastern Nebraska, then subtracted 1 hour

116 Use with pages 402–403.

Name ______________________________ **Extend Your Thinking 9-9**

Decision Making

Make some gifts! Fifi's Fabric Shop has fabric for simple projects like making dinner napkins or pillow covers.

Amount of fabric	Cotton prints 45 in. wide $5.95 per yard	Linen solids 60 in. wide $12.95 per yard
$\frac{7}{8}$ yard	Enough for 6 napkins or 3 pillow covers	Enough for 8 napkins or 4 pillow covers
$\frac{1}{2}$ yard	Enough for 3 napkins or $1\frac{1}{2}$ pillow covers	Enough for 4 napkins or 2 pillow covers

A pillow cover has two separate pieces of the same size that are sewn together.

1. a. Which fabric costs more per yard? **Linen**
   b. How much more? **$7 more per yard**
2. Suppose you want to make solid blue napkins. Which fabric should you choose? Why?
   Linen; It's the only one that comes in solid colors.
3. a. You want to make 4 pillow covers, each with one solid pink side and one flowered side. What fabric should you buy?
   $\frac{1}{2}$ yard of linen; $\frac{7}{8}$ yard of cotton
   b. Will there be enough leftover fabric to make another pillow cover? If so, what kind of pillow cover would it be?
   Yes; Cotton print on both sides
4. Suppose you have $15 to buy fabric.
   a. What fabric will you buy? ____________
   b. What will you make?
   a.–c. Answers will vary.
   c. How much of it will you need? ____________

Name ______________________________ **Extend Your Thinking 9-10**

Visual Thinking

These shapes have been made by joining together letters of the alphabet. All of the letters are upper-case. Some of the letters may have been flipped. Write the two letters which have been joined.

1. **A and T**
2. **Y and U**
3. **V and A**
4. **N and D**

You can solve messages in code by drawing the missing half of each letter. Decode these words.

5. **WAIT**
6. **HOME**
7. **CODE**

Name ______________________________ **Extend Your Thinking 9-11**

Decision Making

The community bulletin board has ads for two jobs that are available right now.

	Baby Sitting	Yard Work
Duties	Make sure children are safe. Feed dinner to children. Do dishes. Entertain children. Put children to bed.	Mow and weed lawn. Trim bushes. Do edging around sidewalks. Rake leaves. Add yard waste to compost heap. Shovel snow in winter.
Hours	Fridays & Saturdays 6:00 P.M.–10:30 P.M.	Saturdays 10:00 A.M.–3:00 P.M.
Pay	$5.25 per hour	$7.50 per hour

1. a. Which job pays more per hour? **Yard Work**
   b. How much more? **$2.25 per hour**
2. a. Which job pays more per week? **Baby Sitting**
   b. How much more? **$9.75 per week**
3. Which job would allow you to read or do homework and still get paid for your time? **Baby Sitting**
4. Why might someone choose baby sitting? **Possible answer: Likes children, doesn't like yard work, wants to keep Saturday afternoons free, needs the extra $9.75 per week**
5. Why might someone choose yard work?
   Possible answer: Likes to work outdoors, wants to keep Friday and Saturday nights free
6. Make a decision. Which job will you choose? Explain your reasoning.
   Answers will vary. Look for consideration of hours, duties, and pay.

Name ______________________________ **Extend Your Thinking 9-12**

Visual Thinking

Draw the next shape in the sequence.

Look for patterns.

1. 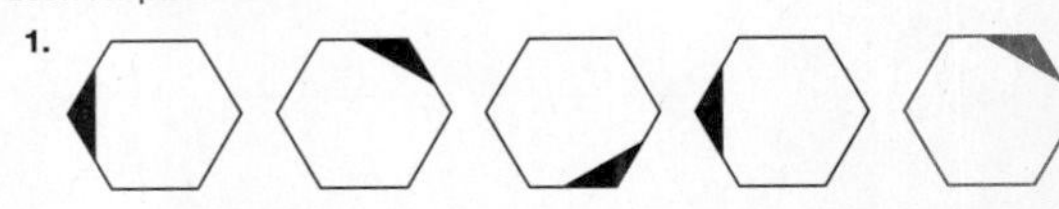
2. 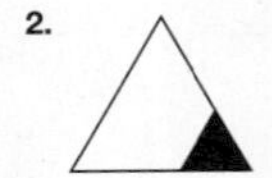   
3. 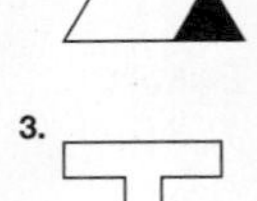  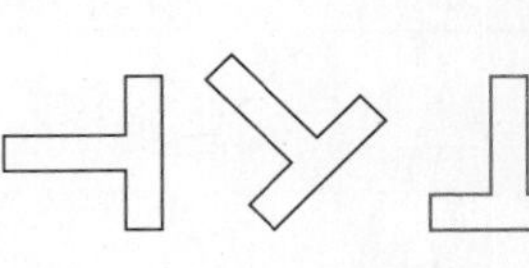
4. 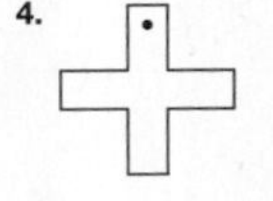 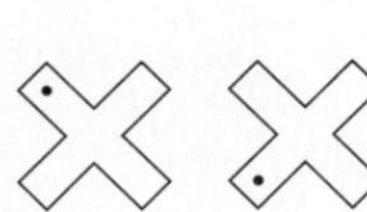 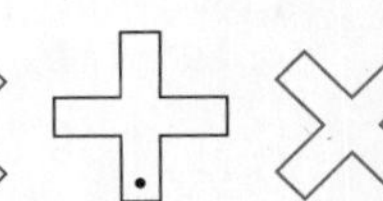
5.  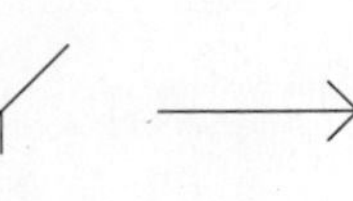 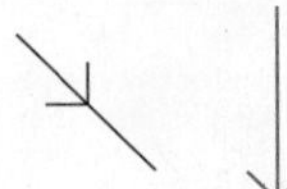

Name ______________________

Extend Your Thinking 9-13

Critical Thinking

Choose a method to solve these problems about feet, yards, and miles.

1. The Boston Marathon race takes place in the streets of greater Boston every spring and covers a distance of 26 miles 385 yards. When it was first run in 1897, the course covered a distance of 24 miles 1,232 yards. How much farther do participants have to run today than in 1897? Explain how you found the solution.
   1 mile 913 yd; subtract 24 miles 1,232 yd from 26 miles 385 yd, change 26 miles to 25 miles 1,760 yd, 1,760 yd + 385 yd = 2,145; 25 miles 2,145 yd − 24 miles 1,232 yd = 1 mile 913 yd.

2. The world record for stacking dominoes is held by Aleksandr Bendikov of Belarus, who stacked 522 dominoes on a single supporting domino. The dominoes were stacked flat, one on top of another. If 4 dominoes equals 1 inch, and about how many feet high was the stack? Explain how you found your solution.
   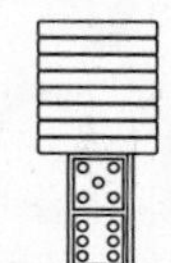
   About 11 ft; 4 dominoes = 1 in., so 522 ÷ 4 = about 130 in., 130 ÷ 12 = about 11 ft

3. The staircase in the Empire State Building in New York City has 1,575 steps. If each step is 8 inches tall, how many feet would you climb if you walked up the staircase? Explain your method of solving the problem.
   1,050 ft; 1,575 × 8 = 12,600 in., 12,600 ÷ 12 = 1,050 ft

Name ______________________

Extend Your Thinking 9-14

Patterns in Numbers

Marco is planning a two-week summer vacation trip to San Antonio. He wants to save $160 for the trip. He has exactly 10 weeks before he leaves for Texas. He wants to save $1 the first week, $3 more the second week, $6 more the third week, $10 more the fourth week, and so on, continuing this pattern.

1. What is the total amount of money Marco will have in the first week? **$1** the second week? **$4** the third week? **$10**
2. How much money does Marco want to save? **$160**
3. What is the total amount of money Marco will have after 5 weeks? **$35**
4. Continue this pattern to show how much Marco will save each week for 10 weeks.
   1, 3, 6, 10, **15**, **21**, **28**, **36**, **45**, **55**
5. Describe this pattern.
   Add 2, add 3, add 4, add 5 and so on.
6. Complete this table using Marco's saving pattern.

Week	1	2	3	4	5	6	7	8	9	10
Amount saved	$1	$3	$6	$10	**$15**	**$21**	**$28**	$36	$45	$55
Total savings	$1	$4	**$10**	**$20**	**$35**	**$56**	**$84**	**$120**	**$165**	**$220**

7. How much money will he have saved after the 10 weeks? **$220**
8. How much over or under the total amount that he wanted to save will Marco save in 10 weeks? **$60 over**

Solve. Make a table to help.

9. Marco's brother Paul wants to save $80 in 6 weeks. He saves nothing the first week, $2 the second, $6 the third, $12 the fourth and so on. If he continues this pattern, will he have reached his goal after the sixth week?
   No; he will only have $70.

Name ______________________

Extend Your Thinking 10-1

Patterns in Numbers

Write the next two numbers to continue the pattern. Then write the rule.

1. $\frac{1}{9}, \frac{2}{9}, \frac{3}{9}, \frac{4}{9}$, **$\frac{5}{9}$**, **$\frac{6}{9}$**
   Rule: **Add $\frac{1}{9}$.**
2. $\frac{11}{12}, \frac{5}{6}, \frac{3}{4}, \frac{2}{3}$, **$\frac{7}{12}$**, **$\frac{1}{2}$**
   Rule: **Subtract $\frac{1}{12}$.**
3. $\frac{2}{15}, \frac{4}{15}, \frac{2}{5}, \frac{8}{15}$, **$\frac{2}{3}$**, **$\frac{4}{5}$**
   Rule: **Add $\frac{2}{15}$.**
4. $\frac{15}{16}, \frac{13}{16}, \frac{11}{16}, \frac{9}{16}$, **$\frac{7}{16}$**, **$\frac{5}{16}$**
   Rule: **Subtract $\frac{2}{16}$ or $\frac{1}{8}$.**
5. $\frac{1}{2}, \frac{1}{2}, \frac{1}{3}, \frac{1}{3}, \frac{1}{3}, \frac{1}{4}, \frac{1}{4}$, **$\frac{1}{4}$**, **$\frac{1}{4}$**
   Rule: **two $\frac{1}{2}$'s, three $\frac{1}{3}$'s, four $\frac{1}{4}$'s, and so on**
6. 0, $\frac{1}{24}, \frac{1}{8}, \frac{1}{4}$, **$\frac{5}{12}$**, **$\frac{5}{8}$**
   Rule: **Add $\frac{1}{24}, \frac{2}{24}, \frac{3}{24}$, and so on.**

Make up your own number patterns with fractions. Leave some blank spaces. Give them to a classmate to solve.

7. ______, ______, ______, ______, ______
8. ______, ______, ______, ______, ______

Check students' patterns.

Name ______________________

Extend Your Thinking 10-2

Visual Thinking

Look at each figure on the left. Then circle the fractional piece on the right that would complete the circle.

1.

2.

3.

4.

5.

6.

Name ______________________ **Extend Your Thinking 10-3**

Visual Thinking

Add each pair of fractions. Then circle the shape that best represents the answer.

1. $\frac{1}{3} + \frac{1}{3} =$ $\frac{2}{3}$

2. $\frac{5}{6} + \frac{1}{6} =$ $\frac{6}{6}$ or 1

3. $\frac{1}{12} + \frac{1}{6} =$ $\frac{3}{12}$ or $\frac{1}{4}$

4. $\frac{1}{5} + \frac{3}{10} =$ $\frac{5}{10}$ or $\frac{1}{2}$

5. $\frac{3}{8} + \frac{1}{4} =$ $\frac{5}{8}$

Name ______________________ **Extend Your Thinking 10-4**

Critical Thinking

A group of 4th grade students were studying the state of Missouri. They took a survey to find out how many classmates had ever visited Kansas City or St. Louis.

Here is what they found out:

- $\frac{1}{2}$ of the class had been to St. Louis but not Kansas City.
- $\frac{1}{6}$ of the class had been to Kansas City but not St. Louis.
- $\frac{1}{4}$ of the class had been to neither city.
- $\frac{1}{12}$ of the class had been to both cities.

Use patterns to complete the table. Then use it to answer the questions.

Part of the Class	Number of Students in the Class			
	12	24	36	48
$\frac{1}{12}$	1	2	3	4
$\frac{2}{12}$	2	4	6	8
$\frac{3}{12}$	3	6	9	12
$\frac{4}{12}$	4	8	12	16
$\frac{5}{12}$	5	10	15	20
$\frac{6}{12}$	6	12	18	24
$\frac{7}{12}$	7	14	21	28
$\frac{8}{12}$	8	16	24	32
$\frac{9}{12}$	9	18	27	36
$\frac{10}{12}$	10	20	30	40
$\frac{11}{12}$	11	22	33	44
$\frac{12}{12}$	12	24	36	48

1. If there are 24 students in the class, how many have been to neither city? **6**
2. If 4 students have been to both cities, how many students are in the class? **48**
3. If 6 students have been to neither city, how many students have been to both cities? **2**

Name ______________________ **Extend Your Thinking 10-5**

Decision Making

Today is Saturday. The roller-skating rink is open from 9:00 A.M. to 9:00 P.M.! You have a party to go to at 3:30 P.M., but there's time to fit in some skating before you go.

Full day	$6.00
6 hours	$4.00
3 hours	$3.00
2 hours	$2.00

1. Zeke and Kye want to skate from 9:00 A.M. to noon, take a lunch break for an hour, and then skate until 3:00 P.M. Should each buy a full-day ticket or separate tickets for the morning and the afternoon? Explain.
   A full-day ticket costs $6. The 2 tickets would cost only $5.
2. Suppose you have $4.00 to spend, Zeke has $2.00, and Kye has $3.00.
   a. How much more time could you skate than Zeke? **4 hours**
   b. How much more time could you skate than Kye? **3 hours**
   c. If you pooled your money, could you all skate for the same amount of time? Explain.
   Yes, for 3 hours each
3. If you went skating at 12:00 noon and paid $3.00, would you have enough time to get to the party if it is a 15-minute walk away? Explain.
   Yes; You would finish skating at 3:00.
4. Which hours would you choose to skate? How much would it cost?
   Check students' answers.

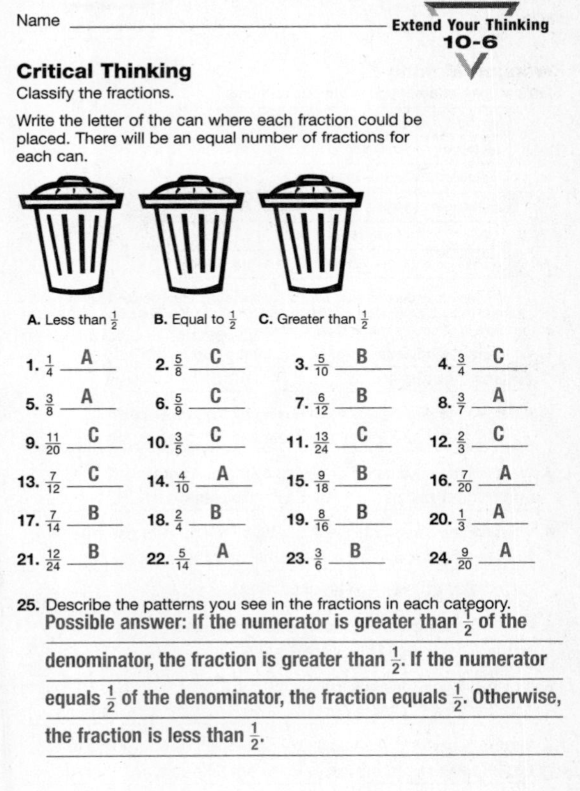

Name ______________________ **Extend Your Thinking 10-6**

Critical Thinking

Classify the fractions.

Write the letter of the can where each fraction could be placed. There will be an equal number of fractions for each can.

A. Less than $\frac{1}{2}$ **B.** Equal to $\frac{1}{2}$ **C.** Greater than $\frac{1}{2}$

1. $\frac{1}{4}$ **A**	2. $\frac{5}{8}$ **C**	3. $\frac{5}{10}$ **B**	4. $\frac{3}{4}$ **C**
5. $\frac{3}{8}$ **A**	6. $\frac{5}{9}$ **C**	7. $\frac{6}{12}$ **B**	8. $\frac{3}{7}$ **A**
9. $\frac{11}{20}$ **C**	10. $\frac{3}{5}$ **C**	11. $\frac{13}{24}$ **C**	12. $\frac{2}{3}$ **C**
13. $\frac{7}{12}$ **C**	14. $\frac{4}{10}$ **A**	15. $\frac{9}{18}$ **B**	16. $\frac{7}{20}$ **A**
17. $\frac{7}{14}$ **B**	18. $\frac{2}{4}$ **B**	19. $\frac{8}{16}$ **B**	20. $\frac{1}{3}$ **A**
21. $\frac{12}{24}$ **B**	22. $\frac{5}{14}$ **A**	23. $\frac{3}{6}$ **B**	24. $\frac{9}{20}$ **A**

25. Describe the patterns you see in the fractions in each category.
    Possible answer: If the numerator is greater than $\frac{1}{2}$ of the denominator, the fraction is greater than $\frac{1}{2}$. If the numerator equals $\frac{1}{2}$ of the denominator, the fraction equals $\frac{1}{2}$. Otherwise, the fraction is less than $\frac{1}{2}$.

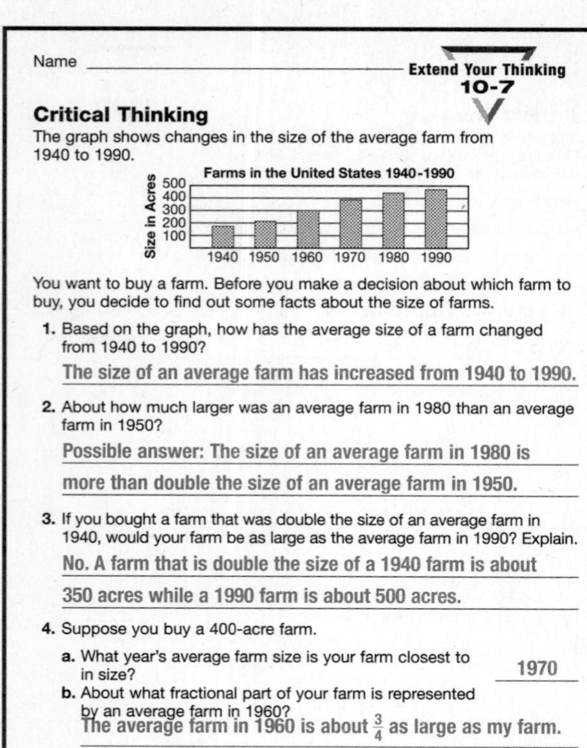

Name ________________ **Extend Your Thinking 10-7**

Critical Thinking

The graph shows changes in the size of the average farm from 1940 to 1990.

You want to buy a farm. Before you make a decision about which farm to buy, you decide to find out some facts about the size of farms.

1. Based on the graph, how has the average size of a farm changed from 1940 to 1990?
   The size of an average farm has increased from 1940 to 1990.
2. About how much larger was an average farm in 1980 than an average farm in 1950?
   Possible answer: The size of an average farm in 1980 is more than double the size of an average farm in 1950.
3. If you bought a farm that was double the size of an average farm in 1940, would your farm be as large as the average farm in 1990? Explain.
   No. A farm that is double the size of a 1940 farm is about 350 acres while a 1990 farm is about 500 acres.
4. Suppose you buy a 400-acre farm.
   a. What year's average farm size is your farm closest to in size? 1970
   b. About what fractional part of your farm is represented by an average farm in 1960?
   The average farm in 1960 is about $\frac{3}{4}$ as large as my farm.
   c. Predict how the size of an average farm in the year 2000 will compare to the size of your farm. Give reasons for your prediction.
   It is likely that my farm will be smaller than an average farm in 2000. This is because the chart shows farms getting larger.

Use with pages 452–453. 129

Name ________________ **Extend Your Thinking 10-8**

Patterns in Numbers

Follow the pattern to find the next three weights. Tell what rule was used to make the pattern.

1. 75 oz, 69 oz, 63 oz, 57 oz, 51 oz, 45 oz, 39 oz
   Rule: Subtract 6 oz.
2. 5 oz, 21 oz, 37 oz, 53 oz, 69 oz, 85 oz, 101 oz
   Rule: Add 1 lb or 16 oz.
3. 8 lb; 2 T 20 lb, 4 T 32 lb, 6 T 44 lb, 8 T 56 lb, 10 T 68 lb, 12 T 80 lb
   Rule: Add 2 T 12 lb or 4,012 lb.
4. 8 T 1,300 lb; 7 T 1,800; 7 T 300 lb; 6 T 800 lb;
   5 T 1,300 lb, 4 T 1,800 lb, 4 T 300 lb
   Rule: Subtract 1,500 lb.
5. 13 oz, 2 lb 5 oz, 3 lb 13 oz, 5 lb 5 oz
   6 lb 13 oz, 8 lb 5 oz, 9 lb 13 oz
   Rule: Add $1\frac{1}{2}$ lb or 24 oz.
6. 432 oz, 384 oz, 336 oz, 288 oz, 240 oz, 192 oz, 144 oz
   Rule: Subtract 3 lb or 48 oz.
7. 34 oz, 50 oz, 82 oz, 130 oz, 194 oz, 274 oz, 370 oz
   Rule: Add 1 lb, then 2 lb, then 3 lb, and so on.

130 Use with pages 456–457.

Name ________________ **Extend Your Thinking 10-9**

Decision Making

Sam's Market offers foods in various amounts.

	1 cup	1 pint	1 quart	1 gallon
apple juice	$0.56	$0.96	$1.79	$6.89
ice cream	$1.49	$2.49	$3.98	$7.59
carrot juice	$0.89	$1.69	$2.99	$9.49
milk	$0.65	$0.89	$1.79	$3.79
orange juice	$1.89	$3.49	$5.99	not available

- The orange juice and carrot juice are freshly made and must be used within 3 days.
- Cups and pints of ice cream come in 5 flavors. Quarts and gallons come in 15 flavors.
- The apple juice comes only in glass containers.

Possible answers shown.

1. What are the advantages of buying by the cup or pint?
   Pay less; get less
2. What are the disadvantages of buying by the cup or pint?
   Higher cost per ounce; don't get the flavors you want
3. What are the advantages of buying by the quart or gallon?
   Lower cost per ounce; need to shop less often
4. What are the disadvantages of buying by the quart or gallon?
   Heavier if you have to walk home carrying groceries; possibility of spoilage before using
5. Why might someone buy carrot juice by the gallon?
   Large family that likes carrot juice
6. Why might someone buy milk by the cup?
   To pack in a school lunch
7. Make a decision. If you had $20, what would you buy? Explain.
   Look for answers that consider convenience, cost, family size, usage, availability.

Use with pages 458–459. 131

Name ________________ **Extend Your Thinking 10-10**

Visual Thinking

Similar figures have the same shape but not the same size. Look at each figure on the left. Circle the similar figure on the right.

1.
2.
3.
4.
5.
6.

132 Use with pages 460–461.

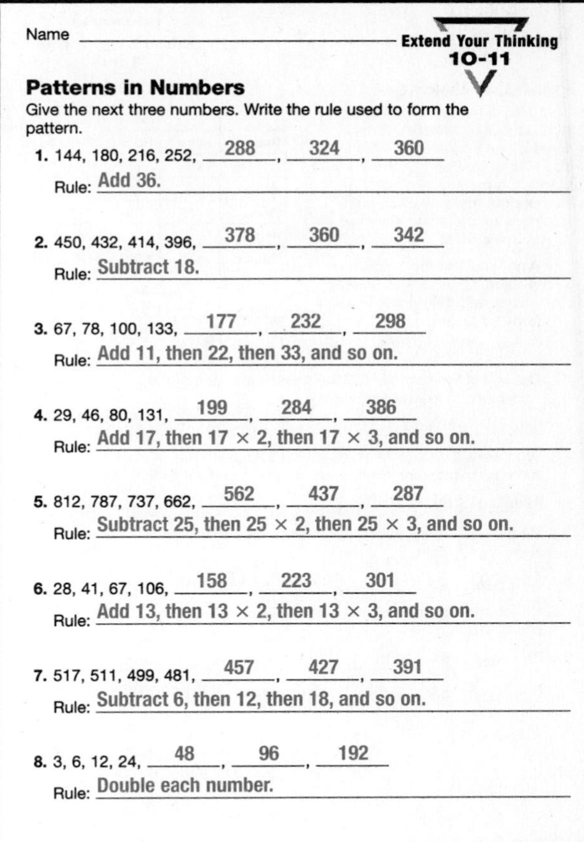

Name ______________________ **Extend Your Thinking 10-11**

Patterns in Numbers

Give the next three numbers. Write the rule used to form the pattern.

1. 144, 180, 216, 252, 288, 324, 360
   Rule: Add 36.
2. 450, 432, 414, 396, 378, 360, 342
   Rule: Subtract 18.
3. 67, 78, 100, 133, 177, 232, 298
   Rule: Add 11, then 22, then 33, and so on.
4. 29, 46, 80, 131, 199, 284, 386
   Rule: Add 17, then 17 × 2, then 17 × 3, and so on.
5. 812, 787, 737, 662, 562, 437, 287
   Rule: Subtract 25, then 25 × 2, then 25 × 3, and so on.
6. 28, 41, 67, 106, 158, 223, 301
   Rule: Add 13, then 13 × 2, then 13 × 3, and so on.
7. 517, 511, 499, 481, 457, 427, 391
   Rule: Subtract 6, then 12, then 18, and so on.
8. 3, 6, 12, 24, 48, 96, 192
   Rule: Double each number.

Use with pages 462–463. 133

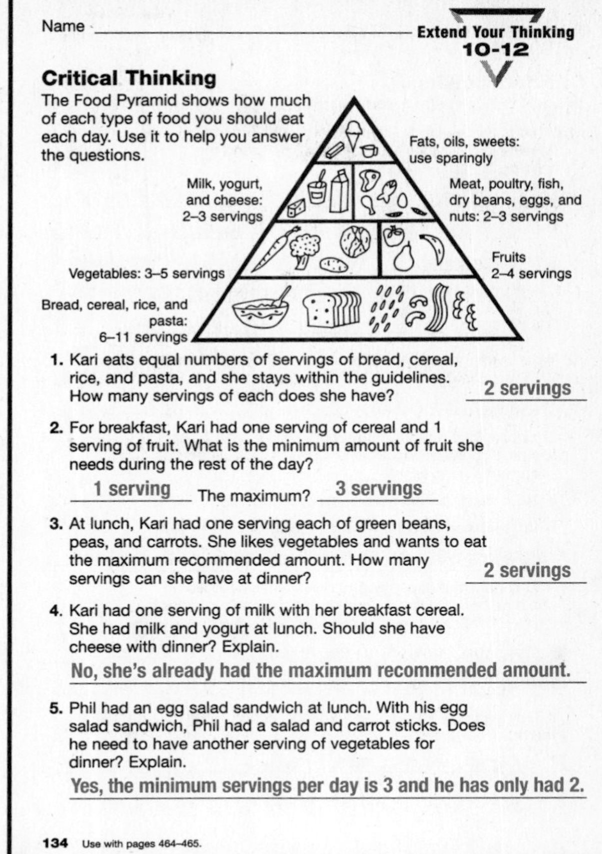

Name ______________________ **Extend Your Thinking 10-12**

Critical Thinking

The Food Pyramid shows how much of each type of food you should eat each day. Use it to help you answer the questions.

Fats, oils, sweets: use sparingly
Milk, yogurt, and cheese: 2–3 servings
Meat, poultry, fish, dry beans, eggs, and nuts: 2–3 servings
Vegetables: 3–5 servings
Fruits 2–4 servings
Bread, cereal, rice, and pasta: 6–11 servings

1. Kari eats equal numbers of servings of bread, cereal, rice, and pasta, and she stays within the guidelines. How many servings of each does she have? 2 servings
2. For breakfast, Kari had one serving of cereal and 1 serving of fruit. What is the minimum amount of fruit she needs during the rest of the day?
   1 serving The maximum? 3 servings
3. At lunch, Kari had one serving each of green beans, peas, and carrots. She likes vegetables and wants to eat the maximum recommended amount. How many servings can she have at dinner? 2 servings
4. Kari had one serving of milk with her breakfast cereal. She had milk and yogurt at lunch. Should she have cheese with dinner? Explain.
   No, she's already had the maximum recommended amount.
5. Phil had an egg salad sandwich at lunch. With his egg salad sandwich, Phil had a salad and carrot sticks. Does he need to have another serving of vegetables for dinner? Explain.
   Yes, the minimum servings per day is 3 and he has only had 2.

134 Use with pages 464–465.

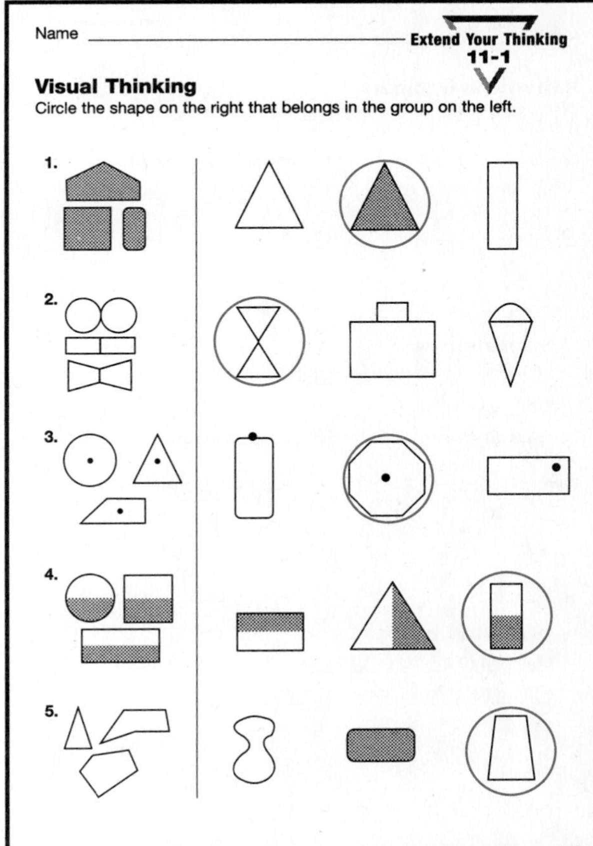

Name ______________________ **Extend Your Thinking 11-1**

Visual Thinking

Circle the shape on the right that belongs in the group on the left.

1.
2.
3.
4.
5.

Use with pages 476–477. 135

Name ______________________ **Extend Your Thinking 11-2**

Patterns in Numbers

Write the next two numbers in each pattern.

1. 0.1, 0.2, 0.3, 0.4, 0.5, 0.6
2. 1.1, 0.9, 0.7, 0.5, 0.3
3. 0.23, 0.24, 0.25, 0.26, 0.27, 0.28
4. 0.09, 0.08, 0.07, 0.06, 0.05, 0.04
5. three tenths, four tenths, five tenths, six tenths,
   Seven tenths, Eight tenths
6. eleven hundredths, twelve hundredths, thirteen hundredths, fourteen hundredths,
   Fifteen hundredths, Sixteen hundredths
7. twenty-two hundredths, twenty hundredths, eighteen hundredths, sixteen hundredths,
   Fourteen hundredths, Twelve hundredths
8. $\frac{4}{10}, \frac{5}{10}, \frac{6}{10}, \frac{7}{10}$, $\frac{8}{10}$, $\frac{9}{10}$
9. $\frac{62}{100}, \frac{63}{100}, \frac{64}{100}, \frac{65}{100}$, $\frac{66}{100}$, $\frac{67}{100}$
10. 0.10, 0.1, 0.20, 0.2, 0.30, 0.3, 0.40, 0.4
11. 0.9, 0.90, 0.8, 0.80, 0.7, 0.70, 0.6, 0.60
12. eight tenths, eighty hundredths, seven tenths, seventy hundredths, six tenths, sixty hundredths,
    Five tenths, Fifty hundredths
13. 0.67, 0.68, 0.69, 0.7, 0.71, 0.72, 0.73, 0.74, 0.75, 0.76, 0.77, 0.78,
    0.79, 0.8
14. Write your own pattern and have a classmate write in the next two numbers.

____

____

136 Use with pages 478–479.

Name ______________________ **Extend Your Thinking 11-3**

Critical Thinking

Tony has collected $5.17 worth of coins.

1. What is the fewest number of coins that Tony could have? What are they? Explain how you found the answer.

   24 coins; 20 quarters, 1 dime, 1 nickel, 2 pennies; Possible answer: The coin worth the most is a quarter, so I found the greatest possible number of quarters in $5.17. Then I found the greatest number of dimes, then nickels, and then pennies possible.

2. What is the greatest number of coins Tony could have? What are they?

   517 coins; They are all pennies.

3. Suppose Tony bought a bottle of juice with his coins. He has nine quarters, eleven dimes, seven nickels, and twenty-one pennies left.

   a. How much did the juice cost? $1.26

   b. What coins could Tony have used to buy the juice?

   Possible answer: 4 quarters, 2 dimes, 1 nickel, 1 penny

4. If Tony only had dimes and pennies in his collection, could he have an equal number of dimes and pennies? Explain. What strategy did you use to find the answer?

   Yes; He could have 47 dimes and 47 pennies; Possible answers: Make an Organized List or Guess and Check

5. If Tony had only 13 quarters in his collection, what could the other coins be?

   Possible answer: 19 dimes, 2 pennies

Name ______________________ **Extend Your Thinking 11-4**

Decision Making

There are seven sprinters on the high school track team. Only three of the sprinters can run the 100-meter sprint in the upcoming meet. The seven runners ran three races to help decide who should be selected to run in the meet.

	Time		
Runner	**Race 1**	**Race 2**	**Race 3**
Heather	17.9	18.12	18.10
Keisha	17.87	17.80	17.99
Darcy	17.82	17.97	17.81
Angelina	17.89	18.10	17.8
Tamara	18.14	17.86	18.12
Marisa	17.91	17.84	17.93
Ming	17.90	17.9	17.88

1. Who were the top 3 finishers in Race 1? Write the runners' names and their times in order, from 1st to 3rd.

   Darcy–17.82, Keisha–17.87, Angelina–17.89

2. Did any of the runners in Race 1 finish the race at the same time? How do you know?

   Yes; Heather and Ming did. 17.9 is the same as 17.90.

3. Who were the top 3 finishers in Race 2? Write the runners' names and their times in order, from 1st to 3rd.

   Keisha–17.80, Marisa–17.84, Tamara–17.86

4. Who were the top 3 finishers in Race 3? Order their names and times.

   Angelina–17.8, Darcy–17.81, Ming–17.88

5. Which three runners do you think should run in the meet? Explain.

   Possible answer: Darcy, Keisha, and Angelina should run in the meet because they each finished in the top three twice.

Name ______________________ **Extend Your Thinking 11-5**

Visual Thinking

Circle the two figures in each row that are alike.

1.   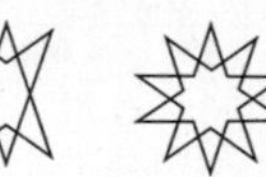 

2. 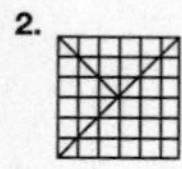 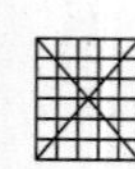 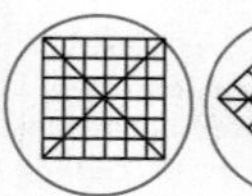 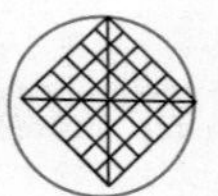 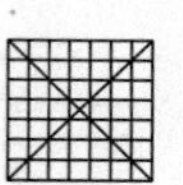

3. 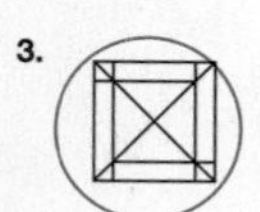 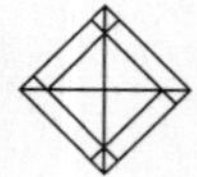 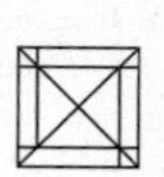 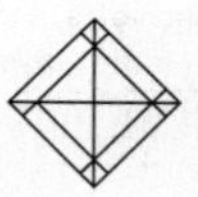 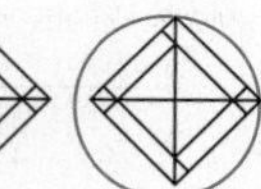

4. 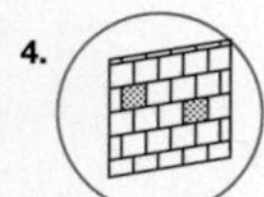 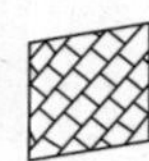 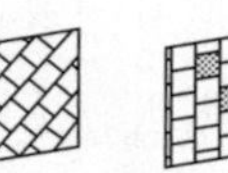 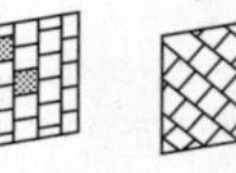 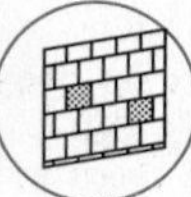

5. 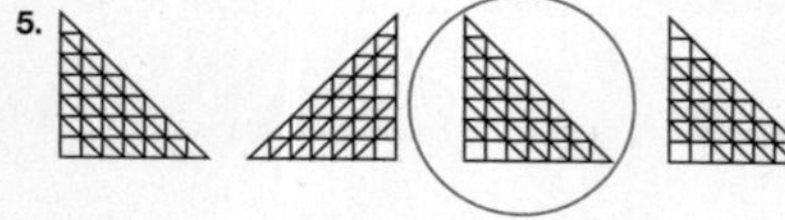

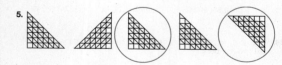

Name ______________________ **Extend Your Thinking 11-6**

Patterns in Numbers

Complete **1–8** using the same pattern used in samples **A** and **B**.

Sample A $\frac{1}{2}, \frac{5}{10}, \frac{5}{1}$, 5 **Sample B** $\frac{6}{5}, \frac{12}{10}, \frac{12}{1}$, 12

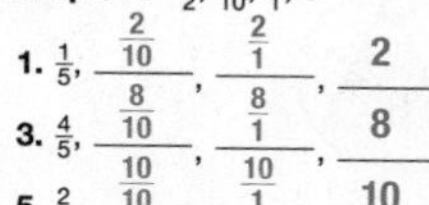

1. $\frac{1}{5}$, $\frac{2}{10}$, $\frac{2}{1}$, 2
2. $\frac{3}{5}$, $\frac{6}{10}$, $\frac{6}{1}$, 6
3. $\frac{4}{5}$, $\frac{8}{10}$, $\frac{8}{1}$, 8
4. $\frac{1}{10}$, $\frac{1}{10}$, $\frac{10}{1}$, 10
5. $\frac{2}{2}$, $\frac{10}{10}$, $\frac{10}{1}$, 10
6. $\frac{8}{5}$, $\frac{16}{10}$, $\frac{16}{1}$, 16
7. $\frac{3}{2}$, $\frac{15}{10}$, $\frac{15}{1}$, 15
8. $\frac{7}{5}$, $\frac{14}{10}$, $\frac{14}{1}$, 14
9. Describe the pattern.

   Changed to a fraction in tenths, changed denominator to 1, wrote as a whole number

Complete **10–15** using the same pattern used in samples **C** and **D**.

Sample C $\frac{1}{4}, \frac{25}{100}, \frac{25}{10}$, 2.5 **Sample D** $\frac{7}{10}, \frac{70}{100}, \frac{70}{10}$, 7.0

10. $\frac{3}{4}$, $\frac{75}{100}$, $\frac{75}{10}$, 7.5
11. $\frac{4}{10}$, $\frac{40}{100}$, $\frac{40}{10}$, 4.0
12. $\frac{9}{25}$, $\frac{36}{100}$, $\frac{36}{10}$, 3.6
13. $\frac{3}{20}$, $\frac{15}{100}$, $\frac{15}{10}$, 1.5
14. $\frac{27}{25}$, $\frac{108}{100}$, $\frac{108}{10}$, 10.8
15. $\frac{37}{20}$, $\frac{185}{100}$, $\frac{185}{10}$, 18.5
16. Describe the pattern.

    Changed to a fraction in hundredths, changed the denominator to 10, wrote as a decimal in tenths

Name ______________________

Extend Your Thinking 11-7

Visual Thinking

For each shape, write the letter of the sentence that describes the shape. Some shapes may fit more than one description.

a. This shape has no right angles.

b. This shape has only one right angle.

c. This shape has 4 right angles.

d. This shape has 2 sets of parallel sides.

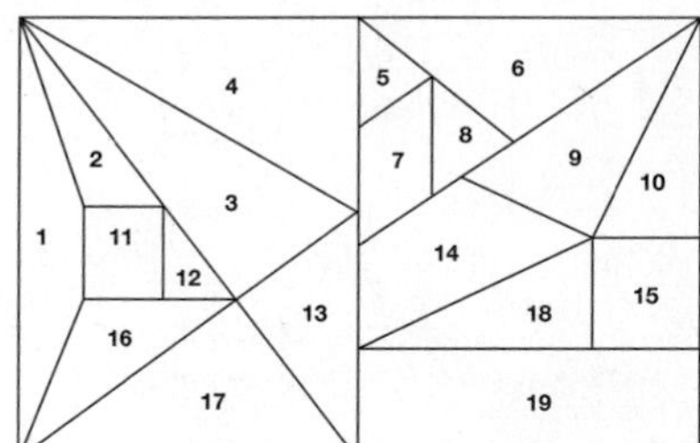

1. a **2.** a **3.** b

4. b **5.** a **6.** a

7. a, d **8.** a **9.** b

10. b **11.** c, d **12.** b

13. b **14.** a **15.** c, d

16. a **17.** b **18.** b

19. c, d

Name ______________________

Extend Your Thinking 11-8

Visual Thinking

The rectangles in the first column are sheets of paper that have been folded in fourths. A hole has been punched out of each rectangle. The designs in column 2 show the sheets of paper after they have been opened up. The dashed lines represent the fold lines. Draw a line from each folded rectangle to its matching design.

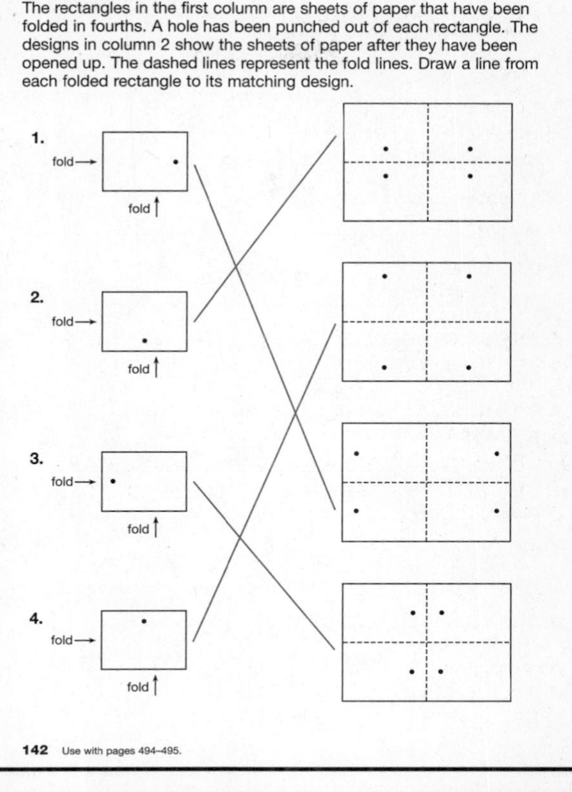

Name ______________________

Extend Your Thinking 11-9

Critical Thinking

1. Write four pairs of decimals to complete each column in the table.

Possible answers:

Sums			Differences		
greater than 1	equal to 1	less than 1	greater than 1	equal to 1	less than 1
0.34, 0.89	0.5, 0.5	0.3, 0.4	6.9, 0.7	3.1, 2.1	1.0, 0.37
4.3, 0.8	0.99, 0.01	0.01, 0.59	1.98, 0.79	1.28, 0.28	5.4, 5.2
0.54, 3.2	0.7, 0.3	0.42, 0.3	12.2, 11.1	7.81, 6.81	4.1, 3.7
0.6, 0.6	0.73, 0.27	0.11, 0.5	8, 0.73	1.01, 0.01	0.98, 0.36

2. Explain how you can tell whether the sum of two decimals is greater than 1 or less than 1.

Possible answers: Greater than 1: there is at least one whole number or you must regroup decimal parts as a whole number; less than 1: no whole numbers and the difference of the decimals is less than 1.

3. Explain how you can tell whether the sum of two decimals is equal to 1.

Possible answer: There are no whole numbers and the sum of the decimal parts equal 10 or 100.

4. Explain how you can tell whether the difference of two decimals is equal to 1.

Possible answer: The decimal parts are exactly the same and the whole numbers have a difference of 1.

Name ______________________

Extend Your Thinking 11-10

Decision Making

Rasheed is building rectangular picture frames. He can build frames with these dimensions:

13.5 cm by 21 cm

19.25 cm by 25 cm

26.5 cm by 34 cm

13.5 cm

21 cm

He has 2.5 m of wood. How can he best use the wood?

1. What is the perimeter of a 13.5 cm by 21 cm frame? **69 cm**

2. What is the perimeter of a 19.25 cm by 25 cm frame? **88.5 cm**

3. What is the perimeter of a 26.5 cm by 34 cm frame? **121 cm**

4. a. How much wood does Rasheed need to build one of each frame? **278.5 cm**

b. Can he build one of each frame with 2.5 m of wood? Explain.

No; he needs 278.5 cm of wood but has only 250 cm.

5. If Rasheed decided to buy 0.75 m more wood, would he have enough to build each frame? Explain.

Yes, he would have 325 cm of wood which is greater than 278.5 cm.

6. Using 2.5 m of wood, how many of each size frame should Rasheed build? Explain.

Possible answer: Two 19.25 cm by 25 cm frames and one 13.5 cm by 21 cm frame, because that will use 246 cm of wood, the most possible.

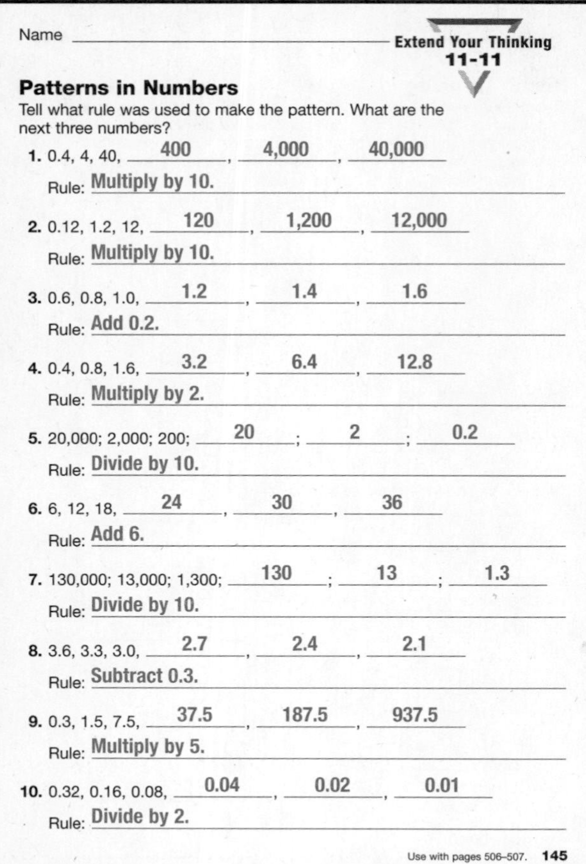

Name ______________ Extend Your Thinking 11-11

Patterns in Numbers

Tell what rule was used to make the pattern. What are the next three numbers?

1. 0.4, 4, 40, 400, 4,000, 40,000
   Rule: Multiply by 10.
2. 0.12, 1.2, 12, 120, 1,200, 12,000
   Rule: Multiply by 10.
3. 0.6, 0.8, 1.0, 1.2, 1.4, 1.6
   Rule: Add 0.2.
4. 0.4, 0.8, 1.6, 3.2, 6.4, 12.8
   Rule: Multiply by 2.
5. 20,000; 2,000; 200; 20; 2; 0.2
   Rule: Divide by 10.
6. 6, 12, 18, 24, 30, 36
   Rule: Add 6.
7. 130,000; 13,000; 1,300; 130; 13; 1.3
   Rule: Divide by 10.
8. 3.6, 3.3, 3.0, 2.7, 2.4, 2.1
   Rule: Subtract 0.3.
9. 0.3, 1.5, 7.5, 37.5, 187.5, 937.5
   Rule: Multiply by 5.
10. 0.32, 0.16, 0.08, 0.04, 0.02, 0.01
    Rule: Divide by 2.

Use with pages 506–507. 145

Name ______________ Extend Your Thinking 11-12

Critical Thinking

Write >, <, or = in each circle to make a true metric sentence.

1. 5 m (>) 50 cm
2. 2.46 cm (=) 0.0246 m
3. 0.23 m (>) 2.3 cm
4. 39.9 cm (>) 0.0399 m
5. 89 m (>) 890 cm
6. 37.2 cm (=) 0.372 m
7. 3820 cm (>) 3.82 m
8. 1.12 m (>) 11.2 cm

Arrange the five numbers in the box from greatest to least. Write the numbers on the lines.

48.7 cm	487 cm	0.0487 m	487 m	48.7 m

9. a. 487 m
   b. 48.7 m
   c. 487 cm
   d. 48.7 cm
   e. 0.0487 m

10. If you had a strip of paper one meter long, how could you show how long a centimeter is? Explain.
    Possible answer: Cut the strip into 100 equal parts because there are 100 centimeters in a meter.
11. Jan said, "I am 1.2 meters tall." Stan said, "No, you're not. You are 120 centimeters tall." Explain why both of them are correct.
    1.2 meters is the same as 120 centimeters.
12. Kelly said, "I'd like to measure the thickness of this book in meters." Jerome said, "You should measure it in centimeters instead." Who is right? Explain.
    Jerome is right. A meter is much larger than the thickness of a book.

146 Use with pages 508–509.

Name ______________ Extend Your Thinking 11-13

Visual Thinking

Complete 1–6 using the same pattern used in Samples **A** and **B**.

Sample A: BUY (shown in four orientations)

Sample B: END (shown in four orientations)

1. GRAM
2. KILO
3. METER
4. DIVIDE
5. MULTIPLY
6. MEASURE

Use with pages 510–511. 147

Name ______________ Extend Your Thinking 11-14

Patterns in Numbers

Complete the pattern. Then write the rule.

1. 3,000 mL 3.2 L 3,400 mL 3.6 L 3,800 mL
   Rule: Add 200 mL or 0.2 L.
2. 5 L 5,500 mL 6 L 6,500 mL 7 L
   Rule: Add 500 mL or 0.5 L.
3. 4,200 mL 5.2 L 6,200 mL 7.2 L 8,200 mL
   Rule: Add 1L or 1,000 mL.
4. 3 L 2,400 mL 1.8 L 1,200 mL 0.6 L
   Rule: Subtract 600 mL or 0.6 L.
5. 750 mL 0.6 L 450 mL 0.3 L 150 mL
   Rule: Subtract 150 mL or 0.15 L.

Write your own mL or L patterns. Have a classmate write in the next two numbers and the rule.

6. ____ ____ ____ Answers will vary. ____
   Rule: ______________
7. ____ ____ ____ ____ ____ ____
   Rule: ______________
8. ____ ____ ____ ____ ____ ____
   Rule: ______________

148 Use with pages 512–513.

Name ______________________ Extend Your Thinking 11-15

Critical Thinking

Complete each sentence with the correct measure. Use g, kg, L, mL, m, cm, °C, or °F.

1. The basketball player was 208 cm tall.
2. The cat weighs about 6 kg.
3. The living room was a comfortable room temperature of 20 °C.
4. The flower vase held about 100 mL of water.
5. The house key was 4 cm long.
6. The horse weighs about 425 kg.
7. The jug held 2 L of water.
8. The gas tank held 60 L of gasoline.
9. A can of tuna weighed 173 g.
10. In the 1996 Summer Olympics, Michael Johnson ran a 400 m run in a little more than 43 seconds.
11. The inside temperature of the refrigerator was 5 °C.
12. The hot soup was 120 °F.
13. The can of soup weighed 300 g.
14. The baseball bat is 1 m long.
15. A jar of honey holds about 600 mL.
16. Swimming is comfortable at 37 °C.

Write a sentence for each unit of measure. **Answers will vary.**

17. kilogram ______
18. °C ______
19. liter ______
20. meter ______
21. °F ______

Name ______________________ Extend Your Thinking 11-16

Critical Thinking

How many stars are there:

1. In the rectangle? 18
2. In the circle? 9
3. In the larger triangle? 14
4. In the circle but not in the rectangle or larger triangle? 2
5. In the rectangle but not in the circle or larger triangle? 9
6. In the larger triangle but not in the rectangle or circle? 6
7. In common to the rectangle and larger triangle but not the circle? 4
8. In common to the circle and larger triangle but not the rectangle? 2
9. In common to the rectangle and circle but not the larger triangle? 3
10. All together in the rectangle and circle? 22
11. All together in the circle and the larger triangle? 19
12. All together in the rectangle and the larger triangle? 26
13. All together in the circle, larger triangle, and rectangle? 28
14. Draw a diagram using a square and a circle. There should be 8 stars in the square, 12 in the circle and 4 in common to both. What is the total number of stars? 16

Name ______________________ Extend Your Thinking 12-1

Patterns in Division

Find each quotient. Tell what rule was used to make the pattern. What are the next two division problems and quotients?

1. 640 ÷ 8, 560 ÷ 8, 480 ÷ 8, 400 ÷ 8, 320 ÷ 8
   Quotients: 80, 70, 60, 50, 40
   Rule: Quotient is 10 less, divisor stays the same.
2. 280 ÷ 7, 350 ÷ 7, 420 ÷ 7, 490 ÷ 7, 560 ÷ 7
   Quotients: 40, 50, 60, 70, 80
   Rule: Quotient is 10 more, divisor stays the same.
3. 18 ÷ 9, 36 ÷ 9, 54 ÷ 9, 72 ÷ 9, 90 ÷ 9
   Quotients: 2, 4, 6, 8, 10
   Rule: Quotient is 2 more, divisor stays the same.
4. 121 ÷ 11, 99 ÷ 11, 77 ÷ 11, 55 ÷ 11, 33 ÷ 11
   Quotients: 11, 9, 7, 5, 3
   Rule: Quotient is 2 less, divisor stays the same.
5. 240 ÷ 2, 240 ÷ 4, 240 ÷ 6, 240 ÷ 8, 240 ÷ 10
   Quotients: 120, 60, 40, 30, 24
   Rule: Divisor is 2 more, dividend stays the same.
6. 600 ÷ 60, 500 ÷ 50, 400 ÷ 40, 300 ÷ 30, 200 ÷ 20
   Quotients: 10, 10, 10, 10, 10
   Rule: Dividend is 100 less, divisor is 10 less.
7. Make up your own division patterns. Leave some blank spaces. Give them to a classmate to solve.
   Answers will vary. Check students' patterns.

Name ______________________ Extend Your Thinking 12-2

Patterns in Numbers

Write the next three numbers to continue the pattern. Then give the greatest number that evenly divides all of the numbers in the pattern.

1. 7, 14, 21, 28, 35, 42, 49
   7
2. 5, 10, 15, 20, 25, 30, 35
   5
3. 90, 81, 72, 63, 56, 45, 36
   9
4. 220, 209, 198, 187, 176, 165, 154
   11
5. 25, 50, 75, 100, 125, 150, 175
   25
6. 20, 30, 40, 50, 60, 70
   10
7. 8, 16, 24, 32, 40, 48, 56
   8
8. 108, 120, 132, 144, 156, 168, 180
   12

Name ______________________ **Extend Your Thinking 12-3**

Visual Thinking

Find the pattern in each row. Draw the next picture to continue the pattern.

1.
2.
3.
4.
5.
6.

Name ______________________ **Extend Your Thinking 12-4**

Critical Thinking

Solve each problem. Explain your reasoning.

1. What is the least number you can divide by 63 and have a 1-digit quotient with no remainder?
   63; 63 ÷ 63 = 1
2. What is the greatest number you can divide by 36 and have a 1-digit quotient with no remainder?
   324; Multiply 36 by 9, the greatest 1-digit quotient.
3. What is the greatest number you can divide by 18 and have a 2-digit quotient under 20 with no remainder?
   342; multiply 18 by 19, the greatest 2-digit quotient under 20.
4. What is the least number you can divide by 72 and have a 2-digit quotient with no remainder?
   720; multiply 72 by 10, the least 2-digit quotient.
5. You have 313 fresh carnations from your garden. You want your friends to take 2 dozen each. You want to pin 1 carnation on your jacket. You don't want any flowers to be wasted. How many friends will have to take flowers?
   13 friends; subtract 1 (the pinned one) from 313 and divide by 24 (2 dozen).
6. You want to give an equal number of 222 origami decorations to 8 friends. You want to keep 5 and give 9 to your sister. How many decorations will each friend get?
   26 decorations; Subtract 14 (9 + 5) from 222 and divide by 8.

Name ______________________ **Extend Your Thinking 12-5**

Decision Making

The fair is in town! If you had $20, and the fair was closing in 3 hours, what would you do?

Ride	Cost in Tickets	Average Time in Line
Ferris Wheel	5	15 minutes
Fun House	3	5 minutes
The Hammer	6	16 minutes
The Chute	4	10 minutes
The Thrill-a-Minute	7	18 minutes
Roller Coaster	9	22 minutes

Food Item	Cost in Tickets
Hot Dog	7
Veggie Burger	8
Lemonade	4
Popcorn	3
Peanuts	5
Frozen Yogurt	6

- Tickets cost 40¢ each. They are needed for all purchases.
- Each ride takes about 5 minutes to complete.
- The wait in the snack bar line is about 10 minutes.

Plan your activities.

1. How much does each ride cost?
   Ferris Wheel—$2.00; Fun House—$1.20; Hammer—$2.40; Chute—$1.60; Thrill-a-Minute—$2.80; Roller Coaster—$3.60
2. How much does each food item cost?
   Hot Dog—$2.80; Veggie Burger—$3.20; Lemonade—$1.60; Popcorn—$1.20; Peanuts—$2.00; Frozen Yogurt—$2.40
3. Make a schedule that shows which rides you would take and which foods you would buy.
   Look for answers that consider costs, time, and interest.

Name ______________________ **Extend Your Thinking 12-6**

Critical Thinking

Order each set of statements from certain to impossible. **Possible answers shown.**
Use: 1—certain, 2—likely, 3—equally likely as unlikely, 4—unlikely, 5—impossible

1. Basketball

1 A college basketball game requires 5 players on a team.
3 You and your friends play basketball inside.
5 Your class team members are selected to play professional basketball next year.
4 Each player scores 25 points in a game.
2 10 points or more will be scored by at least one team.

2. Baseball

1 Baseball is played with 4 bases.
3 The baseball game is played on Monday, Wednesday, or Friday.
5 A baseball game must be played with 27 players.
2 There is at least one home run in a professional game.
4 The pitcher strikes out every player.

3. Choose a different sport or game. Write 5 sentences for a classmate to order from certain to impossible. **Answers will vary.**

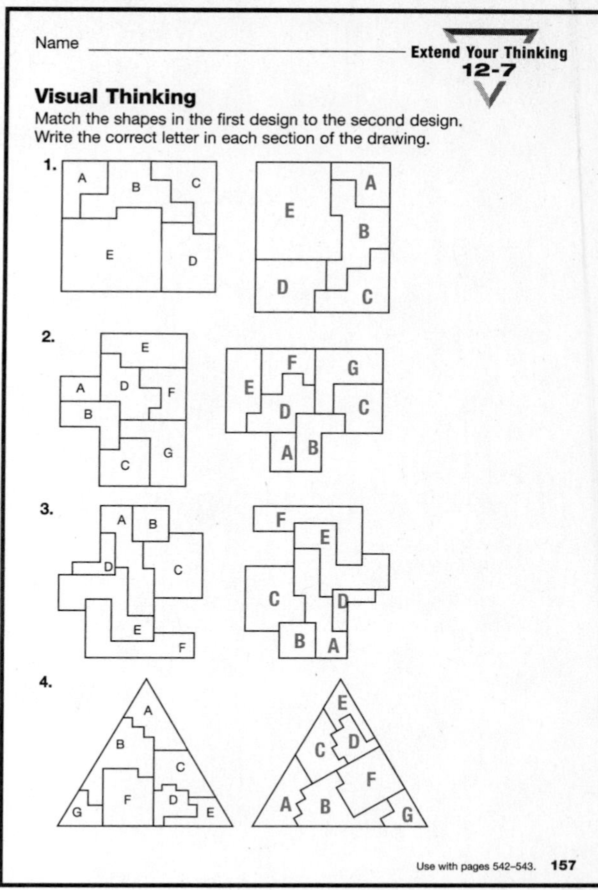

Name ______________________

Extend Your Thinking 12-7

Visual Thinking

Match the shapes in the first design to the second design. Write the correct letter in each section of the drawing.

1. A B C E D — E A B D C
2. E A D F B C G — F G E D C A B
3. A B D C E F — F E C D B A
4. A B C G F D E — E C D F A B G

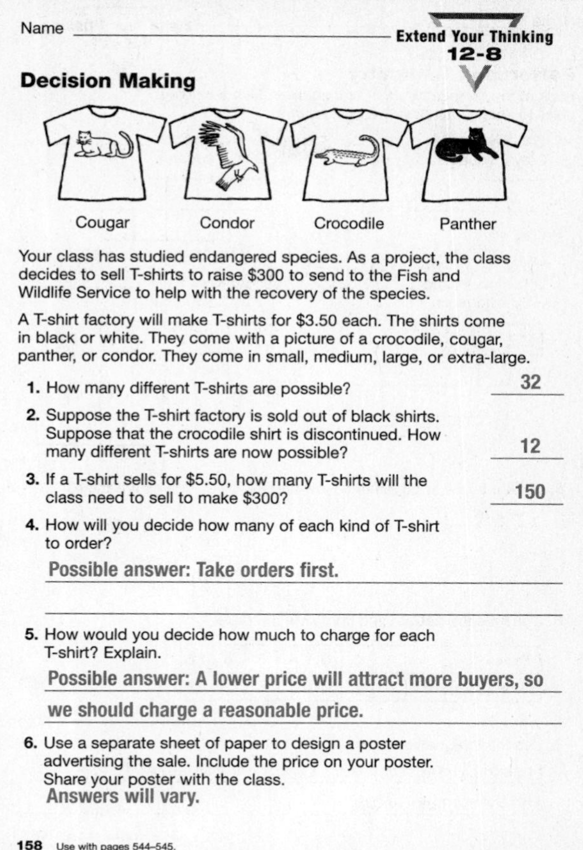

Name ______________________

Extend Your Thinking 12-8

Decision Making

Your class has studied endangered species. As a project, the class decides to sell T-shirts to raise $300 to send to the Fish and Wildlife Service to help with the recovery of the species.

A T-shirt factory will make T-shirts for $3.50 each. The shirts come in black or white. They come with a picture of a crocodile, cougar, panther, or condor. They come in small, medium, large, or extra-large.

1. How many different T-shirts are possible? **32**
2. Suppose the T-shirt factory is sold out of black shirts. Suppose that the crocodile shirt is discontinued. How many different T-shirts are now possible? **12**
3. If a T-shirt sells for $5.50, how many T-shirts will the class need to sell to make $300? **150**
4. How will you decide how many of each kind of T-shirt to order?
   Possible answer: Take orders first.
5. How would you decide how much to charge for each T-shirt? Explain.
   Possible answer: A lower price will attract more buyers, so we should charge a reasonable price.
6. Use a separate sheet of paper to design a poster advertising the sale. Include the price on your poster. Share your poster with the class.
   Answers will vary.

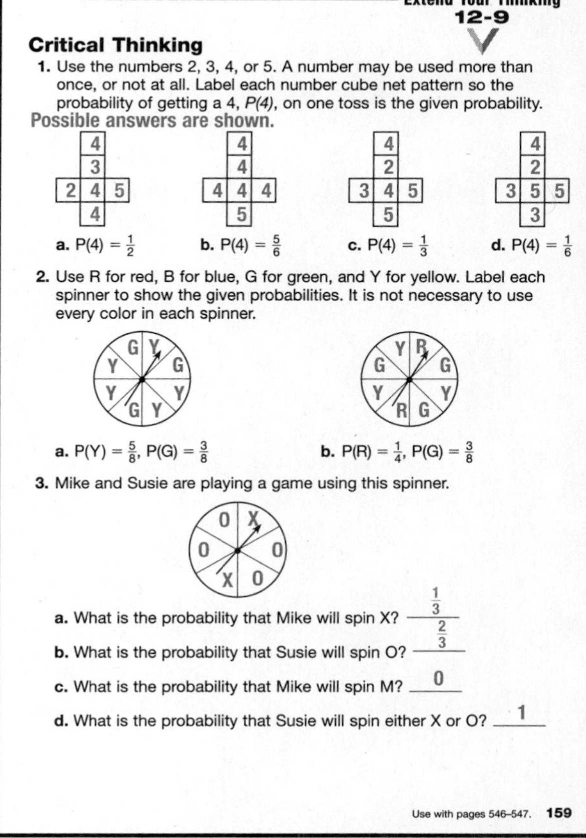

Name ______________________

Extend Your Thinking 12-9

Critical Thinking

1. Use the numbers 2, 3, 4, or 5. A number may be used more than once, or not at all. Label each number cube net pattern so the probability of getting a 4, *P(4)*, on one toss is the given probability.
   Possible answers are shown.

   a. $P(4) = \frac{1}{2}$ b. $P(4) = \frac{5}{6}$ c. $P(4) = \frac{1}{3}$ d. $P(4) = \frac{1}{6}$

2. Use R for red, B for blue, G for green, and Y for yellow. Label each spinner to show the given probabilities. It is not necessary to use every color in each spinner.

   a. $P(Y) = \frac{5}{8}$, $P(G) = \frac{3}{8}$ b. $P(R) = \frac{1}{4}$, $P(G) = \frac{3}{8}$

3. Mike and Susie are playing a game using this spinner.

   a. What is the probability that Mike will spin X? **$\frac{1}{3}$**
   b. What is the probability that Susie will spin O? **$\frac{2}{3}$**
   c. What is the probability that Mike will spin M? **0**
   d. What is the probability that Susie will spin either X or O? **1**

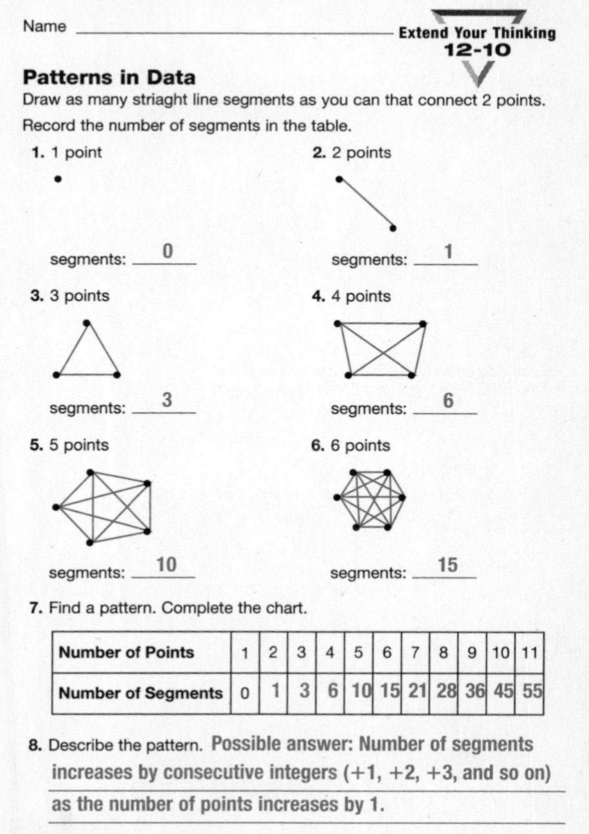

Name ______________________

Extend Your Thinking 12-10

Patterns in Data

Draw as many striaght line segments as you can that connect 2 points. Record the number of segments in the table.

1. 1 point — segments: **0**
2. 2 points — segments: **1**
3. 3 points — segments: **3**
4. 4 points — segments: **6**
5. 5 points — segments: **10**
6. 6 points — segments: **15**
7. Find a pattern. Complete the chart.

Number of Points	1	2	3	4	5	6	7	8	9	10	11
Number of Segments	0	1	3	6	10	15	21	28	36	45	55

8. Describe the pattern. **Possible answer: Number of segments increases by consecutive integers (+1, +2, +3, and so on) as the number of points increases by 1.**

Name ______________________ Extend Your Thinking 12-11

Patterns in Geometry

Look at the arrangements of unit squares. Use a different color to shade each larger 2 by 2 square.

1. One row has zero 2 by 2 squares.

2. Two rows have two 2 by 2 squares.

Check students' shadings.

3. Three rows have four 2 by 2 squares.

4. Four rows have six 2 by 2 squares.

5. Draw a 5-row arrangement. How many 2 by 2 squares are there?
eight

6. Continue the pattern and complete the table.

Rows	1	2	3	4	5	6	12
2 by 2 Squares	0	2	4	6	8	10	22

7. Describe the pattern.
Possible answer: Subtract 2 from the product of 2 and the number of rows.

Use with pages 550–551. 161